POPULAR MECHANICS
SHOP NOTES

FOR 1915 VOL. 11

Algrove Publishing ~ Classic Reprint Series

Algrove Publishing Limited
1090 Morrison Drive
Ottawa, Ontario
Canada K2H 1C2

Canadian Cataloguing in Publication Data

Main entry under title:

    Popular mechanics shop notes for ...

(Classic reprint series)
Includes indexes.
Originally published: Chicago : Popular Mechanics Co., 1905-
"Compiled from the "Shop notes" department of Popular mechanics
    magazine, and "Written so you can understand it;" tells easy
    ways to do hard things" --Added t.p., v. 1.
Contents: v. 1. 1905 - v. 2. 1906 - v. 3. 1907 - v. 4. 1908 - v. 5. 1909 - v. 6. 1910 - v. 7. 1911 -
    v. 8. 1912 - v. 9. 1913 - v. 10. 1914 - v. 11. 1915 - v. 12. 1916 - v. 13. 1917 - v. 14. 1918 -
    v. 15. 1919 - v. 16. 1920 - v. 17. 1921 - v. 18. 1922 - v. 19. 1023.
ISBN 0-921335-87-3 (v. 11) - ISBN 0-921335-91-1 (v. 12) - ISBN 0-921335-94-6 (v. 13) -
ISBN 0-921335-96-2 (v. 14) - ISBN 0-921335-98-9 (v. 15) - ISBN 0-921335-93-8 (v. 16) -
ISBN 0-921335-95-4 (v. 17) - ISBN 0-921335-97-0 (v. 18) - ISBN 0-921335-99-7 (v. 19) -

    1. Do-it-yourself work. 2. Industrial arts. I. Title: Shop notes for ... II. Series: Classic reprint series (Ottawa, Ont.)

TJ1160.P66 2000   600   C99-900763-7

Printed in Canada
#10400

Publisher's Note

Virtually every woodworking magazine in the English-speaking world has a shop notes section and has published an accumulation of them in book form. This was all started in 1905 with the first annual issue of *Popular Mechanics Shop Notes*, a compilation of advice on jigs, fixtures, methods of work, processes and projects. The earlier issues focussed primarily on metalworking, but with tips for a variety of other trades liberally sprinkled throughout. As years went by, the contents shifted more and more to woodworking and handyman projects. Each book is profusely illustrated. The line drawings of the earlier issues were supplanted by superb engravings until photographs started to creep in during the 1920s. Each year has its charm but all issues share the attribute of being clear, concise and widely informative.

Leonard G. Lee, Publisher
Ottawa
September, 1999

WARNING

This is a reprint of a book compiled in the early 1900s. The book describes what was recommended to be done in accordance with the knowledge of the day.

It would be advisable to treat all corrosive, explosive and toxic materials with much greater caution than is indicated here, particularly any materials that come in contact with the body.

Similarly, some of the recommended projects were dangerous then and remain so now. All of this material should be regarded with a judicious eye and necessary precautions taken.

POPULAR MECHANICS

SHOP NOTES

FOR

1915

EASY WAYS TO DO HARD THINGS

OF DAILY USE
TO EVERY MECHANIC

Vol. XI — Table of Contents, Pages 2263-2271

POPULAR MECHANICS, CHICAGO

This Volume is Reprinted from the
Shop Notes Department
of
Popular Mechanics
Magazine

Edited by H. H. WINDSOR

A Home Garage

By FRANK L. RUSSELL

The housing of an automobile must be taken into consideration when a new machine is purchased and would-be owners in a city often face this problem first, with the result that the cost of keeping the machine in a garage discourages many, who could afford it, from buying one. The limited space on an ordinary residence lot or that allotted to an apartment dweller is inadequate for a large home garage, yet, in many places, a small one could be erected or space could be procured on a near-by lot at a small rental for such a building, the cost of which would fall far short of the expense of

rior of the automobile and do small repairs.

The first thing to be considered is the foundation, or base, which is made of concrete. The earth should be excavated for a depth of 6 in. and to the exact dimensions given for the floor plan. The hole is then filled with cinders, well tamped in and leveled on top. A frame, about 4 in. high, is built up of cheap lumber, so that the space within measures 12 ft. wide and 16 ft. long, except at the double-door opening where a sloping runway is formed for the easy entrance of the automobile. A 2-in. layer of concrete—a mix-

A Garage That will House One Automobile and Provide Space Enough for Light Repairing and for Washing the Exterior, the Concrete Floor Being Better for This Work Than a Floor Made of Plank

keeping the machine in a public garage.

The home garage shown in the illustration is designed for housing one machine, and to give a little space about it so that a person can clean the exte-

ture of 1 part cement, 2 parts sand, and 4 parts gravel or crushed stone—is placed on top of the cinders, and a neat mixture of cement and sand, ½ in. thick, is placed on the concrete and made perfectly level. When putting in the concrete, ½-in. bolts, about 5 in. long, are set in the edge with the threaded end extending about 3 in.

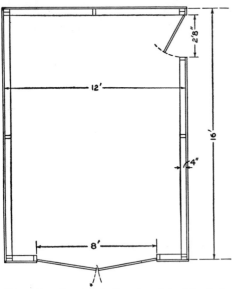

Floor Plan, Showing the Location of the Sills, Studs and Corner Posts on the Concrete Floor

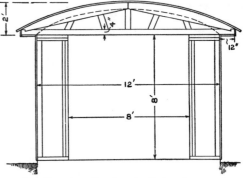

End Elevation, Showing the Rafter Construction and the Finishing Facia Boards on the Eaves

above the upper surface of the cement and in line with the center of the 2 by 4-in. timber used as a sill. The detail of this construction is shown in the sketch. About four of these bolts should be set on each side, three on the end, and one on each side of the double doors.

The corner posts and studs are cut so that their length, together with the thickness of the sill and the two pieces for the plate, will measure 8 ft. This is the proper length to cut the boards without waste from standard lengths of lumber. After raising the corner posts and studs, and nailing the plate pieces on top, the siding boards are nailed on vertically to the plate and sill, and the battens nailed over the joints.

The rafters are built up in a manner similar to that used on large garages now so popular. Each one, or each pair, consists of a crosspiece that rests on top of the plates at the sides and is notched at the ends, to receive the ends of the convex rafter pieces. The pattern for one of these pieces, with dimensions, is shown in the drawing. After fitting the three main parts to form one rafter across the building, they are fastened together with short pieces of boards, which can be cut from scrap. The rafters are set on the plates 16 in. apart from center to center.

The sheathing boards are nailed to the curved edges of the rafters lengthwise, and as the material list calls for

Material List

CONCRETE FLOOR:	WINDOWS:
2 bbl. cement.	4 single casements.
4.5 cu. yd. cinders.	
2.2 cu. yd. sand.	FINISHING PIECES:
4.3 cu. yd. gravel.	2 frieze boards, 18 ft. long, ⅞ by 1 ft.
SILLS, PLATES AND STUDS:	2 facia boards, 18 ft. long, ⅞ by 4 in.
6 pieces, 16 ft. long, 2 by 4 in.	4 facia boards, 8 ft. long, ⅞ by 1 ft.
4 pieces, 12 ft. long, 2 by 4 in.	8 corner boards, 8 ft. long, ⅞ by 4 in.
20 pieces, 8 ft. long, 2 by 4 in.	6 door facing boards, 8 ft. long, ⅞ by 4 in.
SIDING:	
90 boards, 8 ft. long, ⅞ by 8 in.	HARDWARE:
90 battens, 8 ft. long.	1 pair of door hinges.
RAFTERS:	1 door lock.
10 boards, 14 ft. long, ⅞ by 8 in.	3 pair of heavy door hinges.
10 boards, 14 ft. long, ⅞ by 4 in.	1 foot latch.
ROOFING:	1 upper latch.
Enough sheathing boards, 12 ft. long, to cover 260 sq. ft.	1 large door lock.
Enough prepared roofing to cover 260 sq. ft.	10 lb. 20-penny nails.
	20 lb. 8-penny nails.
	10 bolts, with double washers, ½ by 5 in.

boards 12 ft. long, one and one-half lengths will cover the rafters and allow 1 ft. projection at each end for the eave. The facia boards are cut on a curve in the same manner as the rafter pieces, and the under side is cut as shown in the detail, so as to make a neat-appearing connection to the end of the frieze boards. Straight facia boards are fastened on the eaves, at the sides, in the same manner, and a frieze board nailed to the under side, the ends being finished as shown in the detail drawing.

Prepared roofing is fastened to the sheathing in the usual manner, beginning the layers at the eave and finishing in the center, allowing the center piece to overlap on both sides.

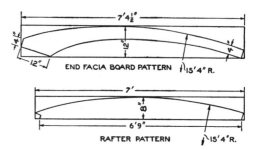

Pattern Layout for the Rafter Pieces and the Finishing Facia Boards for the Eaves at the Ends

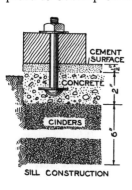

SILL CONSTRUCTION

The windows consist of four single casements, two being placed on each side. These can be of any size to suit the builder, and can be bought from a mill ready to be set into the openings cut for them.

The doors can be made up of the same material as that used for the siding and battened together, or, if a more elaborate door is desired, they can be purchased at a reasonable price, paneled and with a glass in the upper part. If paneled doors are used, 18 boards can be deducted from the siding-material list. The double doors will require fastenings at the center, and, in placing the concrete floor, a keeper should be set in the surface cement for the foot latch. The upper keeper can be attached to the end rafter crosspiece. The usual hardware is necessary for the small door at the opposite end.

A garage built up in this manner and well painted will last for years, and if it becomes necessary to move it, nothing will be lost except the concrete floor, as the building can be lifted from the bolts and taken away bodily.

A Plane Gauge

The gauge consists of a hardwood board, A, $\frac{3}{8}$ in. thick, the length and width being determined by the plane on which it is to be used; a thumb nut, B; a well made butt hinge, C, and some sheet steel. If the plane is made of iron, two holes are drilled through the side of the body, to correspond with the holes in the hinge. A semicircular piece, D, is cut from the sheet steel, so that its center will coincide with that of the hinge pin when it is bolted to the board A with the hinge, the other wing of the hinge being fastened to the plane. Another piece of sheet steel is cut and fastened on the plane, with the hinge, extending up high enough to hold the end of the bolt carrying the thumb nut, B, as shown. With this arrangement the gauge is readily set at any angle, and if a scale of the various degrees is marked on the

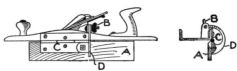

The Gauge as It is Attached to the Side of an Iron Plane

semicircular piece, the adjustment is quickly made without the use of a protractor.—Contributed by John V. Loeffler, Evansville, Ind.

Bracing a Plate-Glass Window

Many times a large plate glass can be saved in a storm or a strong wind, if it is braced lightly, but the bracing

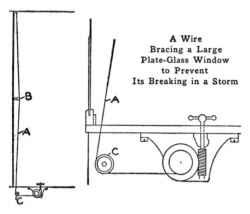

A Wire
Bracing a Large
Plate-Glass Window
to Prevent
Its Breaking in a Storm

is rather inconvenient and unsightly when done in the ordinary manner. It is best to provide an arrangement such as shown in the sketch, which is ready for use at any time. The device consists of a strong wire, A, tied at the top to a hook which is fastened in the ceiling in the middle of the window opening close to the glass. A small bracket is placed in the exact center, B, of the glass, and the wire is drawn taut over the bracket. The part of the bracket in contact with the glass is covered with rubber or felt.

The lower end of the wire passes through a hole in the floor close to the glass and opposite the hook in the ceil-

the worm extends through the floor and is fitted with a hand wheel for drawing the wire taut.

The wire can be released and unhooked at the top when desired. This protection for a large glass is as good as can be made and, unless the storm is very violent, will keep the glass from breaking.—Contributed by Charles Homewood, Cedar Rapids, Ia.

Grader Attachment on a Utility Car

The manner of equipping a general-utility car, used to haul materials on a short electric line, with a grader that serves both for grading and as a snow-plow, is shown in the sketch. The scrapers are held free to swing on a 2-in. iron post set in a casting that is fastened to the bottom of the car. The lower end of the post is also braced from the drawbar on each end of the truck. The scrapers can be raised and lowered with the detachable crank shown at the right of the car, which turns a rod, having lift chains and ratchet wheels to hold the scrapers at any desired height. The material dropped can be sheared to both sides of the track by adjusting the scrapers on a shear cut as in Fig. 1. When placed in the position shown in Fig. 2 the foremost scraper is fastened to the journal box with a piece of metal in the shape of an inverted U. By this arrangement the material is thrown to one side of the track. If both outer

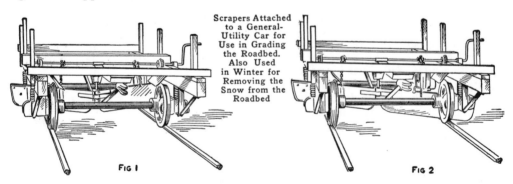

Scrapers Attached to a General-Utility Car for Use in Grading the Roadbed. Also Used in Winter for Removing the Snow from the Roadbed

FIG 1　　　FIG 2

ing, and then over a small pulley, C, to a drum, or cylinder, which is revolved by a worm gear. A small shaft from

ends are fastened to the journal boxes all the material will be held and deposited in the center of the track.

When the scrapers are dropped on the rails at their outer ends, the inner ends at the center pin will be 1 in. higher than at the former.

As a plow, the car was used with success during the winter for clearing the track, throwing the snow to either side of the track. A piece of boiler plate was attached at the outer ends of the scrapers so that the snow could be pushed quite a distance from the roadbed. These plates were made to be raised at the ends so as to be out of the way when crossing a bridge.— Contributed by Frank H. Renninger, Montoursville, Pa.

The Cows and Horses cannot Pass through the Passage to Follow the Person Doing the Feeding

horse or a cow could not make the turn. The small swinging gate can be fastened to one side, to make a permanent inclosure for the smaller stock. —Contributed by H. S. Long, Bazile Mills, Neb.

Plumb-Bob Protector

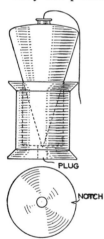

The chainmen of a surveyor's crew carry the plumb bobs in their pockets and the sharp point soon wears holes in the cloth and the bob is lost. An ordinary spool makes a good protector for the sharp point and also provides a place to wind the cord. The hole in one end of the spool is plugged and the other end enlarged to admit the bob. Two notches are cut in the spool rim and the cord is run in them before it is wound on the spool. The spool protects the sharp point and the bob can be carried in the pocket or with other tools. —Contributed by Charles Motton, Toronto, Can.

Gate for a Stock Farm

It is often desired to separate the smaller stock from the larger at feeding time, and in providing a passageway for this purpose, I devised a plan to make the gateway so that I could pass through with a milk pail in each hand while the cows could not follow me. This plan was realized as shown in the sketch. The smaller animals, such as hogs, chickens, and sheep, can pass through the V-shaped part, but a

An Emergency Tire

An old casing filled tightly with pieces of old inner tubes makes a better spare tire for emergency use than a new one, for the reason that an air-filled tire never holds pressure for a great length of time and must be pumped up when it is put on the wheel. A casing filled with inner tubes is ready as soon as it is fastened in place.

Wood Soles to Keep Shoes from Damp Floors

As it was necessary for me to work in a place where there was always some water on the floor, I made a pair of wood soles to keep my feet dry. The soles were made of ¾-in. wood, shaped like the shoe soles and having straps to attach them to

the shoes. Two cleats, 1 in. wide, were fastened to the bottom of the wood sole to raise the shoe high enough to be out of the water.—Contributed by Louis Travers, Corona, L. I.

Mold for Forming a Chimney Top

The outside corners A of the mold are made of sheet steel, about 18 in. long and 3 in. wide, bent in the center

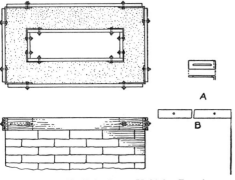

An Adjustable Take-Down Mold for Forming Cement Tops on Chimneys

at right angles. The ends of these pieces are slotted to adjust themselves on bolts. The inside corners are made in the same manner, except that they are 10 in. long. The sides B are made of wood, 3 in. wide and ¾ in. thick, with a hole in each end for a bolt. The length of the outer side pieces is about 18 in., the length of the end pieces, 12 in.; the inner side pieces are about 9 in. and the ends 6 in. long.

The parts are assembled as shown, the slots in the ends of the metal corner pieces allowing considerable adjustment for making different-sized chimneys. A thin strip is slipped in between the mold and the top of the chimney to hold the former in place while the cement is poured in and until it sets. The mold is taken apart by removing the nuts from the bolts. —Contributed.by W. E. Crane, Cleveland, O.

To Prevent Water Barrels from Falling to Pieces

The following method will prevent water barrels from "going to staves" when they become dried out and the hoops loose. Procure some wire and wind it spirally around the barrel, fastening each alternate stave to the wire with a small staple. The wire will keep the hoops in place even when they are loose.

This method is also applicable to wood tubs, buckets, casks, round washing machines, etc., and is more effective if the wire turns are run parallel for two or three courses at the ends. —Contributed by J. W. Whitaker, Francesville, Ind.

Making the Marks on an Old Square Show Plainly

Cover the surface of the square thoroughly with blue chalk, then rub off the surplus. This will leave the division marks clear and distinct in a bright blue, and they will remain in this condition much longer than would be expected.

Another and a more permanent method is to paint the square with red lead and allow it to dry for 5 or 6 hours, then dampen a soft cloth in kerosene and wipe off the surface coat. The paint will adhere in the marks and figures, thus making them plainly visible.—Contributed by H. J. Blacklidge, San Rafael, Cal.

Homemade Fire Extinguisher

It is not generally known that carbon tetrachloride makes a very efficient fire extinguisher. The vapor of this chemical is very heavy and will remain so for a considerable length of time and prevent combustion. The liquid is not injurious to furniture.

A simple fire extinguisher may be made with the use of the tetrachloride in a seltzer siphon. The siphon bottle is filled about two-thirds with the liquid and the metal top screwed tightly in place, whereupon air is pumped on the liquid with an ordinary bicycle pump. Enough air can be forced in to be able to expel the liquid contents, since the liquid has a low specific gravity and the bottle is constructed to stand a high pressure. The nozzle on the bottle should be reduced by soldering the tip of an oil can to it.

This extinguisher possesses many advantages over the common carbon-dioxide reversible ones. It will put out gasoline, benzine and similar fires —in fact the liquid has been used for fireproofing these liquids; articles will not be ruined if they accidentally come in contact with the liquid, and one always knows how much liquid remains within.—Contributed by Arthur Woreschek, New York City.

Using Oil in Compression Grease Cups

It is often desired or necessary to use oil in compression grease cups, and this can be easily done by first filling the cup with waste, or, better still, with a small fine sponge, then turning in the oil and using the cup as with grease. The sponge or waste will hold the oil until the cap is screwed down to squeeze it out.—Contributed by H. F. Hopkins, N. Girard, Pa.

Locating Buried Pipes

The caps of the shut-off pipes for gas and water mains leading into residences often become buried, and sometimes it is very difficult to locate them. Usually a great deal of digging has to be done and the lawn is practically ruined. A little tool which will save the lawn and much unnecessary digging in the location of buried caps, can be easily made as follows:

Procure an old shovel handle and saw it off at A, as shown in the sketch. A piece of steel rod, ⅜ in. in diameter

and 3 ft. long, is inserted in a $\frac{5}{16}$-in. hole bored in the end of the handle. A hole is drilled through both rod and

A Tool for Finding the Location of Earth-Covered Pipes or Service Boxes

handle and a pin driven in to hold them together. The end of the steel rod should be ground to a sharp point. In use, the pointed end is driven into the earth at the location of the cap until it is struck.

Window-Pole Hanger

Window poles used in large office buildings, schools, etc., are usually kept standing in a corner and are not always easily found when wanted. In a telephone exchange a hanger was provided as shown, which was made of a wood block, ⅝ in. thick, 3 in. wide and 2½ in. high, beveled on the outside edges and fitted with a brass clip shaped to receive the knob on the window pole. This provides a hanger

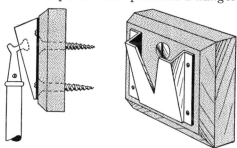

Providing a Place to Keep a Window Pole Where It is Easily Found When Wanted

that keeps the pole clear of the wall and near where it is used.—Contributed by Theodore Woolman, Newark, New Jersey.

A Harnessmaker's Clamp

A very handy, as well as easily constructed, clamp for holding leather is shown in the sketch. The clamp con-

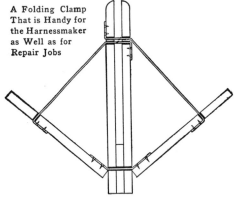

A Folding Clamp That is Handy for the Harnessmaker as Well as for Repair Jobs

sists of two jaws, two levers, a separating block, and a piece of leather, ¾ in. wide and 3 ft. long. When not in use the parts fold up out of the way. In use, it is placed on a chair with the levers under and just back of the knee joint.—Contributed by A. S. Thomas, Gordon, Can.

Bag Holder for a Round Spout

The round metal spouting of a feed mill furnishes a very nice opening to attach a bag with the holder shown in the illustration. It is the idea of a correspondent of American Miller and

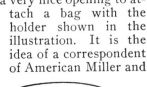

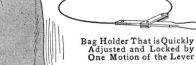

Bag Holder That is Quickly Adjusted and Locked by One Motion of the Lever

is constructed of spring wire and a toggle-joint lever. The lever is made of stake iron, 1 in. wide and ¼ in. thick. The end of the spouting must have a flange at the bottom. When the bag is in place and the holder adjusted the lever locks itself and has no tendency to open. Square spouting can be fitted with round ends to fit the bags.

Permanent Marks on Concrete Floors

The aisles of a manufacturing plant must be kept open for the trucks, and a white line is usually marked on the floor beyond which nothing is placed. These lines will require renewing often, as they wear away quickly. The owners of one factory overcame this difficulty and made a line that could not be worn away in the following manner: Two iron straightedges were placed on the floor, about ½ in. apart, and held down with weights while a compressed-air chisel was used to cut a slit in the cement, ¼ in. deep. White paint was placed in this groove. The depression prevents any wear on the paint and a permanent line is the result.—Contributed by J. C. Moore, Wilkinsburg, Pa.

Removing Lime from Used Brick

An old cleaver with teeth cut in the edge, as shown in the illustration, makes a good tool for removing lime from old brick. The teeth should be

cut about 1 in. deep and the points about 1 in. apart. This makes the best kind of tool for this work.—Contributed by J. N. Bagley, Superior, Neb.

How to Make a Wire Cable

When erecting a smokestack for our heating plant in connection with a greenhouse, some cable was necessary for the guys. We had a lot of fence wire and I decided to make the cables from the wire. We used a general-utility gasoline engine which had a flywheel with 5 spokes. One wire, 200 ft. long, was tied to each spoke in the wheel, the other ends of the 5 wires being fastened to a large post. The engine was started, and in a short time we had a cable of 5 strands nearly 200 ft. long. When the wires became nicely twisted they would break at the wheel and cause no serious trouble.—Contributed by Ed Lampert, Xenia, O.

Cleaning Lead Pipes

Old lead pipes and connections in a bathroom can be cleaned of the green tarnish, so that they will look like new, in the following manner: Procure some ammonium sulphide and add to it a few ounces of salt or at least enough to make a pasty solution. Yellow ammonium sulphide should be purchased, and after it is mixed with the salt it should be rubbed briskly over the pipes. After sufficiently cleansed, the pipes should be polished with a dry cloth. The mixture is harmless and will not hurt the hands though it will stain them, if not washed off quickly after the mixture is applied.

A Pulley-Measuring Stick

Many times it is desired to find the diameter of a pulley that is on a shaft and running. This can be easily accomplished with a measuring stick as shown in the illustration. The stick is made of a piece of wood, 4 in. wide, ¾ in. thick, and of suitable length to reach the shafting. A V-shaped notch is cut in one end large enough to accommodate the largest shaft and then graduated with inch marks starting at the bottom point of the V-notch. The angles on the notch should be cut perfect so that the center of the shaft will be at a true right angle to the scale line. The manner of using the stick is clearly shown, the distance determined being the radius, or one-half of the diameter.—Contributed by Walter A Olsen, So. Boston, Mass.

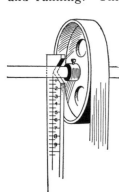

¶Short brads can be easily held for starting by inserting them through a heavy piece of paper to serve as a handle.

Window for a Dairy Barn

A practical dairy-barn window is made by placing the hinges at the lower edge of the sash, as shown, and

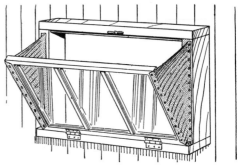

A Window That will Admit Fresh Air and Prevent Draft on the Stock

attaching canvas at the ends so that the cloth will hold the sash partly open. This will deflect the air currents upward toward the ceiling and prevent draft on the stock.—Contributed by Ralph V. Crane, Ypsilanti, Mich.

Straightening an Automobile Wheel

Through accident, warping or poor construction, the road wheel of a car may run out of true sideways. Where the hub is not bent, a simple correction can be made until such time as the wheel can be out of service and the spokes reset or replaced.

Ascertain which is the high side of the wheel, loosen the bolts that hold the flange and hub and fill in with paper, cardboard or tin, AA, then tighten and test, repeating the operation until the wheel is straight. The drawing shows a liner inserted on two opposite sides. At the highest part the greatest thickness should be used, ta-

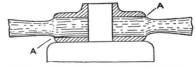

Thin Wedges, Placed under Opposite Sides of the Hub Flange on a Wheel, Straighten the Rim

pering off until the ends of the packing extends under about one-half of the circle. Shellac or paint is good to use in connection with the paper filling.

Setting Disks True in a Chuck

After turning the outside diameter of a piece of work in a lathe chuck, the face must be trued, and the piece can 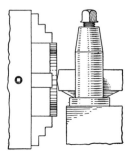 be quickly set in the manner shown. The piece is placed in the chuck jaws which are set tightly, then the tool is turned in the post, and the back end forced against the piece while the lathe is in motion. The work will adjust itself quickly, and it only remains to clamp it tightly in the jaws of the chuck. Thin washers and disks of good-sized diameter which must be faced can be set true in this manner and it does not require much time.—Contributed by E. A. Strauss, Chicago, Ill.

Replacing Broken Ventilator Rope

Many times the ropes controlling ceiling ventilators, skylights, etc., become broken near the ceiling, and, in  the absence of a long ladder, the problem of fastening a new rope to the broken end is often a difficult one.

The following device has proved a good one for overcoming the difficulty. A staple is fastened in the end of a long stick of wood, a rope passed through the staple and a slip noose made as shown. The stick is raised and the noose passed over the hanging end of the broken rope. The long rope is then drawn to tighten the slip noose, which can be pulled tightly, as the knot is too large to pass through the staple. The stick is then drawn down and the staple slipped off the lower end of the rope. The best results are obtained by using a rope a little smaller in diameter than the original one.—Contributed by W. O. Nettleton, Washington, D. C.

Sediment Collector in a Lubricator Pipe

The lubricator is a delicate and sensitive instrument, and any sediment that may collect in its small oil and water pipes will cause trouble. This trouble is more apt to occur where the feed water is treated with soda ash, or other chemicals, to prevent the foaming.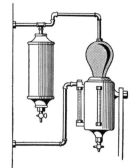

The sketch shows an inexpensive attachment that will provide a protection against the accumulation of sediment in the lubricator. The arrangement requires a few extra pipe fittings. A large-size nipple, fitted on each end with reducers to connect into the lubricator steam line, and a drain cock provide a mud drum for collecting the dirt. The drain cock is opened once or twice and the steam allowed to blow out any sediment collected. Then there will be no danger of this material entering the lubricator.

Repairing Broken Flange Pulley

Some repairs had to be made on a sawmill located in the woods about 20 miles from a station. There was found among the broken parts one 18-in. flanged pulley with one flange broken off and three arms cracked. As time and price were considered above 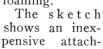 appearance, a new wood pattern was out of the question. The old pulley was broken beyond repair, but it had value as a pattern. About 30 ft. of pasteboard, ⅛ in. thick, was procured and cut into strips, 4 in. wide. These were laid on the face of the pulley and coated with shellac, and each layer tacked to the previous layer. When the space was filled to the size of the flange the wheel was ready for the molder. In this case the rim was cast solid and the metal turned out to form the two flanges.

Applying a Draft Surface to a Curved Pattern

It often becomes necessary when making a curved pattern hastily to apply a draft, and in the ordinary manner this would require considerable time. A draft surface that will answer the purpose in many instances can be made quickly in the following manner: Glue a cord at the center and then glue heavy wrapping paper over

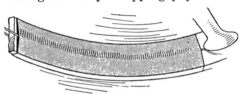

The Cord and Paper Applied to a Curved Pattern Produces a Satisfactory Draft

it as shown. This is for rough and quick work and can be used to advantage for repairs.—Contributed by Ralph E. Mosher, Port Deposit, Md.

Applying Calcimine Evenly

When applying calcimine, alabastine or paint, if it is to be rubbed down, put on the different layers at right angles. The first coat, when dry, is composed of fine ridges of color. When the second coat is applied these ridges hold the color between them, thereby causing the surface to be covered evenly and thoroughly. — Contributed by Jas. M. Kane, Doylestown, Pa.

❡When lapping casehardened steel emery alone will not take hold, but if mixed, half and half, with Portland cement, it will do good work.

An Eraser Holder

Having some fine erasing to do on some drawings, I converted an old drawing pen into an eraser holder

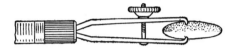

The Nibs of a Discarded Drawing Pen are Cut Off and Shaped to Hold the Eraser

which enabled me to do the erasing neatly. The nibs were cut off close to the adjusting screw and their points turned in slightly. The eraser, which may be of any kind, is shaped as desired and inserted between the points, whereupon these are drawn together on the eraser with the adjusting screw. —Contributed by A. Espey Crozier, Louisville, Ky.

Repairing Holes in Concrete Ceilings

Where it becomes necessary to repair a ceiling that has a hole caused by the falling out of some of the concrete, the following method, described by Concrete Cement Age, will prove satisfactory. The method is to pour a thin grout through a hole drilled through the concrete, the grout being kept in place until it sets by a light panel sup-

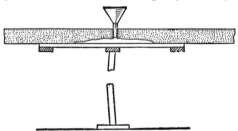

A Panel is Supported by an Upright against the Ceiling over the Hole, to Hold the Grout

ported with an upright from the floor. The upright can be of such length as to be sprung lightly in place, or it may be wedged up from the floor.

Jaw Holder for a Drill Chuck

A certain type of chuck will cause some trouble by coming apart when 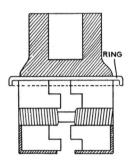 running without holding a drill, or when a beginner turns it in the wrong direction. This trouble may be easily overcome by shrinking on the chuck a ring having a recess that will allow the jaws to back up just far enough to admit the size drill which it is intended to hold.

Recording Telephone Calls

Desiring to know if there had been a call on the telephone in my absence I devised the arrangement shown in  the illustration, to record the call. When I returned it was only necessary to call those from whom a call was expected.

The recording device consists of a strip of carbon paper cut together with a tissue-paper protection, about ½ in. wide, both being rolled on an ordinary pin, provided with a cardboard disk at the head and stuck into the wood of the bell box of the telephone. The pin should be placed so that the end of the paper can be pulled between one bell and the clapper, as shown, and it should be pushed in until the cardboard disk acts as a retarder on the paper.

When leaving the house, the end of the paper is drawn in position, and if a call has been made, the clapper records it on the end of the tissue paper. This end can be torn off and the strip placed on top of the bell, out of the way, until it is necessary to use it again. Any one of the various forms of paper clips fastened to the end of the strips will keep them together.—Contributed by Hazel Kolar, Maywood, Ill.

Depositing Copper on Plaster of Paris

A new method of depositing copper on plaster-of-Paris articles is the result of experiments made by a correspondent of Chemical News. The plaster article is thoroughly dried and then warmed, after which it is placed in a bath of melted paraffin, heated to about 150 deg. F., which causes the paraffin to permeate the plaster and render it waterproof.

After removing the article and allowing it to cool, it is next coated with a thin layer of collodion, diluted with ether and alcohol, whereupon it is allowed to dry. The surface is then coated with electrotyper's plumbago, the copper wires for conducting the electricity are attached, and a second coating of plumbago applied.

The plaster article is now placed in a 10-per-cent solution of aluminum sulphate for a few minutes, and then in a copper bath, made of sulphate of copper and sulphuric acid. The solution should contain from 5 to 8 per cent of sulphuric acid. A current density of 1 ampere for every 4 sq. in. of surface is used on 3 volts. The coating can be polished or given an old copper finish, the same as plate on metals.

Extension Wrench

The wrench end A consists of a hydrant clamp, tapped for a ⅜-in. pipe. The ends BB of the clamp are cut 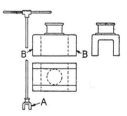 off, and a length of ⅜-in. pipe threaded on both ends to receive the clamp and a ⅜-in. tee. Two 6-in. lengths of pipe are screwed into the tee for a handle. The hydrant clamps can be procured in a variety of sizes and one can be selected to fit any of the common nuts.

How to Make Small Paneled Doors

The usual method of making small paneled doors necessitates a great deal of careful joining and the use of a rabbet plane, usually not found in the home shop. However, these doors can be very easily made, if the following directions are carefully followed.

Instead of using the rabbet plane to cut the slots, the frames are built up, as shown at A, Fig. 1, and fastened together with glue and dowel pins, or screws covered with plugs. For ordinary doors, three pieces of the desired material, ⅜ in. thick, will make substantial frames.

In making up the doors, three frames should be joined with miter joints, after which operation the panels should be slipped in, as shown at B, Fig. 1, and

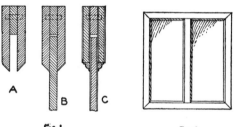

Fig.1   Fig.2

Rabbet Plane Not Necessary in Making Paneled Doors of Veneers and Built-Up Frames

the fourth piece put in place. Nothing but the best furniture glue should be used for all the joints. If expensive woods, such as mahogany or curly birch, are used, their veneers can be purchased at a moderate cost and put together, as shown at C, Fig. 1. Molding of the same wood should be run around the edges. If a more elaborate panel is desired, matched, beaded material may be used. A completed door is shown in Fig. 2.—Contributed by Olaf Tronnes, Evanston, Ill.

Moving a Truck Out of Soft Ground

One of the best methods of moving a truck when it is stuck in soft ground is described by the Automobile. A plank is put under each rear wheel as far as it will go and then it is tied in the manner shown in the sketch.

When the wheels start to revolve they will carry the plank under the wheel

Starting a Wheel Out of Soft Ground with the Aid of a Plank and Rope

with them and the result will be that traction is automatically given.

Coating Black Pipe Fittings with Solder

While putting up some galvanized pipe to serve as a rose trellis for a person who insisted on all parts being galvanized, I found that no fittings could be purchased in the city but the ordinary black-metal kind. As the customer was in a hurry, I planned to coat the tees and ells necessary to complete the job. A strong solution of sal ammoniac was made up, and the fittings placed in it and left there over night. The next morning I removed and dried them, and then they were dipped in a strong solution of muriatic acid, after which I placed them in a pot of melted solder, the kind called half-and-half. When taken out, the fittings would pass anywhere for galvanized.—Contributed by F. H. Bronner, Portland, Ore.

Repairing a Leaky Boiler Tube

Where a bead breaks off on the end of a boiler tube and its replacing with a new one would cause a serious delay a temporary repair can be made as follows: Procure, or make, a band that will enter the hole in the tube and place a 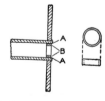 thin copper strip, AA, around the band B, driving them into the end of the tube. This will make a repair that will last indefinitely.—Contributed by J. S. Grant, Winchester, Va.

A Concrete Wall

A very convenient way to build a wall for a back-yard fence, or for a windbreak for stock, is described by Cement Age. The wall is built up in

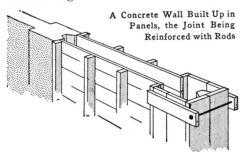

A Concrete Wall Built Up in Panels, the Joint Being Reinforced with Rods

panel sections, about 12 ft. long, with a foundation extending 3 ft. in the earth. Supporting one end of this panel, and built up at the same time, is a large concrete post. The other end of the panel is keyed into the mortise in a similar large post molded at the previous operation, as shown in the sketch.

The forms for the panel are simply two independent walls of 1-in. siding fastened on uprights of 2 by 4-in. material, spaced about 2 ft. apart. The mold for the post is a box open on one face and at both ends. The open side butts against the end supports of the panel forms. To the inside of the board opposite the open face is nailed a wedge-shaped timber which forms the lengthwise mortise of the post, into which the next panel is keyed. Two 2-ft. lengths of $\frac{3}{8}$-in. rod are inserted through holes bored in the face of the wedge, one 3 in. from the top and the other 3 in. from the bottom, allowing 1 ft. of the rods to enter each panel.

In starting the wall, use the post form only and carefully plumb it, using the rods as reinforcing for the first panel.

Bushing a Roller Bearing

When the lining of a roller bearing becomes worn, the shaft turning in the bearing is usually worn also. In most cases it is advisable to procure new parts, but in some instances the parts can be repaired at small cost. Turn the shaft off to the largest diameter it will make and be true and round. Remove the old lining, or sleeve, and caliper the bore of the housing from which the lining was removed. The difference in the diameter of the shaft bearing and the diameter of the housing bore is the amount to be filled with the new lining which must be made to take up the lost motion. Subtract one diameter from the other and take one-half the difference, which will be the thickness of wall of the piece of tubing that must be ordered of a diameter equal to the bore of the housing. In case tubing is used, it is best to turn the shaft to a diameter in sixteenths or eighths, so a stock size of tube may be obtained and the repair job thereby greatly simplified.

Quarter-Turn Belts

A quarter-turn belt will run properly, if the following simple rule is followed. Consider separately each pulley as the driver, then the belt must be delivered from the face of the driver into the plane of the driven pulley. This applies to parallel shafts, at right angles to one another. The plane of a

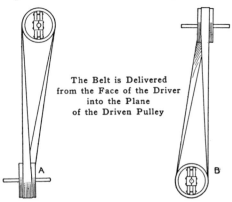

The Belt is Delivered from the Face of the Driver into the Plane of the Driven Pulley

pulley is an imaginary one at right angles to the shaft and passing through the center of the pulley. This rule is clearly illustrated in the sketch.

⊄A good mucilage can be made of acetic acid, $\frac{1}{2}$ oz.; dextrin, 1 oz ; alcohol, $\frac{1}{2}$ oz., and water, $2\frac{1}{2}$ oz.

Drawing Water into a Dry Well

Having a well that would fail in water supply during a drouth and not caring to dig it deeper, I decided to try out a plan for drawing water into the well. I made an air-tight covering for the top and lowered a box of shavings, soaked in gasoline, to the bottom with a fuse attached that could be ignited through a gimlet hole in the covering material. The burning of the shavings caused a vacuum which drew the water through the earth in the bottom of the well, and when I uncovered it, I had plenty of water and have not been without water since that time.—Contributed by J. W. Bauholster, Gresham, Oregon.

Magnetic Plumb-Line Holder

A handy little device for holding a plumb line is shown in the sketch. It

is especially valuable to one working alone around iron structures or in places where a plumb line cannot be tied to iron work. It consists of a rectangular piece of tool steel bent to a U-shape, the ends squared and a hole drilled in the center of the bend for a screweye. After hardening, the screweye is riveted in place and the steel magnetized. The size of the magnet will depend upon the weight of the plumb bob used.—Contributed by M. J. McGall, W. Orange, N. J.

A Lawn Sweeper

Not having any use for an old lawn mower I converted it into a lawn sweeper that served the purpose of

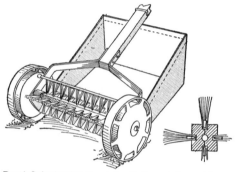

Brush Substituting Revolving Cutters on Lawn Mower for Sweeping and Picking Up Leaves

picking up leaves and pieces of cut grass in a satisfactory manner.

The sweeper was easily and quickly constructed with little expense in the following way: I removed the revolving blades and substituted a brush. The center part for holding the bristles of the brush consisted of two pieces of wood, cut to the length of the old blades and then grooved to fit over the mower axle. They were fastened together on the axle with glue and nails, after which a hole was drilled through the wood and axle and a pin driven in to prevent the finished brush from turning on the metal axle.

The tufts of bristles were taken from a couple of old brushes, $\frac{3}{16}$-in. holes, $\frac{9}{16}$ in. deep, were bored into the four sides of the wood axle $\frac{3}{4}$ in. apart and the tufts well glued and inserted in them, then further secured with wood pegs or wedges. The ends of the bristles should just clear the knife on the mower when they are revolving.

In running this machine over the lawn the brush will throw the leaves into the apron at the rear.—Contributed by Warren E. Crane, Cleveland, Ohio.

Indicator for a Mail Box

An indicator showing when mail has been deposited in a mail box makes it unnecessary to step outside to see if any letters were left by the postman.

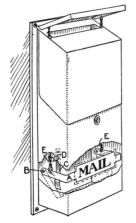

The indicator consists of a piece of heavy tin, A, ½ in. in width and long enough to work up and down freely when placed in the box in the position shown. The center of the tin is cut to a size and shape to correspond with the opening in the front of the box. The ends of the indicator are hinged on rivets, B, so that it will swing as shown by the dotted lines.

A spring clip, C, is riveted to one side of the box in a position to hold the indicator up, and a push button, D, to release it when the mail is removed from the box is provided. Small chains, EE, connect the indicator with the cover of the letter slot, so that when the latter is raised it sets the indicator, which is held in the position shown until released by the button D.—Contributed by F. L. Matter, Portland, Oregon.

Protecting Glass While Painting Window Sash

The modern bungalow door with its square sash and many panes of glass makes a very tedious job for a painter since at least five coats of stain, filler and varnish are required. The following is a method I am using in the case of plate glass: Common-weight manila paper is brushed with linseed oil and dried, then cut into sheets the same size as the glass. A piece of the paper is placed in the open sash, then the sheet of glass and another sheet of paper on top of the glass. The glass is fastened in the usual way. The pane of glass is now protected on both sides and remains so until the finish is completed and dry, when the paper is cut out by following the edges of the opening with a blunt-pointed knife held at right angles to the glass. The result is a bright, clean job and a moisture-proof packing between the glass and the wood. The paper is translucent and transmits enough light to work by easily.—Contributed by I. L. Sears, Waverly, Ill.

Siphon for Large Tanks

A swimming pool, or any tank having its drainage overflow at the surface of the water instead of at the bottom, is easily siphoned dry for cleaning purposes by using the device shown in the sketch. The drain pipe passes through the side of the reservoir A, beginning of course near the bottom. The outer end of the tube must be lower than the bottom of the tank A, and is immersed in a small box of water B. At the top of the bend C is a small air hole which can be opened or closed readily.

In operation, if a constant stream of water is flowing, the tank A fills to the level D and the water trickles

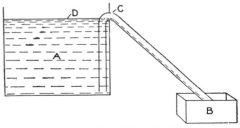

The Siphon is Started by Filling the Tank above the Highest Bend in the Pipe

down the tube. If the small air hole at C is open the water will only flow out to a certain level. If it is desired to empty the tank, no laborious pumping is required to start the big siphon.

Merely plug the air hole C, and the running water drags practically all the air out of the overflow pipe. It then fills with water and acts as a siphon until the tank A is emptied.

If there is no constant flow of water, the siphon can be started by turning on a temporary stream until sufficient air is taken out of the drain tube. It is evident that, unless the outer end of the tube is covered with water, the siphon cannot be started in this way.
—Contributed by Harry W. Holmes, Richmond, Ind.

A Fire Escape

A very serviceable fire escape can be made of stake iron and long bolts in the manner shown. The iron forming the side bars, Fig. 1, should be 15 in. long, 1½ in. wide and ¼ in. thick. A ½-in. hole is drilled near each end of the two pieces and bolts, 12 in. long and ½ in. in diameter, are used for the connecting parts or rungs, as shown

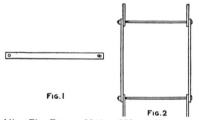

FIG. 1

FIG. 2

Folding Fire Escape, Made of Metal, That can be Quickly Attached to a Window Sill

in Fig. 2. The upper end pieces are bent and pointed so that they can be hooked on a window sill. A fire escape of this kind, when folded, will not occupy much space, and can be attached to a window sill and lowered almost instantly.—Contributed by Wm. Jenkins, New York City.

Lock for Double-Entrance Doors to a Bathroom

A bathroom having two entrance doors should be provided with a device for locking both doors at the same time from either entrance, and this provision made when the building is in the course of construction. If the doors are

located at right angles, a bell-crank lever must be used at A which is joined with two rods, B B, running to

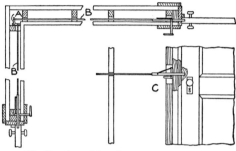

The Locking of One Door Causes the Other to be Locked Simultaneously

the latches at the doors. A lever, which is duplicated on both doors, is made as shown at C. When one door is locked by turning its lever, the other door is locked also.—Contributed by J. E. Carter, St. Petersburg, Fla.

Sliding Display Board on a Show Case

Show cases used for displaying metal goods or any material that is apt to scratch the glass may be fitted with a protector on which articles are placed when they are shown to a customer. A board can be easily made by a carpenter or a handy man, of the same material as the show case and finished in the same manner. The end cross-pieces are rabbeted, as shown at A, and mortised to receive the ends of the centerboard, which can be finished in natural wood, or ribs may be put on the edges to form a depression to re-

GLASS

The Board can be Used at Any Place on A the Top of the Show Case

ceive a piece of heavy felt. The protector can be slipped along on the show case and used at any place for showing the goods.

Homemade Gauge Tester

The large number of air and water gauges about my plant made it necessary to have a gauge tester, says a correspondent of Power. I constructed a

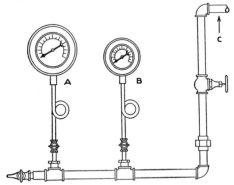

Standard or Test Gauge and Gauge to be Tested on the Pipe Line from a Boiler

tester at home and connected it to the boiler as shown in the sketch. The standard or test gauge is located on the pipe line at A and the gauge to be tested at B. The boiler connection is at C. Gauges may be tested at different pressures by partially closing the valve in the steam line and opening the drain cock at the end until the desired pressure is obtained, as would be shown by the gauge A. All gauges can be kept in perfect working order with very little trouble and expense by using this tester.

How to Cut Dovetails in Metal

Dovetailing in a piece of metal is a very common construction for repairs and for new work, but is usually a slow and exacting job. The task can be

made easier by drilling and sawing out the part for the dovetail insertion. After laying out the dovetail mortise, as shown by the dotted line in the sketch, two holes are drilled at the corners in such a position that a part of them will be left after the dovetail slot is finished. This is seldom objectionable, leaves a much stronger corner, gives clearance for dirt, and

cuts the metal out where it is hardest to work. Two saw cuts are taken just inside of the dotted layout lines. The metal between these lines can be roughed out by any convenient process, drilling, milling, chipping or planing, removing the metal to the lower wave line. In this manner very little stock is left to finish, and the work can be done to the best advantage, as there are no corners to be cut out.

Care of Rain Pipes

The rain pipes of a house should have attention from time to time, and be covered with a coat of good paint inside and out at least once a year. If this is neglected particles of paint will be removed in time, and the unprotected surface of the tin will rust and make a hole rapidly.

If a hole does appear, it should be repaired immediately, in the manner shown at A and B. The surface of the pipe around the hole is thoroughly cleansed of oil, paint and rust, then a

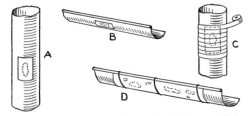

Patches as They are Applied to the Surfaces of Rain Pipes and Gutters over Rusted Parts

piece of tin is cut to cover the opening, allowing a sufficient margin for fastening with solder. After soldering the patch in place the repair is well covered with a coat of paint on both sides.

If no soldering outfit is at hand or one is unable to do soldering work, the repair can be made as shown at C. Coat the piece of tin and pipe around the hole with tar and, while the tar is still in a liquid state, place the tin over the hole and secure it in place by winding some tire tape or electrician's tape around the pipe. The tar will prevent leakage and the tape will hold the tar in place in very warm weather.

When a pipe has been neglected

until it has rusted so that it cannot be cleaned for soldering, it can be repaired as shown at D. A piece of galvanized metal is procured, long enough to cover the part damaged and with sufficient ends to lap on the part not rusted, and bent to the shape of the pipe or gutter, as the case may be, whereupon the inside is coated with tar and the piece placed over the holes. Secure the piece with wire and apply the tape at both ends to prevent the tar from running out. Coat the inside of the gutter with tar and apply a coat of paint on the metal part. A little attention in time will save the cost of a new system.—Contributed by Edward Sieja, Chicago, Ill.

A Glass Cutter for Circular Work

By F. W. BENTLY, Jr.

A cutter for making glass disks is almost a necessity for a repair shop of any kind. The varieties of work requiring the use of such a device are quite numerous, but in a great many instances work of this kind is very crudely done by means of an unguided cutter.

A detail sketch of a circular cutter that can be constructed cheaply is shown in Fig. 1. The supports A A are made of 1-in. round iron, flattened at the lower end and bent so as to allow the cutting bed B to be fastened to them. The upper ends are threaded for a standard 1-in. nut, and by means of 8 of these nuts the guide plates C C are securely held. In addition to acting as a bearing for the cutting shaft D, the plates are rigid supports for the upper part of the cutter.

circle, the center of all circles, of course, to be in line with the center of the cutting shaft D.

The guide plates are shown in Fig. 3, and a detail of the main cutting shaft in Fig. 4. A hole is drilled in the lower end of this shaft to receive the cutting arm shown in Fig. 5. At the end of the cutting arm E, Fig. 1, a hole is drilled of sufficient size to hold a common wheel glass cutter. The supports AA, Fig. 1, are shown in detail in Fig. 6.

A light spring, Fig. 1, should be used to automatically raise the shaft D after the cut has been taken. The device can be instantly set to cut a circular piece of glass to any diameter, limited only by the size of the cutting board B. The cutters may be cheaply replaced when they become worn.

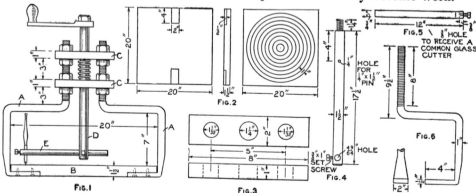

Details of Different Parts for the Construction of a Frame to Hold a Glass Cutter and Drive It in a Circle for Cutting Circular Disks of Glass to Replace Circular Gauge Glasses, and Various Similar Work

The detail of the wooden cutter bed is shown in Fig. 2. The circular guide lines should be scratched with a difference of 1 in. in the diameter of each

⦅The reed of an automobile horn may be renewed by flattening it with a hammer, then filing the edges to fit closely into the opening without touching.

Temporary Book Index

In the study or translation of a book in a foreign language it becomes necessary to refer constantly to the notes

Bill Clips Make an Interchangeable Tab for Indexing, as well as for Holding Divisions of a Book

and vocabulary or index, which many times causes one to lose the place in the text. The use of a few ordinary bill clips, as shown in the illustration, makes it easy to locate instantly any part of the book to which it is desired to refer. The clips separate the unused part of the book from the used and the handles may be labeled as desired. Various sizes can be used, but it is best to select the smallest that will hold the number of pages desired to be clamped together.—Contributed by Harry Schectman, W. Orange, N. J.

Fish Spear with Removable Points

The main part of the spear is made of $\frac{3}{16}$-in. machine-steel rod, and, in the construction of the three-point spear,

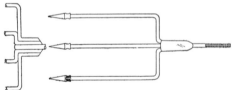

The Points on the Prongs are Hardened Steel and may be Removed and Sharpened

the center rod runs straight and the two outside prongs are bent in the shape shown, then bound to the center rod with fine wire, whereupon the joint is brazed. The four-pronged spear is made in the same manner with all four prongs bent and brazed to the end of the center rod. The points are turned from $\frac{1}{4}$-in. drill rod, then drilled and tapped. The ends of the prongs are threaded to receive the points. After making the points they are tempered. An extra set of points may be kept on hand and used for re-

placing points that become broken or bruised on rocks.—Contributed by F. S. Cummings, Detroit, Mich.

Stopping a Leak in Nickelplated Pipe Connections

The connection between two nickelplated pipes in a newly installed lavatory leaked and all attempts to stop it with pipe-thread lubricant failed. The walls of the pipe were so thin and the coupling so short that any substance in the threads would tend to spring the metal out of place. The leak was successfully stopped by inserting a babbitt-metal sleeve, or washer, between the ends of the pipe in the coup-

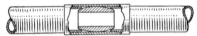

A Babbitt Sleeve in a Coupling between the Ends of Thin Nickelplated Pipes

ling. The babbitt was cast in oval shape and a hole drilled through the center. When the ends of the pipe were turned into the coupling against the babbitt, the sharp edges imbedded themselves in the metal and made a tight joint.—Contributed by J. S. Grant, Winchester, Va.

Fan Blades on an Ordinary Pulley

Having an idle pulley on a rapidly running line shaft, I fitted it up as a fan. Three blades of ⅜-in. white pine, cut as shown at A, were fastened on the pulley B at an angle of about 45 deg. Braces were nailed on for added security. No attempt was made to smooth up the blades, but the fan, nevertheless, gave good satisfaction.

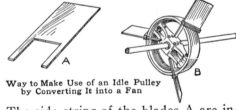

Way to Make Use of an Idle Pulley by Converting It into a Fan

The side strips of the blades A are intended to be nailed to the sides of pulley having no spokes.—Contributed by James M. Kane, Doylestown, Pa.

Segment Work in Pattern Making

By J. H. SHELLY

There are certain kinds of pattern work that require considerable strength, and, for convenience in finishing, it is best to build up the parts in segment courses. This method is to fill in successive layers or courses of wood, their total being equal to the thickness of the piece required and each course divided into a convenient number of pieces called segments. The courses are built up with the segments of one course overlapping the joints of another in a manner similar to laying bricks in a wall. There should always be an equal number of segments in each course. The object of this method is to have the straight grain of the wood to follow, as near as possible, the outline of the pattern, thus eliminating end wood and minimizing the short grain, two factors that usually weaken a pattern.

To turn out this kind of work successfully it is necessary to keep in mind a few general rules, which hold good when applied to all classes of work. It is necessary to use thick, hot glue to obtain the best results, and for the smaller-surfaced segment work the thickest glue should be used. Wherever it is possible to do so, nail the segments together as they are put on, but if for any reason nails cannot be used, it becomes necessary to use toe-

starting another course, but by toe-nailing one course to another the process may proceed without interruption.

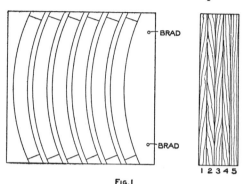

Fig. 1
Cutting Segments with the Grain of the Wood So That There will be No Waste

Use five nails or brads to each segment, three on the outside and two on the inside. The locations for the three outside nails are one at each end and one in the center, the inside ones being placed between the locations of the others. Start the nails before applying the glue and, when nailing, do not drive them in flush, but allow the heads to project about $\frac{3}{16}$ in., so that they may be drawn when the glue is set. Always size the joints between the segments by daubing the ends with glue and rubbing it into the wood with the finger tips. Unless this is done, the

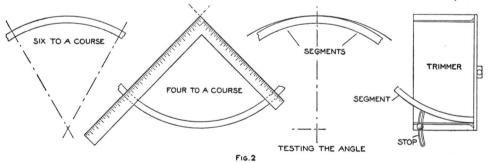

Fig. 2
Manner of Laying Out and Trimming the Segments, Also Fitting Large Segments in Place with the Use of the Trimmer after Setting the Stop to Obtain the Proper Angle

nails or, as a last resort, screw clamps. With the screw clamps it will be necessary to wait for the glue to set before starting another course, but by toe-

inside corners at the butted joints are apt to chip off in finishing, especially if they are to be turned on the inside.

For circular work, the most convenient number of segments to a course is six. The radius of the circle being approximately ⅙ of the circumference,

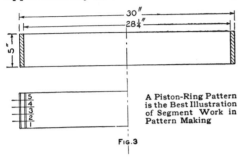

A Piston-Ring Pattern is the Best Illustration of Segment Work in Pattern Making

FIG. 3

it is easy to lay out this number of segments, but for very large circles it will be found more economical to divide into eight or even more segments. Small pieces, that are to be turned on the outside only, may be built with four segments to the course, but for inside turning this will not be found satisfactory, as there is too much short grain at the ends of the segments to make a good job.

The number of courses in any particular job will have to be regulated by the thickness of the stock at hand, but three is the smallest number that should ever be used, unless it is something that is to be screwed or otherwise permanently fastened to another piece that will help to strengthen it and keep it from warping.

In marking off segments preparatory to sawing, always use a template made of a piece of thin stock, unless they are very small and can be conveniently laid out with a pair of dividers. If the segments are thin, the stock may be dressed a little full of the required thickness and cut a little longer than the segment length, then after fastening them together with brads much time will be saved in marking them out from the template and in sawing. When cutting the segments in this manner be sure to saw them to length first, allowing $\frac{1}{16}$ in. or more for trimming. This part of the work is fully illustrated in Figs. 1 and 2.

A saving in thickness may be effected by dressing large segments after they are sawn from the rough plank, and a considerable saving in time by setting the trimmer to the right angle and trimming the ends of all the segments at one setting. This is done by setting the stop on the trimmer as near as possible to the right angle and making the final adjustment by trimming one end of two segments, butting them together and trying them on the circle until the right angle is struck. This makes it necessary to fit but one segment in each course, the last one being trimmed to length.

A piston-ring pattern is a good illustration of this work. The one shown in Fig. 3 is to be finished 30 in. in diameter on the outside, 28¼ in. inside diameter, and is 5 in. deep. Lay out the full-sized section of one side, or half of the ring, adding ⅛ in. for machining, inside and out, at the top, and $\frac{3}{32}$ in. at the bottom; and make an extra allowance of ⅛ in., inside and out, for turning the pattern. The allowance for machining at the bottom is for draft. The segments are cut out as described, a face turned up and the center located. Do not remove the faceplate from the lathe, but set the trammels and strike a circle, the diameter of which is equal to the rough outside diameter of the pattern. In this case it will be about 30½ in. Divide this circle into six equal parts and at each division paste a piece of newspaper about 2 in. square. The joints between each segment should fall in the center of these squares and be glued to them at the ends. This will be found sufficient to hold the ring to the faceplate while turning, and the joint is easily broken with a sharp chisel when the job is finished. Put on the first course of segments, toenailing them to the faceplate, and then face off for the second course which will be nailed to the first, but, in facing off, be sure to use a diamond-point tool taking a light cut for roughing.

The courses that follow require no explanation, and by the time the job is built to the proper height, the glue in the paper joint should be dry enough to start turning, but if there is any uncertainty on this point, it would be better to use a few screws to hold it on the faceplate.

Always build segment jobs on the faceplate in the lathe, unless there is some very good reason for doing otherwise, as there is nothing that consumes so much time as rolling a large faceplate back and forth between the lathe and the bench.

Filler for Cracks in Furniture

Pour boiling water over a quantity of sawdust placed in an earthenware vessel and allow it to set for about one week, thoroughly stirring the mass frequently, then boil it over a fire until it has the consistency of thick paste. Pour this in a coarse cloth and squeeze out the excess moisture. When required for use mix a little of it with a solution of glue water and fill up the cracks or holes with the mixture. When this dries out it has the appearance of wood.—Contributed by Clarke Hill, Weston, Can.

Holding a File without a Handle

Accidents without number have occurred from running the tang of a file into the hand. It is always best to have a handle on the file, but if none is at hand, the file can be safely held as shown in the sketch. It will be noticed that the tang end is not in the hand, and that the hand grasps the file a little farther up, so that if the wrist is turned slightly away, no injury will result even though the file receive a blow on the end. Filing without a handle on work in a lathe is most dangerous of all, but is perfectly safe if done in the manner described. Apropos of filing without a handle, it is interesting to note that filing absolutely perfect

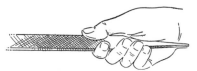

Manner of Holding a File without a Handle
to Prevent Injury to the Hand

fect flat surfaces in a vise is best done without a handle. The extra length of a handle means extra leverage, acting opposite to filing flat.

Drill Press Used for Light Punching

Having a number of oblong holes to punch in some thin brass strips, I devised a die that was used in a drill

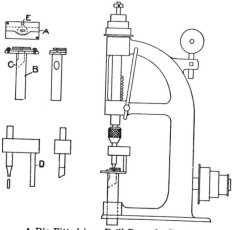

A Die Fitted in a Drill Press for Punching
Oblong Holes in the Brass

press in the manner of a hand bench punch. The die and guide plate A was fastened to a stem, B, that was turned to fit the hole in the drill-press standard. The stem was drilled, as shown by the dotted line C, for releasing the punchings. The guide D passes through the slot E in the die A, so that the whole device may be readily set in the drill press and the punch coincide with the die.—Contributed by A. G. Sherk, Irvington, N. J.

Test for Leather Belting

Place a small strip of leather in strong vinegar and if it is of a good quality, it will not change, except to turn a darker color; but if the leather is of a poor quality, the fibers will quickly swell and the leather will soon become a gelatinous mass.—Contributed by Frank J. Taylor, Las Vegas, Nevada.

Wire Stretcher

This stretcher is especially adapted to draw wires taut on an old fence, but can be used for ordinary work in

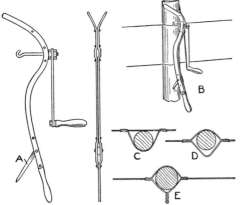

A Stretcher for Tightening Loose Wire on Old Fences, or for Stretching New Wire

putting up a new fence. The handle consists of two pieces of strap iron, about 1 in. in width and 20 in. long, shaped to form a fork at one end and a handhold at the other. A crank, with a shaft and hook, is fitted at the center of the bend, and a projection is pivoted at A. The stretcher, as it is applied to a post, is shown at B. A piece of wire is attached to the main wire around a post, as shown at C, then drawn into the shape shown at D, by the leverage of the handle and the projection A set in the post. This wire is then twisted, as shown at E, until the main wire is stretched tightly.

Correcting Typographical Errors in Typewriting

A time-saving arrangement for correcting typewritten manuscript, where pen or pencil alterations are not allowed, has been used by an ingenious stenographer. A set of typewriter type was procured from the type founders who keep in stock fonts for different makes of machines. A little holder was made for each type, for greater convenience in handling, but this can be dispensed with, as a little care in handling the type itself will suffice. Then

an ordinary rubber-stamp pad was procured and by using the proper amount of ink a shade similar to the impressions made from the typewriter ribbon was easily obtained. The erroneously printed letter is erased and the correct letter stamped on by using the metal type, having, of course, first pressed the type upon the pad.

Where only one or two letters are to be changed on a page and a large number of pages are to be corrected, a material saving of time can be made, the necessity of putting the sheet in the typewriter and adjusting it in the proper position being obviated. The use of the device is of course restricted to the correction of errors where but few wrong letters have been struck.— Contributed by Geo. H. Thornton, Buffalo, N. Y.

Vacuum Cleaner for Removing Loose Sand from Molds

When setting cores in a sand mold there are always some loose particles that fall into the depressions of the mold which, if not removed, will cause a dirty or ragged part on the finished casting. In some instances these particles fall into places where it is impossible to remove them with a molding tool. I rigged up a device that is giving entire satisfaction and can be used in any part of an irregular mold for drawing out loose particles in the same manner as a vacuum cleaner. The device consists of pipe and fittings, con-

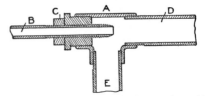

Loose Sand in a Mold is Easier Drawn Out with a Vacuum Than with a Tool

nected as shown and used on an air-pressure line of the shop.

The body of the device is a ¾-in. tee, A, which is fitted with a reducer, C, to admit the end of a ¼-in. pipe, B, having a long thread and a pointed end.

The end of this pipe should extend over the opening in the branch pipe E. The amount of this extension can only be determined by testing it for best results, whereupon the pipe B is fastened permanently with a locknut or a pin. The air rushing through the pipe B causes a vacuum in the pipe E, which is used in the mold. The end of the latter pipe can be fitted with a flexible hose so that it may be more easily handled. The suction set up by this device is sufficient to remove any loose particles from a mold.—Contributed by Eugene J. Desmond, Philadelphia, Pa.

A Hand Scraper for the Woodworker

A very handy scraper, described by a correspondent of the American Carpenter and Builder, is made of a piece

The Scraper is Easily and Quickly Made and Used in a Manner Similar to a Plane

of ordinary ash, 2 in. wide and 6 in. long, with a notch cut in it and a scraper blade fastened with screws in the notch. The blade has slots for the screws instead of holes, so that it may be adjusted for the cut. The notch is located near one end, where the user holds the tool and pushes it along as a plane.

A Small Expansion Arbor

Small gears, as shown in Fig. 1, or similar work, where specifications call for the hole to be ground first and the outside finished last, require a very accurate expanding arbor. Such an arbor, which consists of two parts and a nut for expanding the sleeve, as shown in Fig. 2, can be easily made.

The outer part or sleeve is turned to a neat fit in the hole of the work after both surfaces are ground, then it is

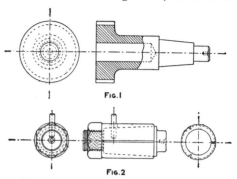

An Expanding Arbor for Holding Small Work That must be Ground Internally Before Finishing

bored tapering. The center, or expanding part, is turned tapering to fit the bore of the sleeve and threaded on the smaller end. A pin is fitted loosely through the sleeve and driven tightly into the center part. This is to hold the parts together and prevent them from becoming lost.—Contributed by C. E. Bradley, Fall River, Mass.

How to Make a Screw-Pitch Gauge

Cut a clean thread with a new die on a bolt and make a slot through the center of the threaded length. Slip the piece of steel to be used for the gauge in the slot, as shown at A, and clamp it in a vise. It is an easy matter to file the threads into the gauge with a new three-cornered file. The metal is then shaped as shown at B. A set of gauges can be made in this manner and attached to a handle. The number of

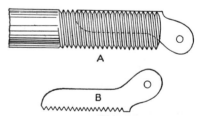

The Threads on the Bolt Make a Guide for Filing the Notches on the Gauge

the thread should be stamped or etched on the gauge.—Contributed by Louis A. Novak, Mahnomen, Minn.

How to Make a Simple Level

By ARTHUR MOORE

The level described in the following article was constructed by the writer and has been exceedingly serviceable in view of the fact that it can be used in a number of cases where the ordinary level is quite troublesome to operate.

Briefly, the level consists of two glass tubes connected at their lower ends by means of a piece of flexible rubber tubing, A. These two tubes are mounted on end on wooden bases and have scales marked on them, the points on the scale being measured from the under side of the base upon which they are mounted. The tubes and connecting hose are filled with water until it rises about halfway in each tube. Two objects can now be adjusted to the same level by placing one of the tubes on each of them and raising or lowering one of the objects until the liquid is at the same height in both tubes.

The level may be constructed as follows: Obtain two pieces of ½-in. glass tubing about 2½ ft. long. Draw one end of each piece down to at least a ¼-in. diameter, in a gas or alcohol flame, and bend it over at right angles to the main portion of the tube. Cut this small projecting piece off so that the remaining portion projects sidewise beyond the side of the main tube about ⅛ in. Turn, from a piece of hard wood, two pieces, that are to serve as bases, similar to those shown in the sketch. Drill a ¾-in. hole in the top of each of these pieces to a depth about ⅛ in. less than the thickness of the piece. Obtain two short pieces of brass tube, and drill a hole in the side of each of the wooden bases, so that the tube B will fit in it tightly and enter the large opening near its bottom. Place the end of the ½-in. tube with the projection on it in the large opening so that the small projection is in the end of the brass tube, and pour a small quantity of plaster of Paris around it. Hold the glass tube in a vertical position and allow the plaster to harden. A scale may now be marked on the glass tube, or one may be marked on a piece of paper and pasted to the tube. The points on this scale should all be located by measurements from the lower surface of the base. A small cap may be provided for each tube with a sight mounted on it so that the two tubes may be used in running a level line, or leveling a point some distance away. Make sure that the end of the tube is not closed up, as the liquid then could not readily pass from one to the other due to the air pressure. The upper edge of the sights must be the same distance from the lower surface of the base in each case. The glass tubes may be protected by mounting two wooden strips, one on each side, on the wooden base.

Calipering Steel Balls

A method used by a correspondent of American Machinist to caliper hardened steel balls is shown in the accompanying sketch.

A piece of spring steel is bent in the form of a pair of tweezers, with holes of different di-

Temperature of Steel Ball Remains Normal; Thus True Measurements are Obtained

ameters drilled in each side and countersunk on the inside. A ball is placed in a hole suitable to its diameter, allowing it to project so that there is no interference with the calipering.

By using the tweezers the heat of the hand does not cause the ball to expand, thus the true diameter may be easily determined.

Washing Pad for Removing Grease from the Hands

Curled hair, such as used in upholstering the finer grades of furniture, is much better than a brush for removing grease and grime from the hands. It penetrates the crevices of the knuckles and nails, and does not abrade the skin at all. To use, simply take a large handful of the hair, apply soap and wet it, then rub over the hands. It will take several days before the wad assumes the form that gives the best results, but once in shape it will last indefinitely. — Contributed by Mabel Hillyer Eastman, Chillicothe, Mo.

Inserting Packing Leathers

It is sometimes very difficult to get a packing leather started into the cylinder. The soft leather will spread  and squeeze out at every attempt to push it and the attached piston into the cylinder. The sketch shows how the leather can be very easily inserted by means of a strip of tin a little larger than the inside circumference of the cylinder. The tin protruding from the opening of the cylinder forms a funnel into which the leather is pressed at all points, thus easily slipping into the cylinder. The tin can be withdrawn with a small pair of pliers. This kink is a time saver when working on all leathers attached to push-up pistons.

Clearing Shellac Varnish

Shellac varnish used in pattern shops has a tendency to hold in suspension impurities that leave dirty streaks on the patterns when the liquid is applied. The liquid can be easily purified by the addition of a few crystals of oxalic acid. The shellac should be stirred, to aid in a thorough mixing, then allowed to settle for several hours. Care should be taken not to use too much acid.

Overhead Location for an Automobile Mirror

The use of a small mirror to reflect a view of the following traffic is fairly common practice, though the location

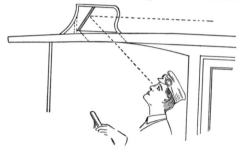

The Mirror Placed on the Roof Makes It Easy to See the Traffic Directly Behind

of such a mirror is not always the best. One difficulty is that traffic close behind a vehicle, equipped with a mirror in the usual position, cannot be seen. In order to obviate this difficulty a driver of a limousine placed the mirror on the roof of the car. The mirror is mounted in a hood which protects it against rain or snow. Through a glass-covered hole in the roof the driver has a good view of the mirror without undue exertion, and the traffic directly behind can be plainly seen.— S. P. McMinn, Brooklyn, N. Y.

How to True Up Triangles

The edges of triangles will become roughened and slightly hollowed out by constant use and must be trued frequently to produce accurate drawings. A very efficient and quick way to true them up is shown in the illustration,

The Edge of the Triangle is Trued by Rubbing It on a Flat Surface Covered with Abrasive

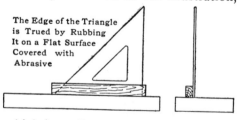

which is easily understood. The abrasive used is a valve-grinding compound that can be procured at any garage.— Contributed by H. M. Briggs, York, Pennsylvania.

Emery-Cloth Ends to Attach in a Hacksaw Frame

A strip of emery cloth, up to 2 in. in width, can be effectively used in a hacksaw frame, if the ends of the cloth

The Strip of Emery Cloth in the Saw Frame is Used in the Same Manner as a File

are held straight to prevent creasing. This may be accomplished by folding the ends over a piece of broken hacksaw blade, then bending a wire clip, to attach it in the saw frame, over the piece of saw blade, as shown in the sketch. In this way a strip of emery cloth may be used like a file.—Contributed by John Steen, Minneapolis, Minnesota.

A Special Die Holder

In some instances it becomes necessary to rethread a stud so placed that it is impossible to get at it with an ordinary die stock. A stud on a cylinder head, for instance, where there are several located, will require a special die holder to turn the die on the stud that needs a new thread. Many times the threads on these studs become bruised or battered in making repairs, and then, too, it may be necessary to reduce the size of the stud to fit some other nut. A special die holder for rethreading these studs is made of a piece of steel or cast iron, bored at one end to receive the die and drilled for a thumb-

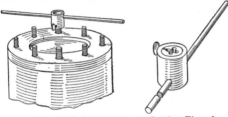

Long Head Diestock for Use in Cutting Threads on a Stud Surrounded by Others

screw. The piece may be of any length and a rod run through a hole drilled in the end opposite the die for a handle.

Lubricating the Stern Bearing of a Motorboat

The usual form of a strut for motorboats provides no means of lubrication for the stern bearing The sketch shows a method by which grease can be very easily fed to the bearing. A piece of ¼-in. copper tubing is cut long enough to reach from the bearing to a point 6 in. above the waterline and the after edge of the strut filed slightly flat. This will make it easier to solder the tube to it. A hole is bored into the bearing of sufficient diameter to receive the tube and another bored through the strut plate A, Fig. 1, the bottom of the boat and the floor. This hole should be small enough to hold the tubing tightly in place. The tube is now forced through the floor, hull and plate, and into the hole in the bearing for a short distance. By tapping very gently with a hammer it can be straightened

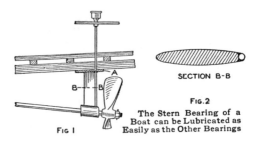

SECTION B-B

FIG. 2

The Stern Bearing of a Boat can be Lubricated as Easily as the Other Bearings

FIG 1

out and pressed against the edge of the strut. Both the tubing and strut should be cleaned with muriatic acid or some good soldering flux, after which they can be soldered together. The solder should be run in freely between the tube and the whole smoothed over, as shown in Fig. 2. A little solder should be run around the tube where it passes through the plate in order to make the point water-tight. A grease cup of the kind preferred is attached as shown. When the bearing needs lubrication, a turn or two of the screw cap in the cup forces the grease through the tube into the bearing. If the solder is smoothed over carefully, the resistance will be no greater than before the tube was attached.—Contributed by Olaf E. Tronnes, Evanston, Ill.

To Prevent Dirt from Entering beneath the Finger Nails

Sometimes a person is called to help repair a machine in a shop where there is considerable dirt and grease. An office man can keep the dirt from getting under the nails by filling the space between them and the fingers with soap. After the work is finished, the soap is easily washed out and the nails cleaned.—Contributed by Loren Ward, Des Moines, Iowa.

Combination Side and End Wrench

A very handy all-around wrench can be made by shaping the jaws from a piece of steel—a piece of buggy spring

The Construction of the Jaws Makes a Side and End Wrench of One Piece

will do—as shown in the sketch. The size and thickness of the wrench will depend on its use. This makes a side and end wrench.—Contributed by C. C. Hall, Eureka Springs, Ark.

Writing Pen for the Draftsman

An old, discarded ruling pen can be easily changed into a pen for lettering or writing on tracing cloth by grind-

The Shape of a Ruling Pen to be Used in Writing or Making Letters on Tracing Cloth

ing away that portion of the nibs shown by the dotted lines in the sketch. To obtain best results, the pen must be held in the hand so that the opening in the pen is vertical and not at an angle.—Contributed by Wm. Rosenberg, Watertown, Mass.

Parallel-Rule Center Gauge

A very handy little tool for locating the center of any piece of round, square, octagon or oval stock is made in the manner of parallel rules. The material required is two pieces of hard wood, 4 in. long, ½ in. wide and ⅜ in. thick; two pieces of metal, 3 in.

long, ⅜ in. wide and $\frac{1}{16}$ in. thick; three wood screws; one bolt with a knurled nut, and a steel point. The parts are

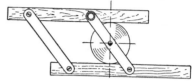

Lines are Scratched across the Ends of the Stock and Their Intersection Marks the Center

put together as shown in the sketch. This will locate centers on stock from ⅛ in. up to 2 in. in diameter. The method of using the tool is easily understood by the illustration.—Contributed by A. Kerbaugh, Allentown, Pa.

Notch to Locate Slots in an Electric Plug

The electric-light extension cord has grown from a convenience to an actual necessity, and there are many varieties, some with faults, some with virtues, some with both. Of the various kinds of plugs one of the commonest is shown in the sketch.

It is inconvenient to connect one of these plugs in the dark, but, if a groove is cut on an emery wheel in the part shown and the raised lettering removed in the same manner, the brass terminals may be easily inserted in the slots.

Pipe Tee Made of an Old Valve

An old discarded valve body will serve as a tee in an emergency. The upper portion A is usually tapped to make a fine thread, but this opening can be rethreaded with a pipe tap and a tee fitting will be the result. In some instances a reducing tee may be made of the valve part.

⫷The approximate wave length of an aerial may be determined by multiplying the height of the aerial by four.

Lining Up Automobile Wheels

The front pair of wheels on all automobiles are "cut under," or have a slight pitch from ½ in. to 1½ in. If

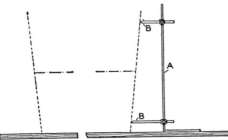

The Pitch of a Wheel is Easily Determined and Its Mate Adjusted to Match It

an axle is bent or twisted in an accident, some means must be employed in the repair shop to get the same "cut-under" to each wheel when straightening the axle. I have used a homemade device which gives the desired results. It consists of a standard, A, to which is attached two sliding pointers, BB. The pointers may be set for any pitch and used in lining up either wheel. The wheels to be lined are placed on a level surface—a straight plank will do—and the device used as shown.—Contributed by T. C. Bevan, Utica, N. Y.

Emery-Cloth Holder for Polishing

The use of a hacksaw frame for holding strips of emery cloth to polish surfaces is a good one, but I find that a decided improvement over this method is to attach the strip of cloth between the ends of a bow. The spring of the wood bow keeps the cloth at a ten-

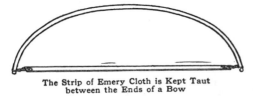

The Strip of Emery Cloth is Kept Taut between the Ends of a Bow

sion and at the same time leaves it sufficient give to allow for inequalities of surfaces and round edges.—Contributed by G. H. Holter, Jasper, Minnesota.

Boring a Deep Hole on a Lathe

When using a boring tool clamped in the tool post of a lathe for boring deep holes, the length of the tool causes it to spring so much that only light cuts can be taken. This makes slow work where there is considerable material to be removed. The following method will hasten the work to some extent.

Instead of setting the tool out far enough to reach the bottom of the hole, set it out far enough to go only halfway. Rough off all the surplus stock with the tool so set, leaving a small amount of material for a finishing cut, then let the tool out and rough the rest of the way, finally taking a finishing cut through the whole length of the hole.

This is well illustrated in the drawing where a casting is to be bored for two bearings A and B. If the tool is set to reach the bottom and used to bore the front bearing, it would not be

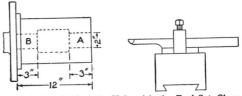

Boring One-Half of the Hole with the Tool Set Close in the Tool Post Hastens the Work

very rigid—it would have a 12-in. overhang, while, if set as shown for the first cut and roughing the bearing A, it will have but 3 in. overhang and the job can be proportionately hastened.

Filling Holes in Castings

Defects in castings may be filled with a paste made of 2 lb. of iron borings, 1¼ lb. of dextrine and ¾ lb. of litharge, the whole mixture being colored with lampblack to the desired shade. The iron borings should be sifted. After the parts are thoroughly mixed, add enough water to make a paste. This is applied to the defects and blow-holes with a putty knife. When the paste has dried thoroughly, it can be machined just as the metal.

Parade Float Representing a Locomotive

An easily constructed and very attractive decoration for an automobile in a parade is a locomotive. The framework, which can be covered in various ways, is built up of thin strips of wood, nailed to curved pieces to shape the boiler part and supported principally on the running board of the automobile. The sand box, steam dome, headlight and smokestack can be shaped of heavy cardboard and fastened to the frame on top, whereupon they are colored or decorated as desired. The bell should be the real article, which will add realism to the feature. The tender is connected on the rear with a short drawbar of wood, the framework being box-shaped and supported on two cart wheels.

The wheels of the locomotive and tender should be raised slightly above the surface and, if desired, they can be made to revolve by connecting them by a rope drive to the rear wheels of the automobile.

The framework is covered with light material, such as cheesecloth, and then any floral decorations may be attached by having the persons in the rear seat of the automobile dressed in the garb of an engineer and a fireman, and by their taking such a position that their heads and shoulders are out of the cab window. The driver of the automobile can observe the road ahead through an opening left in the slats at the smaller end of the boiler over the fire box. The front end provides air circulation for the automobile radiator.

Destroying Moles

An excellent way to exterminate moles is as follows: Procure a small can of calcium carbide, which can be purchased from an automobile or bicycle dealer, open the hole where the mole has been digging and place some of the carbide in it. Pour 2 or 3 gal. of water into the hole and close up the opening. In about 15 or 20 minutes open the hole and immediately ignite the gas formed. Be careful in lighting the gas. A gas lighter or a match placed in the end of a long stick should be used. The gas will burn for a few

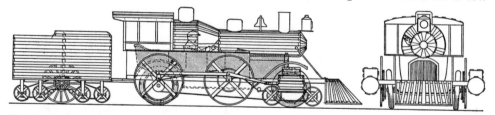

The Framework is Built Up in the Shape of a Locomotive Which Covers the Automobile and Furnishes the Groundwork for Any Decoration, Which may be Plain or Profusely Covered with Flowers

as desired. The groundwork can be covered with ferns and the working parts with flowers. The attractiveness of the float can be greatly enhanced seconds and then it will back-fire in the hole. There will be no more trouble from the mole.—Contributed by W. H. Whitmer, Portland, O.

To Keep a Large Flag Close to the Pole

The school board of our city was at a loss to know how to attach their large flag to the pole so that it would hang close and not bag. I submitted a plan which was accepted, and its results were entirely satisfactory. The plan is as follows:

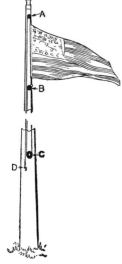

A pulley, A, was attached to the pole about 1 ft. below the copper ball on the top, and a second pulley, B, attached about 12 ft. 8 in. below the first pulley, or a few inches more than the width of the flag. The third pulley, C, was placed about 5 ft. from the ground, and at one side of this pulley a large staple, D, was driven into the pole. The pulleys used were the iron-block type, and they were fastened to the pole with lag screws.

After the pulleys were in place a piece of $\frac{3}{16}$-in. wire rope was run through the pulley B and the bottom pulley C, and the ends tied to an iron ring, 1½ in. in diameter, to form a continuous rope line around the two pulleys. Another piece of rope was procured, long enough to reach from the staple D up to and through the pulley A at the top and down to the pulley B, where the end was fastened to the ring of the first rope. The lower end of the rope at the staple was made up into a ring so that it could be fastened with a padlock.

To lower or raise the flag, an extra piece of marline rope is attached to the ring after it is unlocked, which allows the wire rope to be pulled down and the flag attached to the long line above the ring where the two lines are fastened. The fastenings for the flag consist of small snaps attached to the long line between the upper pulleys about 1 ft. apart, and small rings are sewed on the flag to correspond with the snaps.—Contributed by R. E. Rhines, Centralia, Wash.

Removing a Small Piece of Steel from the Eye

While working at an emery wheel a small particle of steel was thrown into my eye and a fellow workman removed it quickly and without pain in the following manner:

He felt along the lapel and front of his coat for a protruding horsehair of the inner lining used as a stiffener. When found he drew it out and formed it into a loop by folding it double. The eyelid was turned back with the end of a lead pencil, and after the speck of steel was located, it was removed by drawing the loop in the hair over the eye.

The horsehair remover has been used by this man in many instances and has never been found to injure the most sensitive eye.—Contributed by Hugh Wrigley, Philadelphia, Pa.

Repairing a Broken Gunstock

If the gun is provided with projecting tangs on the top and bottom and these are broken with the stock, braze the parts together and provide a piece of steel, cut as shown at A and then bent to fit in between the tang irons

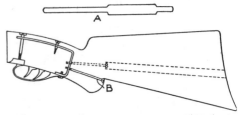

Repairs on a Broken Gunstock That will Make the Parts Rigid and cannot be Seen

and anchored to them with screws. The wood must be removed so that this added piece will fit snugly in place. A hole B is then bored to receive a long screw or bolt, after which the U-shaped piece of steel is drilled and threaded to admit the threads of the screw.

If the stock is of the old style without a grip, the screw can be run in as shown by the dotted lines. This kind of a repair not only makes the parts rigid, but the joint cannot be readily seen.—Contributed by Edward Anderson, Deadwood, S. D.

Aeroplane Angle Indicator

The indicator is used on an aeroplane to designate when the machine is climbing or descending, and to show the amount of angle. A glance at the bubble will tell the airman if he is getting into a dangerous position.

The instrument is made as follows: A piece of glass tubing, about ¼ in. in diameter and about 6 in. long, is bent to the arc of a circle the radius of which is about 6 in. The tube is then

The Bubble Tube is Similar to That of a Level and a Degree Scale is Placed Behind It

filled with water or some colored liquid, allowing sufficient air to remain inside for a small bubble that acts as a pointer. A cork is sealed in each end by covering it with sealing wax. A graduated scale is placed behind the tube.

Make another similar instrument, but bend the tube to a quadrant, and the greatest angle read will be 45 deg. This instrument is placed at right angles to the first so that the lateral angle, or "bank," can be determined.— Contributed by H. W. Hahn, Chicago.

Preserving Cut Flowers

The fragrance and freshness of a bouquet can be retained for many days if the following plan is observed: Arrange the stems loosely in a glass of water, place the glass upon a flat, shallow dish and fill the dish around the glass nearly full of water, then invert a

large glass bowl or fruit jar over the flowers, fitting it evenly upon the dish. The water will rise inside and outside,

The Moisture Rising from the Water will Preserve the Flowers Within for a Long Time

thus forming an air-tight receptacle for the contents. The moisture continually produced inside of the bowl envelops the flowers in a mistlike atmosphere, which prolongs the life and color to a surprising length of time. —Contributed by Renice Radcliffe, Laurel, Md.

Key Bars

With two key bars of the shape shown in the illustration the work of fitting and removing keys from flywheels, driving gears, etc., becomes an easy task. The bars may be used for either large or small keys and are both made of tool steel, ⅝ in. thick, 1¼ in.

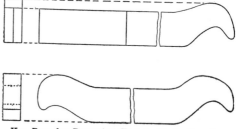

Key Bars for Removing Keys in Shafts Carrying Flywheels, Gears and Pulleys

wide and 2½ ft. long. These are forged into the shape shown and tempered. —Contributed by George Jager, Woodside, L. I.

Bathtub under the Floor

For the house of limited space, or for the summer camp, a bathtub placed under the floor is very convenient. The

The Bathtub is Out of Sight under the Floor When Not in Use

ordinary plumbing is carried out with all attachments beneath the floor, and a trap door covers the tub when not in use.

The rim of the tub should be placed close against the under side of the flooring boards, and it is best to fit boards closely around the curves on the ends.—Contributed by Manley K. Haskins, Syracuse, N. Y.

A Contractor's Sand Car

With a sand car, made as shown in the sketch, a much more even layer of sand can be applied on the surface of a sidewalk than by throwing it on with a pail in the ordinary manner. The box of the car is built up in the usual way, with the exception of the bottom, which consists of two pieces placed on a slant toward the center, where a space of about ⅛ in. is provided for the sand to pass out. This slot is covered with a

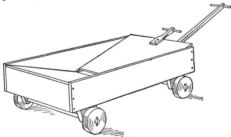

The Sand Cart will Apply an Even Coat of Sand on the Surface of a Cement Sidewalk

slide operated by a handle. The thickness of the sand layer may be controlled by the width of the slot and the speed of the cart.—Contributed by Edwin F. Jones, Waterbury, Conn.

Oxidizing German Silver

German silver does not oxidize with the usual immersion dips, such as liver of sulphur, says the Metal Industry. It is customary to copperplate the German silver for a short time, then oxidize in a cold solution, consisting of 1 gal. of water, 1 oz. of liver of sulphur, and $\frac{1}{16}$ oz. of ammonia.

This will produce a black tone. If the finish is to show more of a gun-metal tone, the oxidized surface should be scratch-brushed after the articles have been washed and dried out.

Soldering-Iron Cover for Coal-Fire Heating

A soldering iron would be used a great deal more than it is for repairing articles in the home, if there were an easy way to heat it. The ordinary fire is not clean enough for heating the copper, but it can be used if a covering is made to hold the copper point while

The Cover When Placed on a Soldering Iron Protects It for Heating in a Coal Fire

it is heating. Such a covering can be made of sheet metal which is shaped and bent to be riveted together at the side and end. A handle is attached at the open end. A soldering iron heated in this device will do as good work as if heated in a gas flame.—Contributed by Luther Turner, Beardstown, Ill.

Holder for Round Stock While Grinding

A useful tool for holding round stock by hand while grinding on a water stone can be easily made by cutting a V-notch in the end of a suitable piece of metal. Revolving the stock with one hand and pressing it against the wheel with the V-shaped tool results in a better job and is a safer way than the usual.—Contributed by Felix Heberlein, Detroit, Mich.

Paving and Pavements

By GEORGE LITTELL

PART I

[The object of this article will be to give the reader a general idea of the course of procedure and the latest methods employed on a construction job of this kind. Only the actual work will be described.—ED.]

Grading

When the excavating gang arrives upon the job it finds that the engineering crew has placed stakes, at regular intervals, along both sides of the proposed street. These stakes are marked with the "cut" to be made at that point and are placed at an offset from the curb line of the finished pavement. This offset may vary with conditions, but is usually about 3 ft.

A pair of stakes are shown in position in Fig. 1, the "cut" 050 being equal to "cut" 0.50 ft., or, to be very plain, cut ½ ft. These cuts are given to the crown, or top, of the finished pavement and care must be exercised when doing the rough grading. When figuring the actual cut to be made, to ascertain the crown of the subgrade, the following method must be used. The given cut to the crown is the surface level of the finished pavement, so that the depth of the cut must be the total of the surface coating, the cushion coat and the depth of the concrete.

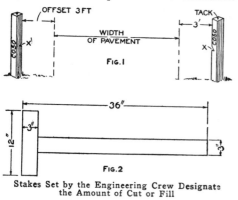

FIG.1

FIG.2

Stakes Set by the Engineering Crew Designate the Amount of Cut or Fill

For example, a brick-paved street using the cut given in Fig. 1 would be as follows:

Given cut 0.50	0 ft.	6 in.
Thickness of brick	0 "	4 "
Thickness of cushion	0 "	1 "
Depth of concrete	0 "	6 "
Actual cut to subgrade	1 ft.	5 in.

To obtain the crown of the subgrade three wooden tees, made as shown in Fig. 2, are used; two being

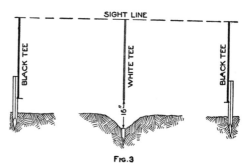

FIG.3

The Crown is Obtained by Sighting over Tees Placed on the Stakes to Adjust a Center Tee

painted black and one being painted white; or they may be painted red, white and blue. The point of a pocketknife is placed into the stake, at X, Fig. 1, on either side of the road, and a black or colored tee is placed upon each. The white tee is then held between them and lined up for height. A stake is then driven down 1 in. less than the actual cut to the subgrade or, using the example, 1 ft. 4 in. This operation is illustrated in Fig. 3.

Stakes are then driven in on the offset line and the actual grading is commenced. If the soil is of clay, or fairly loose, an ordinary grading plow is used, but if it is composed of stone, pieces of block asphalt, cinders, etc., as is often the case, a router plow is called into action. One of these plows is illustrated in Fig. 4.

The plows are started one after another up one side of the road and down on the other, leaving a hard road in the center for the use of the teams. After the sides are plowed up, the wagons use one side of the road while the plows loosen up the center. The same route is covered again and again until the subgrade is reached. Scrapers are also used, sometimes, but not to any great extent when a heavy cut is to be made.

The wagons are usually lined up and

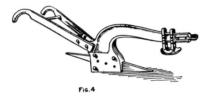

FIG. 4

Implement Used Instead of the Plow for Loosening Up Earth Packed Hard by Traffic

a crew of about 10 laborers is placed on the head or lead wagon; about eight laborers on the next wagon; about six laborers on the third, and about four laborers on each of the others. This method of loading keeps the teams continually on the move and the earth is speedily removed.

When the rough grading is finished, the tees are again used and stakes are set 10 in. higher than the subgrade. The gutters are cut to grade by using a line set on the bank, and quarter

FIG. 5

The Tees are Again Used after Rough Grading to Set the Stakes on a Higher Level

stakes are set midway between the gutter and the crown of the road, Fig. 5, and experienced graders, with mattocks and shovels, trim off the few remaining lumps and fill up the depressions until the finished grade is smooth and even. Different soils settle to different depths when the roller is put upon them, but if the grade is finished ¾ or 1 in. higher than the desired subgrade it will usually press down until it is nearly correct or, at most, ½ in. high. This will necessitate only 5½ in. of concrete instead of 6 in. and, while not materially weakening the foundation of the pavement, means a considerable saving of concrete if the job is a large one.

Trenching

After the finished grade is obtained the next operation is trenching for the drain tile. The width and depth of this trench is shown in Fig. 6, at A. The drain tile, broken stone, concrete and curbing are shown in position at B.

The drain tile comes in 1-ft. lengths and is simply laid on a foundation of gravel, chips from curbing, old concrete or some similar material; covered with 1 or 2 in. of the same material and then with about 4 in. of fine earth, well tamped. The concrete base for

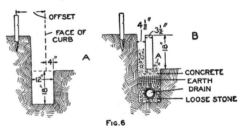

FIG. 6

Trenching for the Drain Tile and Its Location with the Fillers in Place

the curb is laid upon this earth, the curb is set and more concrete is tamped in behind it.

Concrete Curbing

While concrete curbing is gaining favor among highway engineers with great rapidity, not only on account of the lower cost of construction, but also on account of a better-looking and more lasting job, its use is not yet universal. A great number of the larger cities have adopted this type of construction while others have not used

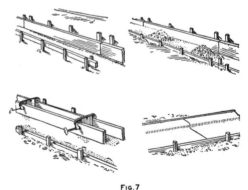

FIG. 7

Method of Using Wood in Constructing a Form to Make a Concrete Curbing it up to the present time, but that does not lessen the popularity of the product.

While concrete curb and gutter forms can be constructed of plank, as any other form or mold for concrete, the cost is very high and for that reason the contractors are using the pressed-steel forms, as the finished product is more satisfactory and from 60 to 70 per cent cheaper.

The illustrations, Fig. 7, show the successive steps in placing wood forms for making concrete curbing. One of the metal forms, set and partially filled with concrete, is shown at A., Fig. 8. This style of form is used mostly in connection with dirt roads or macadam highways, while the curb form shown at B is used in place of the old-style stone curb.

When this form is used the excavation is made as for the stone curbing, but a little wider; the forms are set up in the excavation, filled with concrete and firmly tamped. As soon as the

concrete is sufficiently set, usually in about a half hour, the forms are removed and the surface troweled down.

As yet the specifications for concrete

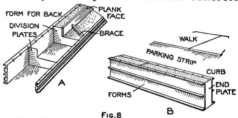

FIG. 8
Sheet-Metal Forms are Much Better Than Wood and Less Expensive to Use

curb and gutters are far from being standardized, but the majority of specifications call for a curb 18 in. high by 6 in. thick, and for combined curb and gutter 12 in. high by 6 in. thick, and the gutter 6 in. thick by 18 in. wide.

When using the combination curb and gutter forms, the face of the curb is made by placing a plank against the form, A, Fig. 8, and this plank is removed as soon as possible and the face troweled down.

(To be continued)

A Tool for Laying Out Mortises and Tenons

A tool for laying out mortises and tenons, and the manner in which it is used, is shown in the sketch. A T-shaped piece, A, is cut from $\frac{1}{16}$-in. sheet steel, and a slot, B, cut longitudinally through the larger part or blade. A shoulder, C, is then cut from $\frac{1}{8}$-in. material, and two pieces of $\frac{1}{16}$-in. sheet steel, D D, are fastened by four rivets to the shoulder C, forming a recess in which the blade of the T-shaped member slides. A hole is then bored in the shoulder C and tapped for a thumb-screw which serves to hold the parts at the desired point. The edges F and G must be filed perfectly parallel, and if in addition the edge H is made perfectly parallel with edge G, the tool may be used as a sliding caliper.

The advantage of this tool over a marking gauge in laying off mortises is that a point of a knife blade may be used for marking instead of the marker on the gauge, which has a tendency to

follow the grain of the wood and thus make a ragged line.

This tool may also be used as a centering tool for round stock. Set the

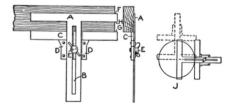

A Mortise and Tenon Laying-Off Tool Which is Also Used as a Centering Tool for Round Stock

tool to the radius of the circle to be centered, as shown at J, and mark a line across the diameter, then move the tool around until it is at right angles with the line just scribed and mark another line on the diameter. Where these two lines intersect is the center. —Contributed by Wm. A. Robinson, Waynesboro, Pa.

⟪If a lump of sal ammoniac is left in a tool box, the tools will rust.

Removing Trouble of a Differential Master Gear

A large number of cars of a certain popular make gave trouble in that the  corner of the teeth of the differential gear would chip out, and the cause of the trouble could not be determined. New parts acted in the same manner and no end of repairs was the result. One garage employe hit upon a scheme that has worked well, and cars fixed according to his method have run a year with no further wear or breakage. The rings, either new or chipped ones, were simply ground on an emery wheel to remove the corners of the teeth on a radius of ¼ inch.

Joining a Pair of Crutches Together

A cripple using two crutches may be able to have one hand free if the crutches are joined together with a piece of metal that is curved to pass around the back. The metal should not fit so closely as to interfere with the forward movement of the lower ends of the crutches.—Contributed by L. A. Palmer, Tacoma, Wash.

Facing a Worm Gear on a Lathe

A worm gear having a large lead, say, 3 or 4 in., may be easily faced on a lathe with the attachment shown in the illustration. Fasten two studs in a plate so that they will enter the screw snugly, and attach the plate to the crosshead of the lathe directly beneath

Keeping Molded Gutter Faces on a Level

A good method to make a gutter that has the desired fall and at the same time a perfectly level molded face is shown in the sketch. The outside gutter A, Fig. 1, of which two styles are shown, is formed so that 1½ or 2 in. of the material will lap on the sheathing; the inside gutter B laps over the sheathing at least 3 in.; its front edge is turned over the standing edge of the outside gutter and is secured by the bolt that holds the hanger in place.

Where the roof has been already laid, all that is necessary is to turn a ¾-in. edge to the inside of both inside and outside gutters, lock the roofing over it and knock it down as in double-seaming. This is shown in Fig. 2. As many different falls can be had as necessary by putting in bottom lines, C

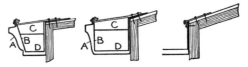

FIG. I   FIG. 2
Gutters Having the Desired Fall with the Outside Molded Face on a Level

and D, between and laying off miters from them where needed.—Contributed by M. C. Walters, Nokesville, Va.

will cause the carriage to travel with a speed equal to the travel of the screw, and the tool can be fed as in ordinary lathe work.—Contributed by D. J. Jones, Massena, N. Y.

❧ A piece of candle is often quite useful for the motorcyclist. It can be

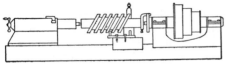 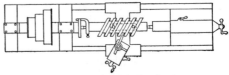

The Worm as It Turns in the Lathe Centers Causes the Proper Feed of the Carriage

the center of the screw, when the latter is set in the centers of the lathe. The proper tool is then placed in the tool post, and the lathe started. The pins

placed in the headlight, or put on the belt for oil, and used to prevent "shorts" by applying to the spark plug in damp weather.

Paving and Pavements

By GEORGE LITTELL

PART II

Stone Curbing

The curbing stone is shipped in a rough state and varies in length from 4 to 8 ft., with an average of about 6 ft. The stones are unloaded from the cars and taken to the place where they are to be used and put in piles. The curb cutters furnish their own tools and do the work for a contract price by the lineal foot. The corner pieces, or the pieces to form an arc of a circle at the intersection of streets or driveways, are cut from a wood pattern, which is first cut out on a 10-ft. radius—the one in general use. One side, the top and the ends are dressed, the bottom and the back being left in the rough. The measuring and marking of each stone is done before it is taken to the setting place so that the stonecutters are credited with the amount of work they have done.

Sidewalk Grade

After the grade has been finished and the curbing set, the ground back of the curb must be graded. This is called the sidewalk grade and is mentioned in the contracts as that strip of land between the curb and the street or property line, as in Fig. 9. Plank walks must be raised or lowered, and all broken planks replaced, to meet the new grade, but the contractor does not have to touch the concrete walks; simply grading from the outside edge of the walk to the curb.

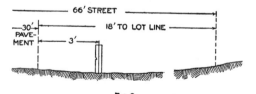

FIG. 9

The Sidewalk Grade is That Part of the Street from the Sidewalk to the Curbing

After the grading is finished and the curbing all set the subgrade must be rolled with a roller, weighing not less than 10 tons, before the concrete can be placed. It should ever be remembered that the concrete will even up the grade, but it should also be borne

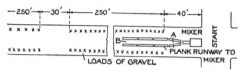

FIG. 10

Location of the Materials and the Mixer on the Street Ready to Lay the Concrete Base

in mind that concrete costs money. In other words, concrete may be depended upon to even up the grade when necessary, but it should not be used for filling in holes, and the like, unless it be a soft spot upon which the contractor wishes to take no chances of failure. In a case of this kind the top is usually dug off and the excavation filled with from 9 to 24 in. of concrete, as the nature of the soft spot may demand.

Placing the Concrete

There are several devices for the mixing and placing of concrete, from the hand method to the big steam mixers with a 20-ft. boom and a running bucket by which the concrete is dropped right into position and the graders simply have to pull over the top of the load and level it off.

The hand method of using large steel mixing boards is well known and familiar to everyone, but it is too slow for present-day work.

It does not make any difference what means or method is used in mixing the concrete, the proportions of the mixture must be the same. The regular mixture is 1:7, although the quantities are left to the judgment of the contractor. A 1:7 mixture is composed of 1 part of cement, a standard grade of Portland being the only kind allowed, and 7 parts of clean gravel with plenty of clean, sharp sand to fill up the voids. If such a gravel is not procurable, the mixture may be specified as a 1:2:5. This mixture is practically the same as the former, but means that 1 part of cement, 2 parts

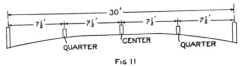

FIG II

Locating the Stakes That Designate the Crown of the Finished Surface on the Pavement

of clean, sharp sand, and 5 parts of gravel must be used. As this mixture is intended for pavement bases only, no one should use such a mixture for building work without consulting an authority on the purpose for which it is to be used.

The method of dumping the gravel or crushed stone is shown in Fig. 10, and for a 30-ft. pavement the loads should just ride each other with a 30 or 40-ft. interval about every 250 ft. This is to allow for a gain of the machine over the stone.

An organization of about 60 men will be necessary to make the best possible time with one of the big mixers, aside from the mixing crew. The men are placed about as follows: Five men are placed back of the machine to spread the concrete, two men to drive grade stakes, one man to empty the bucket, one man to empty the cement into the hopper, two men to wheel cement into the hopper, 15 men to wheel gravel or crushed stone to the hopper, and 30 men to fill the wheelbarrows. A man is stationed at A, Fig. 10, to

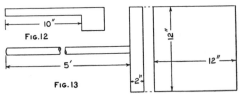

FIG.12

FIG.13

Stick Used by the Gutter Graders and the Tamper Used for Packing the Concrete

assist anyone whose wheelbarrow may have run off the track and to supervise the laying of the planks when the mixer is moved to a new location. One assistant foreman is stationed at B, to see that the men are working, and two men

are stationed, one on each side of the hopper, to assist the men dumping the material into the hopper.

In grading the concrete, the stakes are driven in as follows: Using Fig. 11 as an illustration, a line is first stretched tightly from curb to curb, the centers and quarters of the line being marked by a knot or some similar arrangement. Using a 5-in. crown for example, the taut line must graze the crown of the finished pavement; therefore, with a brick pavement, 4 in. must be allowed for the brick and 1 in. for the sand cushion, or 5 in. for both, the amount necessary to drive the stakes below the line. As the pavement at the curb is 5 in. lower than the crown, the quarter stakes are driven ½ of 5 or 2½ in. below the line. Expansion

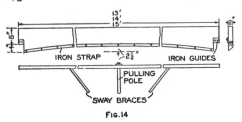

FIG.14

The Guides with the Lute or Screen on Top of Them for Filling in the Sand

joints must be left across the pavement at least every 100 ft., and preferably every 75 ft. A stick, cut as shown in Fig. 12, is used by the gutter graders and is run along the top of the curb to keep the concrete down its full 10 in. After the concrete has set for about one-half hour it is tamped with large wood tampers, as shown in Fig. 13. The concrete is then left to set 7 days before the sand or other material is hauled over it in wagons. During this time it should be sprinkled over at least twice each day in warm weather, to prevent cracks due to the heat. Hardening or setting is also assisted by the use of water.

Sand Cushion

As the cushion is required to be only 1 in. in thickness, care must be exercised to see that all stones and lumps are removed; even at the cost of screening all the material used for the cushion.

It now becomes necessary to have six timbers, 16 ft. long and 4 in. square, and one lute, or screen. The timbers are to be used as guides for the lute, which gives the sand the rounded surface that is required in the finished pavement.

The sand is first spread over the concrete, the guides are placed in position, as in Fig. 14, and the lute pulled along, one man keeping enough sand ahead of it so that no depressions are left. The center guide should just touch a line stretched taut from curb to curb, while the gutter guide should be about 3¾ in. below the top of the curb. De-

tails of the lute are shown in Fig. 15. It may be well to know that the sand used for the cushion must be perfectly dry when placed. If it is damp, the

Fig. 15

The Lute Forms the Crown to the Sand as It is Drawn over the Guides

pressure of the brick being dropped into place will pack it down so that it will be next to impossible for the roller to even up the pavement when completed, and a rough finished job will be the result.

(To be continued)

A Flush-Tank Float

Finding the copper float in the flush tank of a soil basin broken and not desiring to call in a plumber, I repaired it by using a large burned-out incandescent electric globe as a substitute float. The brass ferrule on the globe was soldered to the end of the rod and then it was thoroughly coated with

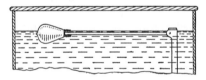

A Float for a Flush Tank Made from a Discarded Incandescent Electric Globe

enamel to prevent moisture entering the cement on the base.—Contributed by W. A. Jaquythe, Richmond, Cal.

Waterproofing Canvas

A good way to waterproof canvas cloth is by the following method: The canvas should be washed and soaped well with any cheap soap, using water to which has been added about 4 oz. of baking soda for each gallon. This soap solution should fill the cloth completely; then, before washing the cloth, it is put to soak in a solution of alum, 10 parts; copper sulphate, 1 part; water, 100 parts; to which about 10

parts of a 10-per cent solution of acetic acid is added. These materials can be purchased at any drug store. After the cloth is soaked in this solution it should be rinsed well and dried. This not only makes the canvas waterproof, but it tends to preserve the cloth. The above treatment may be applied to old as well as new tents.—Contributed by Loren Ward, Des Moines, Iowa.

A Tap Wrench

The parts are each shaped from ¾-in. cold-rolled square, about 6 in. long, the handles being turned round for about 4 in. of their length. The square part of both pieces are clamped together and holes drilled and tapped for ¼-in. bolts. The holes should be accurately drilled so that, when the pieces

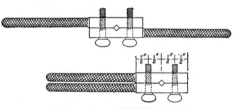

Adjustable Parts for a Tap Wrench to Form a Double or Single Handle

are turned as shown in the lower part of the sketch, they will form a single-handle wrench.—Contributed by E. H. Wolever, Norristown, Pa.

Paving and Pavements

By GEORGE LITTELL

PART III

Sheet Asphalt

Asphalt, as it is known to the American people, is composed of ½ in. of binder, of fine broken stone, mixed with about 16 per cent of asphalt cement; and a wearing surface, or top, of 2 or 2½ in. of fine stone sand, thoroughly incorporated with about 12 per cent of asphalt cement.

The method of laying this pavement is so common that it would be a waste of time to go into the detail required to give a comprehensive view of the subject. Suffice it to say that the concrete is placed first, as described in a previous chapter; then the ½ in. of binder, which bonds the bare concrete and the surface coat together; and finally the 2 or 2½ in. of topping, which is then thoroughly rolled.

Brick

The actual paving of a brick street, that is, the placing of the brick, is done by skilled mechanics called brick droppers, or pavers. The bricks are carried onto the pavement in piles of four, stacked with the spreaders, or teats, on the same side and the best face of each brick turned down. They should be placed upon the pavement with the spreaders facing the brick dropper, as these men grasp the brick with the left hand, turn the brick completely over and drop it into place with the right. This brings the down side of the brick, as carried onto the job, upward, and the spreaders are toward the brick dropper. The bricks are piled four high because most pavers run four courses across the street at one time.

Expansion joints, about ½ in. in width, must be placed at least every 75 ft., or the changes of temperature will cause the pavement to crack and heave, thereby ruining the pavement in a very short time.

After the brick is all placed, a light roller, weighing about 3 tons, is run over the pavement, forcing all the brick into place and making the pavement smooth.

A grout, composed of equal parts of cement and sand, or one part cement to two parts sand, is mixed in a semi-fluid state, then run over the pavement and forced into all the openings in the pavement, around the bricks, with stiff push brooms. The pavement is then left in the care of a watchman for at least 10 days, or until the engineer in charge orders it opened to the public. When the street is ordered opened, it passes from the contractor's hands into the city's and his responsibility ceases, except that he must maintain and repair it until his guarantee expires. The guarantee on a paving job varies from 5 to 10 years.

A 26-ft. brick pavement will require the following material:

132 brick, 4 by 4 by 9½ in., per lineal foot.
.0825 cu. yd. of sand per lineal foot of cushion 1 in. thick.
.4802 cu. yd. of concrete per lineal foot of 6-in. base.

The material for a 30-ft. pavement is as follows:

154 brick, 4 by 4 by 9½ in., per lineal foot.
.0928 cu. yd. sand per lineal foot of cushion 1 in. thick.
.5555 cu. yd. of concrete per lineal foot of 6-in. base.

Block Stone

Block stone, or medina sandstone, ranks first for a pavement having an excessive amount of heavy trucking, or for paving heavy grades. While granite, trap rock, sandstone and limestone are all used for this style of paving, the sandstone is the most popular and is most generally used.

The advantages of this block-stone pavement are many: it is adapted to all grades; is easily cleaned; requires small outlay for repairs; is suitable for all classes of traffic; affords a good foothold for horses, and yields but little dust and mud.

The usual size of these blocks is 4 by 4 by 8 in., and they are laid in place in a manner similar to the brick. No spreaders are necessary on the blocks, as the rough sides of the blocks prevent them from jamming together. This pavement is laid upon a cushion coat, rolled and grouted in the same manner as for the brick pavement.

Asphalt Blocks

Asphalt blocks are composed of a mixture of asphaltic cement and crushed stone in the proportions of about 10 per cent of cement to 90 per cent of stone. The mixture is then heated to about 300 deg. F., run into pressure molds and plunged into cold water. These blocks are usually about 3 by 4 by 12 in. and are laid the same as brick and block stone, but need not be grouted, as the heat and traffic soon incorporate the blocks into one solid mass. These blocks are a great help to a contractor who cannot afford to go into the asphalt-paving business in the regular way, as he can lay a better pavement at considerably less expense than he could sheet asphalt. This pavement is better able to withstand the wear of heavy traffic than is sheet asphalt and can be more easily patched up, if excavation has to be made.

Macadam pavement, as it is commonly known, consists mainly of broken stone spread in layers and thoroughly packed together with at least a 10-ton roller. As the voids comprise about 35 per cent of the volume, fine stuff, such as stone dust or fine sand, are spread on top of each layer and swept into the voids with the aid of water and push brooms. After each layer is rolled, it is sprinkled freely with water and rolled again, the desired result being mainly to solidify the stone and fine stuff into one solid mass.

Asphalt Macadam

Asphalt macadam, roughly speaking, is merely an ordinary macadam upon which hot tar instead of fine sand is poured to fill in the voids. If too much tar is used, however, the result will be a sticky, wearing surface during the hot summer months.

Repairing an Automobile Frame

When a welding outfit is not at hand automobile frames can be repaired as follows: For a frame, say, 3 in. by

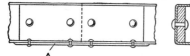

Where Welding cannot be Done, a Frame may be Repaired with a Patch, Hot-Riveted in Place

$1\frac{1}{4}$ in., of $\frac{3}{16}$-in. material use a piece of flat steel, $\frac{1}{2}$ in. thick. This is fitted to the inside of the channel snugly. The piece and frame are then drilled and hot-riveted, using no less than two rivets on each side of the break.

As an aid in fitting the steel in the channel a piece of soft wood is first cut to fit in the channel and over any rivets that may interfere. The wood can be cut and carved to fit the place much easier than the steel. The piece of wood can then be easily duplicated in steel.

An inside patch is much better than one fastened on the outside, for the two reasons, that an outside patch is not easily fitted to the channel, and that it does not make a neat repair. Some-

times it is desirable to put a piece, A, on the bottom of the frame in addition to the one in the channel. This will assist in preventing the frame from sagging. Always use as long a patch as can be fitted in the channel at the break.

Homemade Level

A level that is sufficiently accurate for ordinary work can be constructed on a triangular frame of light wood, as shown in the illustration, on which a plumb bob and line is attached. The center line on the base crosspiece can be found by placing the level on a smooth

surface, then making a temporary mark when the bob comes to rest, whereupon the level is turned around or in an opposite direction and another mark made where the bob comes to a rest. If there is a slight difference in the marks made, find the exact center between them and draw a permanent line.—Contributed by William Jenkins, New York City.

Keeping Food in Hot Weather without a Refrigerator

Many dwelling houses are located where ice is not easily obtained, but in its absence food can be kept in al-

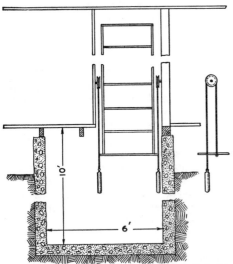

The Shelves of the Elevator When It is Raised to the Top Coincide with Those in the Pantry

most as good a condition in a cave or cellar, although the inconvenience of these prevents their use in all instances. I have for several years used an elevator, placed in one corner of my pantry, which when lowered enters a cement-lined hole in the earth beneath the house. The hole is 6 ft. square and 10 ft. deep. The cement walls are built up to fit closely to the floor so that no vermin can enter.

The elevator is constructed with sufficient shelving to care for all of the perishable food for the family. The framework is counterbalanced with weights, as shown, so that it is easily drawn up or lowered into the hole.

If it is possible to secure ice during the winter, the hole should be of sufficient size to store enough to last through the hot weather and leave a space for the elevator. If this is done, a temperature of 40 deg. can be maintained. In doing this, provision must be made to cover the opening in the floor tightly where the elevator passes through.—Contributed by Leslie Wells, Alfred, N. Y.

Gluing Abrasive Sheets on Grinder Disks

Trouble is often experienced in gluing sandpaper and emery cloth on the disk of a grinder so it will stick until it wears out. The following method will give good results in making the abrasive disk adhere to the entire surface of the metal disk. Apply a thin coat of common hot glue or liquid glass on both the emery cloth and the disk. Lay two layers of cotton batting, or some other soft and yielding material, on a perfectly flat surface. Place the disk on this with the abrasive side of the cloth or paper facing the padding material, and lay some heavy weights on the disk to give the necessary pressure, 50 lb. usually being sufficient. The padding will give a uniform pressure and make the contact perfect over the entire surface.—Contributed by A. C. Morrison, Minneapolis, Minn.

Parallel and Series Battery Connections

In order to get the greatest possible efficiency from dry or wet cells they should be connected up either in parallel or in series according to the work which they are to do. By parallel connection is meant the arrangement of two or more cells as shown in Fig. 1 of the sketch. All the zincs are connected in one line and all the carbons

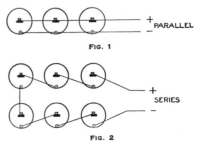

Batteries Connected as Shown in Fig. 1 Produce a Large Amperage, and as in Fig. 2, a Large Voltage

in another. Series connection is the arrangement of two or more cells as shown at Fig. 2. The connections are made from carbon to zinc, carbon to zinc, and so on.

Parallel connection should be used where the external resistance is small in comparison with the internal resistance of a single cell. The current thus furnished will not be greater than that of a single cell, but just equal to that of one cell. Series connection, on the other hand, should be used where the external resistance is large in comparison with the internal resistance of a single cell, and the current thus furnished will be N times that of a single cell, if N represents the number of cells in the series.—Contributed by Olaf E. Tronnes, Evanston, Ill.

A Broken-Tap Extractor

A broken tap that is tightly wedged in the metal cannot be easily removed and sometimes even a hammer and chisel will not start it from the hole. The device illustrated can be depended upon to remove the most stubborn broken tap. The device is made of a selected piece of steel, in which a hole is bored centrally equal in diameter to the size of the tap at the base of the cutters. The outside diameter is the

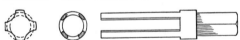

The Prongs of the Tool are Slipped into the Flutes of the Tap for Removing It

same as that of the drill size for the hole being tapped. The hollow part of the tool is then slotted to make four prongs that will slip into the flutes of the tap. When a tap is broken and a part of it remains in the hole the prongs of the tool are slipped into the flutes and the part removed by turning it.— Contributed by Lawrence Annette, Port Huron, Mich.

Springs to Prevent Base Chair from Tipping

Having a base chair to repair and finding the regular spring too weak to hold it from tipping, I used a pair of supplementary springs made of coils taken from an old wire mattress. The ends of each coil were bent into such shape as to receive a screw, and one

spring applied to the front part of each rocker and the base as shown. Any strength may be secured by changing

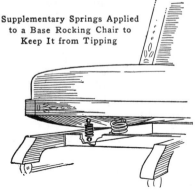

Supplementary Springs Applied to a Base Rocking Chair to Keep It from Tipping

the location of the spring from the center to the front part of the rocker. After these springs had been attached a person could sit on the back of the chair without fear of its tipping over. —Contributed by J. W. Wyllie, Port Arthur, Can.

Parallel-Rule Attachment for a Drawing Board

A parallel rule may be attached to an ordinary drawing board with the use of a straightedge, four grooved pulleys and some flexible wire cord. The pulleys are attached flat on the under side of the board, one at each corner, and the cord run around them as shown. The ends of the straight-

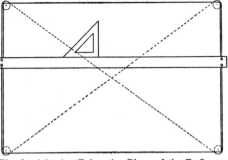

The Straightedge Takes the Place of the T-Square and can be Moved over the Board to Make Parallel Lines

edge are clamped to the cord that runs along the ends of the board.—Contributed by Leonard Den Bleyker, Paterson, N. J.

Self-Cleaning Cuspidor

A self-cleaning cuspidor, suitable for the shop or for public places, can be made with the usual flaring top, a 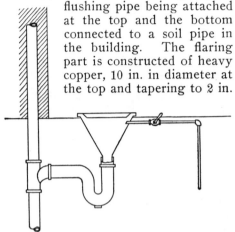 flushing pipe being attached at the top and the bottom connected to a soil pipe in the building. The flaring part is constructed of heavy copper, 10 in. in diameter at the top and tapering to 2 in.

The Top of the Cuspidor is Placed Level with the Floor or Above It as Desired

at the bottom. A 2-in. brass nipple is soldered over the lower end, which in turn is soldered to a 2-in. trap that is vented in the usual manner.

If the flushing pipe enters the top at an angle, the water will have a whirlpool motion which will thoroughly clean the cuspidor and trap. Where the cuspidor is in constant use, a small stream of water is allowed to flow all the time.—Contributed by George M. Crowley, Jr., Newark, N. J.

Removing Automobile-Engine Valves

Various devices for removing the valves from motors for grinding or repairing are being sold and all of them

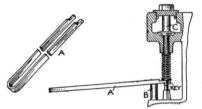

Application of the Lever on the Valve Spring to Compress It When Removing Key

make provision for controlling the spring, so that the key can be removed.

The owner of a car that very rarely needs such a device, can make an outfit that will do the same work at slight cost. The outfit, as it is used on the familiar T-head motor, is shown in the sketch, the cylinder head being in cross section. A piece of steel, A, about 1/4 by 3/4 in., is procured and bent into a U-shape with parallel sides about 5/8 in. apart, the whole being 7 or 8 in. long. Two short blocks of wood, B and C, which may be pieces of a broom handle, complete the outfit.

Remove the cap over the valve, insert the block C and then put the cap back loosely by hand. This holds the valve down, and when the piece B is set up on the crank case and the lever A applied the spring can be compressed at will and the key removed. In replacing valves the same process is repeated and the key inserted. It may be necessary to shape the end of B to suit the motor.

Concrete Garbage Furnace

A suburbanite solved the problem of garbage disposal by making a furnace of concrete. The only requirements for its construction were some second-

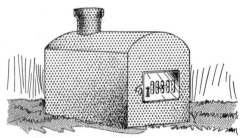

A Concrete Burner for the Disposal of Garbage That will Not be Affected by the Weather

hand grates and an old furnace door, cement, sand, gravel, and cheap lumber for the forms. A length of terra-cotta tile set in the cement roof at the opposite end from the door constitutes the chimney. The ashes accumulate so slowly that their removal requires little attention.

⟨White lead makes a good lubricant for heavy worm gears.

To Fill Pores in Stone

Stone and brick are porous, so much so that they are not suitable as liquid containers, and if used outdoors, they take up water which freezes, causing small bits to crack and fall off. It is often desirable to fill these pores, and this may be done with a solution of paraffin and naphtha. This solution is readily soaked up, and the naphtha evaporates, leaving the pores filled with the paraffin.

If the rock or brick is treated with soft soap and then washed with alum, an insoluble compound is formed, which also acts as a good filler. A solution of sodium silicate, or water glass, applied to sandstone and allowed to dry, then followed with a wash of calcium chloride, forms another insoluble protecting surface.—Contributed by Harry N. Holmes, Richmond, Ind.

A Portable Boat Landing

For those using power boats on rivers and tidewater bays, a correspondent of Power Boating describes a practical landing which is easily adjusted so that it may be adapted to any desired height.

The water end of the landing is supported on a roller, which consists of a wire-cable drum. The timbers are 2 by 4-in. material, the stringers being 18 ft. long and the longest upright 2 ft. between the lower support and the platform. The platform is 2½ ft. wide. The landing can be rolled back and forth on the shore as the water rises

Breaking Up a Thick Concrete Floor

Some improvements being made in a factory necessitated the removal of a concrete floor 1 ft. thick. The work

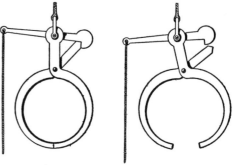

Release Grip for Dropping the Weight When It is Carried High Enough for a Heavy Blow

could not be accomplished with picks and wedges, so a piece of metal was cast, about 2 ft. in diameter and ½ ft. long, which weighed about 1 ton and was used as a hammer to break up the cement.

A very ingenious release grip was made to use in connection with the overhead traveling crane for lifting the weight, which was carried to a height of from 35 to 50 ft. before it was dropped. The illustration clearly shows the construction of the clamp and how it is tripped when the weight is at the proper height.—Contributed by J. C. Moore, Wilkinsburg, Pa.

Fastening Hose on Pipe

A hose can be easily fastened to a pipe, if the latter has a sharp thread cut and is of a size that will fit tightly in

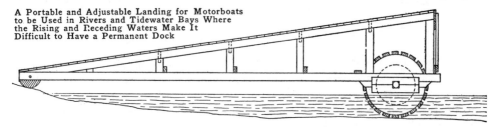

A Portable and Adjustable Landing for Motorboats to be Used in Rivers and Tidewater Bays Where the Rising and Receding Waters Make It Difficult to Have a Permanent Dock

and falls. The taper or slanting platform makes it possible to have some part of it on a level with the deck of the boat making a landing.

the hose. The hose is then bound with wire so as to press the rubber into the threads.—Contributed by W. K. Hook, Florence, S. C.

A Camper's Sleeping Outfit

A piece of canvas, unbleached muslin, a blanket, or any other piece of goods, and 75 ft. of strong sash cord are all the materials necessary. No

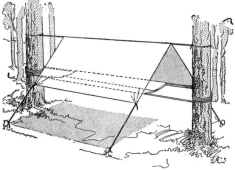

A Hammock Bed Placed between Two Supports, and a Covering, Shaped Like a Tent

sewing is required and the outfit can be erected in a few minutes. It is light and can be carried anywhere.

Select two trees, or two poles, and tie the end of the rope to one of these; then run the rope around the other three times, draw it taut and run the end back to the first support and fasten it. Thus two parallel cords at any desired height will be formed between the two supports.

Spread out the cloth on the ground under the two ropes so that the side of the material to form the inner part of the hammock is uppermost. Lift one side of the goods and place the edge over one of the cords far enough to overlap about one-third the entire length of the material. Lift the opposite side and turn its edge over in a

A Quickly Constructed Stretcher, the Only Articles Necessary Being Two Sticks and a Sheet, or Blanket

like manner and both edges will overlap in the center, as shown in the sketch which also illustrates the way to make up a stretcher quickly. The weight of the body on the edges causes friction enough to prevent the cloth from slipping.

Two sticks of wood are placed between the parallel ropes at the ends of the cloth to hold them apart as in a hammock. Place a pillow at one end and enter, being careful not to disturb the overlapped edges of the cloth.

After hanging the hammock bed stretch another rope between the supports, about 2 ft. above the parallel lines. A sheet of canvas or waterproof material is thrown over this rope and the hanging edges are weighted or staked to the ground, lines of cord first being attached to the corners. One of the illustrations shows the finished bed and cover.—Contributed by V. W. Killick, Los Angeles, Cal.

Turning Elliptic Spokes on a Metal Lathe

The sketch shows an attachment that may be constructed and fitted to any small lathe for turning a spoke elliptical at one end and round at the other, the change from one to the other shape being gradual on the full length.

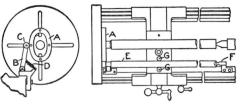

A Lathe Attachment Which Automatically Controls the Feed of the Cutter for Turning Elliptic Spokes

The ring A is an elliptical cam, the difference of the diameters being equal to the difference of the diameters of the elliptical end of the spoke. An arm, B, has a roller, C, which is held against the cam by a strong spring D. The shaft E is attached to the lever B at one end, while the other is supported by the upright piece F, ending in the ball and socket joint. Two rollers, G, G, are attached to the cross slide on each side of the shaft E, to work the feed of the cutting tool as the spoke turns.

When the carriage is at the left end of the shaft E, practically all of the motion of the roller C is transmitted to the tool, while at the other end of its travel the tool will have no motion and the finished spoke will be round.—Contributed by W. C. Dixon, Blacksburg, Va.

Glass Towel Rack

Materials discarded from an engine room as useless furnished the parts for making a good towel rack. A steam-gauge glass that was broken off too short to be used on the boiler was hung in two brass bracket clips, cut as shown at A and bent to hold the gauge glass

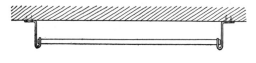

A Glass Towel Rack Made of Discarded Parts from an Engine Room

after they were fastened with screws to the wall. The illustration clearly shows the manner of construction.—Contributed by Frederick M. Perros, Mansfield, Mass.

Drawknife Guard

To protect the edge of a drawknife from being nicked against other tools in a chest, or to prevent accidents, make a guard from a piece of springy wood to fit closely between the handles, as shown in the sketch. The ends of the guard are cut concave, as shown at A, so as not to slip off the handles. The wood, when sprung in place in

Wood Guard Sprung Between the Handles Makes the Tool Safe to Handle and Protects the Edge

front of the edge, protects it, and makes the tool safe to handle when not in use.—Contributed by W. A. Henry, Galesburg, Ill.

◖A large peach basket makes a good protection for growing vegetables.

Increasing the Efficiency of a Blower

The blower of a cupola was not large enough to keep the blast at the right pressure and increased speed would not give the required results. The difficulty was overcome by adding small pieces of sheet  metal to the fan in the space between the housing and the blades. An increased pressure sufficient for the furnace was obtained.

Removing Obstruction in a Pipe

Many times a steam or water pipe becomes so blocked with iron scale or other loose material, that it is almost impossible to clear it with the steady pressure from a force pump, and in some instances long stretches of pipe must be taken down to reach the obstruction. The illustration shows a method of loosening up the scale and

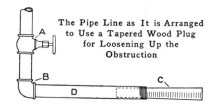

The Pipe Line as It is Arranged to Use a Tapered Wood Plug for Loosening Up the Obstruction

washing it out without very much work. The valve A—or valves, as the case may be—is left open, and if there is an angle in the line, a brace is placed against the elbow B, parallel with the piece D; whereupon the line is disconnected at some joint and a long and slightly tapered plug, C, fitted into the pipe. Allow sufficient water to run in and fill the pipe between the obstruction and the plug. A sharp blow of a heavy hammer loosens up the sediment and scales so that it can be washed away.—Contributed by James E. Noble, Toronto, Can.

Holding Drawings Flat in Drawers

A very effective way to hold blue-prints or pencil drawings in cabinet drawers, so as to keep them from being

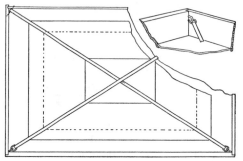

The Drawings are Kept Flat in the Drawer by the Tape Which Does Not Interfere with the Filing

damaged, is to use heavy tape, diagonally attached to the upper part of the drawer sides. In the corners at the back part the tape is attached with a nail driven in across the corner, as shown. The other end of the tape has a ring which is slipped over a screw-hook turned into the diagonally opposite corner. The tape will hold the corners of the drawing down flat and prevent them from catching in the cabinet when the drawer is pulled out.— Contributed by Edward Sieja, Chicago.

Kerosene Carburetor for a Gasoline Engine

The carburetor illustrated can be fitted to almost any gasoline engine with the result that at least three-

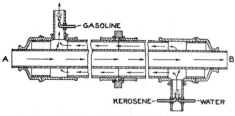

A Carburetor for Using Gasoline Alone or a Combination of Gasoline and Kerosene

fourths of the fuel used will be kerosene. It consists of ordinary pipe and fittings.

The engine exhaust pipe is attached at A and this connection should be as close to the cylinder as possible. The exhaust passes through the pipe and out at B. The carburetor is made over the center pipe so that there will be a space of $3/8$ or $1/2$ in. between them. The inlets for the gasoline and kerosene are shown in the sketch. The adjustment can only be determined by experience.

After the engine is run on gasoline until the exhaust pipe gets hot, the gasoline is gradually turned off and at the same time, the kerosene turned on until a mixture is obtained which causes the engine to miss occasionally. Then the valves are left set and a very small amount of water turned on.

A saving of the more expensive fuel will result if the carburetor is properly installed and adjusted.—Contributed by L. C. Price, Jr., Lexington, Ky.

Cutting Left-Hand Screws

When left-hand screws are desired and only a right-hand screw plate is available, the left-hand plate shaped as follows will produce the threads very satisfactorily: A screw is first cut with the right-hand die and a tap made from it by cutting away the

threads on two opposite sides of the metal as shown in the sketch. The tap should be tempered and a hole of the same diameter as the body drilled in a piece of steel of the proper size. The tap is then placed in the hole and turned to the left, while applying considerable pressure. The tap should be turned slowly and the pressure applied steadily in order to insure a clean cut. If necessary the plate thus made can be shaped and slotted, after which it should be tempered. The screws cut by this plate will not be quite perfect but will do in an emergency.—Contributed by J. H. Bebee, Rochester, New York.

⊄Calcimine should be stored in a dry place, as moisture ruins the glue in the mixture.

Removing a Hanging Telephone Pole

While out on a repair trip on a telephone line we were detailed to remove a certain pole that was almost rotted in two about 2 ft. above the ground and was kept in a hanging position with four wires as the only means of support. As we did not dare to climb the pole, some one suggested breaking the insulators by shooting them off with a gun. A rifle was procured and the insulators shot to pieces which allowed the pole to fall.—Contributed by Herbert L. Spencer, Whitney Point, New York.

Sharpening a Scraper Iron

It is almost impossible to sharpen a scraper iron with a file so that it will cut properly. The best way is to file it and rub the surface on a stone, then turn the edge over a little, as shown at A, on a smooth piece of iron. An iron sharpened in this manner 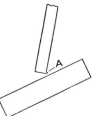 will take hold and cut smoothly, and leave a surface that can be easily finished with sandpaper.—Contributed by G. H. Clemons, Storm Lake, Iowa.

An Emergency Chuck for Engravers

If it is desired to do some engraving on a signet ring and no engraver's  chuck is at hand, the ring can be held in a grip made of a cork fitting in a large-neck bottle. A notch is cut in the top of the cork to receive the ring tightly after which it is pressed into the bottle neck. Because of its slight taper, the cork will grip the ring tightly when it is pushed in, and will not mar the metal.—Contributed by C. F. Gronemann, Elgin, Ill.

Laying Out Pipe-Flange Gaskets

It is often a difficult matter to lay out and mark rubber gaskets correctly for pipe flanges when they are in place, as the parts are hard to separate. A very good method for marking a perfect gasket is shown in the illustration. It is only necessary to spring the flanges apart far 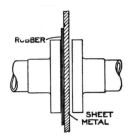 enough to allow a thin piece of sheet metal to be inserted behind the gasket. The gasket can be firmly pressed against one of the flanges where it can be marked for the outside diameter as well as the holes for the bolts.

An Improved Milk Strainer

The dirt and sediment in milk will fall into the sieve of a milk strainer and some of it is forced through with the milk. A milk strainer can be improved so that the dirt will not get into the sieve and clog it, or be forced through with the milk. Remove the rim and  sieve from an ordinary strainer and attach a solid bottom the same size as the rim with sides about 2½ in. deep. Holes are cut in the side with their lower edges ¾ in. above the solid bottom and these are covered with the strainer sieve. The dirt and froth will be caught in the bottom, and the milk will run out freely through the strainer holes.—Contributed by A. P. Benson, Stewartville, Minn.

⊄ To fill fine cracks in mahogany mix dry venetian red in gum arabic mucilage, forming a putty, which is forced into the cracks. The same method is used for other woods, the color being substituted to suit the color of the wood.

A Sack Chute

Many times it is desired to lower filled sacks from one floor to another in a mill, and a correspondent of American Miller 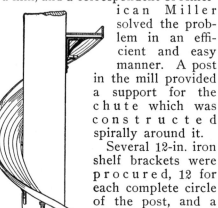 solved the problem in an efficient and easy manner. A post in the mill provided a support for the chute which was constructed spirally around it.

Several 12-in. iron shelf brackets were procured, 12 for each complete circle of the post, and a piece of wood attached to the upper arm of each, to make a base for receiving the nails for fastening the bottom boards in place. The brackets were fastened to the post, being spaced one-eighth of the circumference of the post apart, and each 8 in. below that next above, beginning at the top. This gave the proper pitch for a post 12 in. in diameter.

The bottom was made up of strips ⅜ in. wide. The strips were soaked in water until each could be bent in place and fastened. Beginning from the outside, one was nailed to the other until the space was filled. The side rail can be made of thin strips or a piece of sheet iron.

To Prevent a Cow from Kicking

A very simple and efficient remedy for a cow that has a habit of kicking the milk pail over is to tie a ¾-in. rope tightly around the cow's body just in front of the hips. When the cow tries to lift her foot the swelling of the muscles causes the rope to tighten, producing such discomfort that she soon stops trying to kick. A few applications of the rope are generally sufficient to break any cow of kicking.—Contributed by T. Todd, Jr., Clayton, Ill.

Cutting Threads for a Wood Screw

Where it is desired to turn a wood screw into a piece of wood that is liable to split, it is best to make a cutter that will cut into the wood and make threads the same as those on the screw. A cutter can be made from one of the screws to be used in the board. Select a screw having a full thread and cut a notch in opposite sides in the manner of making a top. When this screw is turned into the wood, the threads will cut out the wood instead of pushing it to one side, consequently, when the cutter screw is removed, another screw may be turned into the threads without fear of splitting the wood.

Substitute for Thumb Tacks

The clip or holder consists of a metal plate—preferably of brass—screwed to the corner of a drawing board or table, which is cut away in such a manner that the surface of the board is flush with that of the clip. This is illustrated in the sectional sketch. The clip, when thus attached to the board, provides sufficient space under its thinner portion to admit the heaviest drawing paper. Underneath the clip is a metal socket with a circular, tapered metal plug. The upper surface of this plug is flush with that of the socket, when

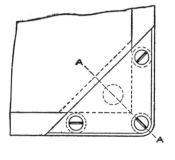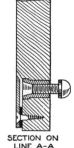

SECTION ON LINE A-A

The Clamping Device Takes the Place of Thumb Tacks and does Not Interfere with the Drawing Instruments

the paper is inserted beneath the clip. As soon as the clip is in position, the screw on the lower side is turned, thus forcing the plug upward until it grips the paper tightly. The paper is held by the pressure of a metal surface, ⅜ in. in diameter, that does not make a hole or tear it like a thumb tack. The surface of the clip being flush with that of the board, no obstacle is met by the T-square or set squares which may be employed above it. The full-size drawings clearly show the construction of the clip, which may be nickelplated if desired.—Contributed by C. P. Chalker, Ottawa, Can.

Clamp Bolt for a Drill Press

The ordinary clamping of metal parts to a drill press for drilling is inconvenient because no two pieces are of the same thickness and the clamp jaw will require different lengths of bolts, a complete supply of which would consist of so many that time would be wasted in looking for the right length. I devised a bolt with many heads, which was cut from a flat

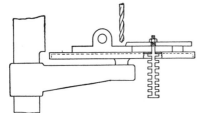

Clamp Bolt in Its First Position for Holding a Thin Piece of Metal for Drilling

piece of metal of suitable size to fit the slots on the faceplate and could be quickly adjusted to clamp metals of reasonably varying thicknesses. The bolt is slipped through a slot in the drill-press faceplate and given a one-quarter turn when set on the clamp at the proper height.—Contributed by E. W. Lawrence, Pittsburgh, Pa.

A Movable Hanging Lamp

In rural districts where a kitchen is long and narrow and the lighting is done with kerosene lamps, the arrangement shown in the sketch is a convenient way of fixing a hanging lamp so that it can be moved from one end of the room to the other, and it may be of help to some one similarly situated.

Hooks were placed in the ceiling several feet apart and a ¼-in. gas pipe

fitted with tees on the ends was hung on the hooks. The lamp was hung on an ordinary cast-iron clothesline pul-

The Hanging Lamp can be Easily Moved Along to Any Location on the Pipe

ley that could be easily moved along on the pipe.—Contributed by Frank W. Harth, W. Simsbury, Conn.

Fuel Economy Demonstrated on Automobiles

A certain agency for automobiles found it to their advantage to equip one of the stock cars with a small tank, holding just 1 gal. of gasoline, and a speedometer to measure the mileage. Anyone interested in the purchase of a car, is given a demonstration of the exact number of miles it will run on that quantity of fuel.

Locknuts for Pipe

When in need of a locknut for pipe fittings one can be made by cutting the bead from the threaded opening of a pipe tee on the line A A. The tee is placed in the jaws of a vise

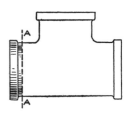

or turned on the end of a pipe and a hacksaw used for removing the threaded part.—Contributed by G. P. Piedmont, Cedar Falls, Wash.

¶Steam jets are being advocated as the best means of cleaning dirt and grease from machinery, shaftings, journal boxes, pulleys, and the like, in shops.

Value of Isometric Drawings

The practical machinist can readily read a mechanical drawing, but the one unaccustomed to this kind of work will

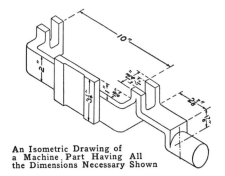

An Isometric Drawing of a Machine Part Having All the Dimensions Necessary Shown

be unable to picture in his mind how the finished part will appear. The isometric drawing can be readily understood by any person. This drawing differs from the true perspective in that the lines representing parallel surfaces will not meet if they are continued, or, in other words, there is no vanishing point. The dimensions can be put on as readily as on any drawing. A little practice will make anyone proficient, and the beginner may, if desired, purchase ruled paper on which to practice. The sketch shows a fair example of an isometric drawing.

The Selection of Emery Wheels

The somewhat prevalent idea that an emery wheel will do for any kind of work is largely erroneous. Of course,

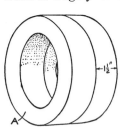

no matter what the grit and grade of the wheel may be, or the kind of work applied to it, the grinding will be accomplished to some extent, and even the amateur who does but a few hours' work a day will gain time by having two or more wheels. But a wheel which will cut cast iron rapidly will be a failure if used on soft steel; a wheel which

grinds hardened tool steel and leaves a smooth finish will, while it is cutting freely without heating, clog up, heat and burn a piece of mild steel. The selection of proper grit and grade is of the highest importance and in this manufacturers are exceedingly willing to coöperate.

An emery wheel is built up of millions of little sharp-cutting particles held in a bond. To do the best and most work, each particle, before getting really dull, should break out of the bond, making way for a new cutter to be brought to the surface. The wheel in which the particles retain their edge longest, yet break out at the proper time before heating and clogging become excessive, is the most efficient and therefore the most economical.

That a wheel may be compounded for a purpose and be good for no other, is illustrated by the following instance: A cup or cylindrical-shaped wheel was made for grinding certain steel articles, the work being applied to the face A. After four months of continuous service the wheel was worn down until nothing but the backing—a plain disk, 12 in. diameter and 1½ in. face—was left.

This was used for another grinding operation on the same places by applying the work to the face of the remaining part of the wheel. This part of the wheel was worn out in 24 hours, which proved that the wheel could be used only as it was intended, if economy and efficiency were desired.

Soldering Flux

A flux that can be used for tinning surfaces of metal without any previous cleaning is made as follows: Dissolve 1 lb. of zinc in muriatic acid and add 22 oz. of sal ammoniac to the solution, which is then allowed to evaporate and crystallize. The yield is about 2¼ lb. The salt is moistened and brushed on the metal to be soldered or tinned. The solder will readily flow wherever the flux has been applied.—Contributed by Frank J. Taylor, Las Vegas, Nev.

Water-Power Vacuum Cleaner

The suction part of the cleaner consists of an ordinary ¾-in. Y-branch, A, to which is fitted a short nipple, B, with a hose coupling attached for making connections to the water faucet. The other upper opening in the Y-branch is equipped in a similar manner for making connections to an ordinary hose. The lower end of the Y-branch is connected to a 6-in. length of ¾-in. pipe for the discharge.

The cleaner end of the hose is equipped with a piece of ¾-in. pipe, 3 ft. long, for a handle, the open end having a flat-shaped funnel arrangement for the mouth. The opening should be about ½ in. wide and 6 in. long, and all seams and the connections to the pipe end well soldered to make air-tight joints.

The cleaner is connected as shown and the water turned on full force. This creates a suction in the branch of the fitting connected to the hose that

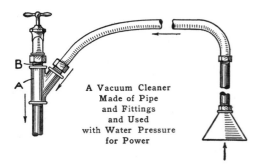

A Vacuum Cleaner
Made of Pipe
and Fittings
and Used
with Water Pressure
for Power

is sufficient to clean draperies and carpets. The dirt collected is discharged through the sink into the sewer.—Contributed by A. H. Waychoff, Lyons, Colo.

A Foot-Power Hammer

A cheap and efficient foot-power hammer or striker may be constructed as shown and will prove a valuable ad-

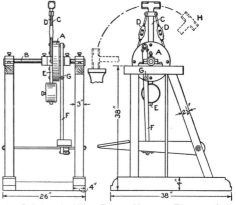

An Inexpensive Foot-Power Hammer That can be Made for the Small Shop

dition to the ordinary shop equipment for welding or heavy hammering. Sufficient dimensions are given to enable the owner of a small shop to construct one suitable for his needs by making the necessary changes.

The main working parts consist of a cast-iron wheel, A, 12 in. in diameter, with a long hub, which turns on the stationary axle B, between two collars, and carries the hammer and counterweight, together with the crankpin and connecting rod to the foot treadle. These parts are supported on a frame made of hard wood, as shown.

The bar C, carrying the hammer, is solidly bolted to the wheel A and is braced with two rods, DD, having turnbuckles. The bar is made of steel, ⅝ in. thick, 1½ in. wide and about 16 in. long. The bar E, carrying the counterweight, is securely bolted to the opposite radius of the wheel. The weight attached to the end of this bar should be about twice the weight of the hammer, and fitted so that it can be adjusted to the proper distance from the center of the wheel to bring the hammer quickly back to the position shown.

The connecting rod F is jointed at G to allow the crankpin to pass over the center and the hammer to recede toward the position shown by the dotted lines at H for a longer stroke; the upper end of the connecting rod forming a rocker arm to bring the crankpin back over the center.—Contributed by Winton Ball, Rugby, Va.

A Forge-Clay Mixture

Mix thoroughly together in a dry state 10 lb. of fire clay, 10 lb. of cast-iron turnings, ½ lb. of house salt, and ¼ lb. of sal ammoniac. Make this into a mortar by adding water, constantly stirring in the meantime. The mixture dries hard, and will outlast any material for a forge.

Repairing Worn Threads by Electro-plating

The threads on a compression screw spigot became worn to such an extent that the compression part would no longer hold the spigot in place. A new spigot was of no use, owing to the worn thread. To avoid expense and inconvenience the following expedient was adopted. A copper strip, about 1 ft. long, was soldered to the spigot, and the outside of the latter and about 6 in. of the strip thoroughly covered with asphaltum varnish. The spigot was hung in an electroplater's bath and given a coat of copper plate. A gauge or template was made to test the deposit so that it was reduced to the correct diameter. The job was a perfect success.—Contributed by Frank D. Henry, Haddon Heights, N. J.

❏To remove ink spots from wood, use sweet spirits of niter. When the spot turns white with the niter, wipe it off with a soft cotton rag. A second application may be necessary.

An Automobile Turntable

A turntable is a necessary adjunct to a garage where there is a limited floor

One garage owner, desiring a turntable, constructed one without any out-

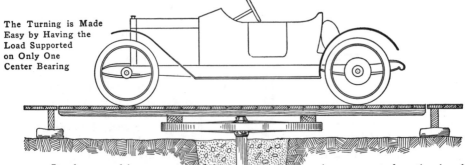

The Turning is Made Easy by Having the Load Supported on Only One Center Bearing

space. It also would come in handy in a private garage, making it unnecessary to back the machine out of the housing, but the expense of erecting a turntable is usually too great for the average garage owner.

lay except for the hauling of some sand and gravel and the purchase of a few bags of cement. An old wheel from a discarded truck wagon with a part of the axle was procured, and the axle part set in a concrete foundation so that the outside surface of the wheel could be built up with joists to carry a floor level with the floor of the garage. The joists can be made to overhang the circumference of the wheel if necessary for an automobile with long wheel base. The hole in the garage floor is cut circular and the turntable floor is made to turn freely in it. It requires very little power to turn the automobile when it is properly centered on the table.—Contributed by Harry E. Corey, Petrolea, Can.

Marker Attachment for a Garden Rake

A good way to make drills or seed rows of uniform width and depth is to have an attachment for the garden rake as shown in the sketch. The device consists of a piece of tin or sheet metal having V-shaped projections on one edge the width of the rows. The other edge of the metal is inserted between the teeth on the rake. Thus it can be

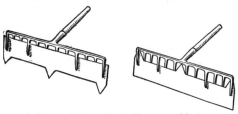

A Piece of Sheet Metal Used as a Marker and Hoe on a Rake

easily drawn over the garden bed to mark the rows. After the seed has been planted reverse the tin and use it as a hoe for filling the row.—Contributed by Bert W. Verne, San Diego, California.

Cone End on a Compass Point

It is sometimes necessary to scribe a large circle concentric with a hole that has been drilled in a piece of metal. This is very difficult to do accurately with the ordinary compass, but if the compass is slightly improved, as shown, the circle can be drawn perfectly true. Cut off one of the legs on a pair of compasses and substitute a straight ¼-in. rod, which is riveted to the compass shank as

shown. Turn up a brass or steel cone to fit on the rod and provide a small thumb screw to adjust its location. A

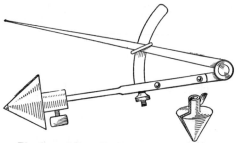

The Cone Adjusts Itself in a Large Hole and Provides a Center for Scribing Circles

slot is cut in the cone to allow the shank of the other leg to be drawn close to the cone's center when small circles are to be drawn. The cone adjusts itself to holes of various sizes, up to those almost as large as its base.—Contributed by H. W. Hahn, Chicago.

Surface Cleaner for Wood Planers

An ingenious superintendent in a wood shop devised the attachment for the planer shown in the drawing. Much of the lumber to be planed had been exposed to the elements, and as a consequence there was an accumulation of loose splinters, grit, dirt, etc., on the boards. This would dull the knives very quickly. The attachment consisted of a cylindrical wire brush, mounted in suitable bearings in front of the feed rollers of the machine and driven by a belt from a pulley on the lower shaft. This revolving brush ef-

The Brush is Mounted on the Planer Where It Cleans the Surface of the Boards

fectually cleaned the boards of all grit, and prevented it from getting in where it could dull the four knives on the cutter head.

A Fruit-Crate Cover

The cover illustrated is for use on fruit or vegetable crates without being nailed. The cover is made so that there

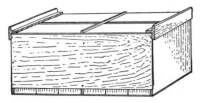

A Crate Cover Fastened without Nails Which Permits Its Use Many Times for Shipping

will be about a ½-in. space in the center, and the boards are fastened permanently on two end pieces of special grooving, as shown. This form of a groove permits the cover to be put on the crate and fastened by turning the crosspiece at the center which slips through the space between the boards and is turned like a button on a door. The crosspiece is fastened with one screw in the center turned into the partition of the crate. A crate having a cover of this kind can be used over and over again.—Contributed by Duncan F. Young, Osyka, Miss.

A Washer to Take Up End Play on a Shaft

A large gas engine developed end play in the crankshaft due to the wearing of the bronze bearing, and the occasional knocking of the flywheel, which weighed about 1 ton, became a serious matter. The wear was all on one side and it was decided to remove

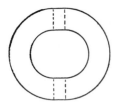 

FIG. I   FIG. 2

A Split Washer to Place on a Shaft Where a Wheel could Not be Removed

the flywheel and put in a bronze washer to take up all the slack. It was found that the wheel was so tight a fit

that it could not be moved with the means at hand. Therefore the bronze washer had to be made in halves so that it could be put on the shaft. The washer was made oval in shape, Fig. 1, split, the ends beveled, and rivet holes drilled. By removing the cap of the main bearing on the side next to the flywheel, it was possible to get at the washer and rivet the two parts together. The completed washer, or collar, is shown in Fig. 2. By making the pattern for the casting in this manner, no boring or turning was necessary to finish the washer.—Contributed by Donald A. Hampson, Middletown, New York.

An Adjustable V-Block

The adjustable V-block shown in the illustration will be found very handy for drilling clevis pins or similar articles. The drill-bushing slide can be adjusted to any distance from the end of the block and is fitted with removable bushings for any size drill desired.

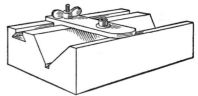

An Adjustable Bushing Slide Makes It Possible to Drill Holes Accurately in Pins

The under side of the head of the pin strikes the end of the V-block and insures a uniform length of pin from the head to the hole to be drilled.—Contributed by Henry J. Marion, Pontiac, Michigan.

Splicing a Garden Hose

If a hose leaks, cut out the injured part and make a splice as follows: Procure a short piece of pipe that will fit snugly in the hole of the hose, and heat it enough to melt the rubber. Then push it into the hose so that the joint will be at the center of the pipe, and cool it in water. The hot pipe vulcanizes the hose and pipe together, making a permanent and neat repair.—Contributed by J. S. Grant, Winchester, Va.

Transmitting a Phonograph's Sound Vibrations over a Wire

A motion-picture operator wished to transmit the sound of a phonograph to the outside of the building for attracting the people, but his endeavors to use a tube failed. The operator's room being about 10 ft. back from the entrance, the phonograph could not be heard for any great distance. The desired results were obtained by substituting a No. 24 gauge steel wire for the tube. The only change made was to remove the diaphragm from the machine and place it in the horn. The wire was run from the needle carrier to the diaphragm.—Contributed by G. Henry Jones, Dadeville, Ala.

Leakage Alarm for Boats

The leakage alarm shown diagrammatically in the illustration will prove very useful to boat owners, as it will give automatically an audible signal when the water in the hull has reached a predetermined level. The alarm consists of nothing more than an ordinary vibrating bell, in series with a battery, a switch, and a contact device which is controlled by the water in the hull. The contact device may be made from a piece of heavy wire, A, bent into the form shown and mounted on an upright, B, that is fastened to one end of this piece of wire, and the other end is bent into such a form that it will cause the two springs, C and D, to make contact when the water raises the cork. Two guides, E, are placed on the sides of

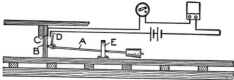

As the Water Rises in the Boat the Float is Carried Up, Thus Making the Electric Contact

the wire carrying the cork so it is free to move only in a vertical direction. Care should be exercised in insulating all parts.

A Fisherman's Detachable Gaff Hook and Spear

The illustration shows how to make a gaff hook, or spear, that detaches from the head and allows the catch to

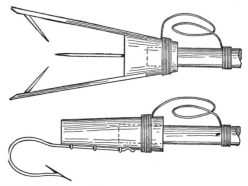

The Gaff Hook or Spear is Fastened to a Detachable Block on the Pole End

be played until it can be landed. The detachable part, on which the hook, or spear, is attached, is fastened to the pole with a line of sufficient length to permit playing the fish at will.

The spear is of a type used by the Siwash Indians and was originally made entirely of wood with the points fire-hardened. The fish is released by spreading the strips. The strips are ⅜ in. thick, 1½ in. wide, and 8 in. long.—Contributed by L. W. Pedrose, Seattle, Washington.

A Remedy for Tacky Varnish on Church Pews

To cure a tacky surface, as a church pew, for instance, coat it with fresh whitewash and allow it to become quite dry, then brush it off and apply a coat of hard-drying varnish. If lime is not at hand, use some whiting mixed in water. Allow this to remain on for several days, then dust it off and apply the varnish. If any of the whitewash or whiting remains on after the dusting, it will do no harm, as it will not show after the varnish is applied.

❡The gear box of a motor should have a mixture of half grease and half oil to cover the shaft.

Erasing Shield with Adjustable Openings

The shield is composed of two ordinary shields fastened together with a grommet at one corner, the shields be-

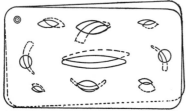

Two Shields Fastened Together so That They will Produce Openings of Any Shape Necessary for Erasing

ing placed in a reversed position. Shifting the shields will produce various-shaped holes which can be adjusted to parts being erased.—Contributed by Wm. Roberts, Cambridge, Mass.

Miter Gauge for Cutting Automobile-Wheel Spokes

A very handy miter device for use in repair shops on automobile wheels is made as follows: The base A consists of a piece of oak, 2 in. thick, 4 in. wide and 2 ft. long, hinged to which is a block, B, having a hole in the center to fit the tenon on the spoke. At the opposite end of the base a piece of oak, C, 2 in. thick, 4 in. wide and 6 in. long, is secured with screws. The distance between the blocks B and C should be the exact length of the spokes from

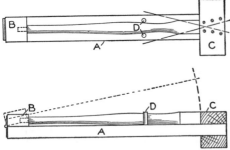

Miter-Marking Device for Laying Out the Slopes to Cut a Spoke for an Automobile Wheel

the shoulder of the tenon. Two pins, D, are fastened in the base, one on either side of the spoke so as to hold it in position.

Procure an old spoke and place it in

position and with a straightedge and pencil mark the lines on the block C extending from the slopes on the spoke. When making a new spoke for repairs, first cut the tenon, then slip it into the hole in the block B, and drop the spoke between the pins D. It is only necessary to use the straightedge to mark the lines on the spoke where it is to be cut.—Contributed by T. P. Mc-Carme, Waurika, Okla.

A Grease Gun

On a small automobile the differential-gear box was supplied with a small hole, about ¾ in. in diameter, through which to admit the grease for the gears. It was an almost endless task to put the grease in without a grease gun, as the box takes about 1 lb. of lubricant at a time. I had no grease gun and I decided to make one.

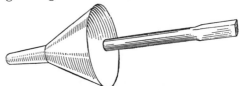

Grease Gun Made of a Cheap Funnel and a Flat-End Plunger Cut from Soft Wood

When completed, it proved to be as efficient as any that could be purchased.

A cheap funnel was procured having a stem that would enter the small hole, then a stick or plunger was whittled to snugly fit the hole in the funnel stem and the end cut straight across at right angles. In using the funnel, it is filled with grease and the stick is used to force the grease into the casing.—Contributed by A. F. Kaler, New Holland, O.

Coating for Cast-Iron Patterns

A coating that will resist any corrosion on cast-iron patterns may be applied as follows: Coat the surface with boiled linseed oil, using a brush, then heat the casting sufficiently to char the oil. The pores of the metal will thus be filled, and no moisture can enter.

Pattern Making

The Core-Box Plane

The core-box plane, as its name implies, is a device that has been confined exclusively to the pattern-making craft, but other woodworking specialists would find it very handy for "getting out" large core moldings, guttering, and work of a similar nature.

The principle on which the core-box plane operates is simple. It is a practical application of the geometrical theorem that "an angle inscribed in a semicircle is a right angle," wherefrom it follows that, if a right angle is revolved with its sides or legs kept against the two fixed points A and B, Fig. 1, the corner C of the angle will describe a semicircle.

Applying this principle to the subject in hand, it will be seen by consulting the drawing of the core-box plane, Fig. 2, that the two wings forming the body of the plane are at right angles to each other and that a cutter is provided which projects slightly below the left-hand wing, but is exactly flush with the opposite one. The grinding and adjusting of the cutter is very important, because, in order to produce a perfect semicircle, the point of the cutter must not project beyond the right-hand wing. In planing a half-round box, all the cutting is done on the left-hand side, and the diameter of the box is the distance between the two

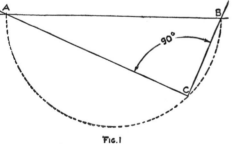

FIG. 1

The Geometrical Fact According to Which the Core-Box Plane Cuts to the Inside of a Circle

fixed points on which the plane is revolved.

The drawings show so clearly the construction of the plane that very

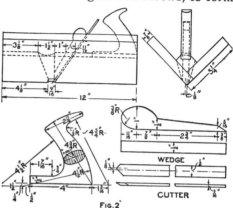

FIG. 2

Detail of the Parts for the Construction of a Core-Box Plane

little explanation is necessary. The wings are made of two pieces, securely fastened with glue and screws, to form a right angle. The block, through which is cut the openings for the throat and cutter, is a separate piece planed to the proper cross section before it is glued in place. The handle should be fitted to this block before it is fastened in place, but not fastened until the throat and opening for the cutter and wedge are worked out. The addition of a knob at the front end of the plane will make it more convenient to handle, but is not absolutely necessary. The cutter is made of $\frac{3}{16}$-in. by $\frac{1}{2}$-in. steel, and it will be noted that it comes to a point $\frac{1}{8}$ in. off center. This throws the throat, cutter socket and handle off center the same amount. The plane here shown is only suitable for semicircles 5 in. or less in diameter, but its capacity may be increased by additions to the wings, held in place by small battens on the inside.

A wing added to a 1-in. rabbet plane forms a core-box plane of easy construction, and answers very well for small boxes. By fastening the wing with two screws and two dowels so that it may be easily removed, the usefulness of the rabbet plane is not impaired.

Core boxes, on which the plane is

to be used, should be laid out in the usual way, with a semicircle on each end and two lines, indicating the diameter, on the face. "Rough out" to

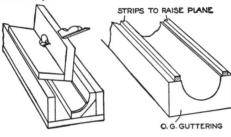

FIG.3   FIG.4

Attachments for the Core-Box Plane to Make Core Molding and for Cutting Out Ogee Guttering

within ⅛ in. of the lines, and start the plane by fastening a thin strip on one of the diameter lines with brads; plane about $\frac{1}{16}$ in. deep, keeping the side of the plane close against the strip, then reverse the strip and repeat the operation on the opposite diameter line. This provides the two fixed points on which the plane is to be revolved. Remove the strip and continue planing until the bottom of the box at the center has been reached, then reverse the box and plane the other side down to the center to complete the job.

Where it is desired to plane a quarter-circle as in the case of a core mold-

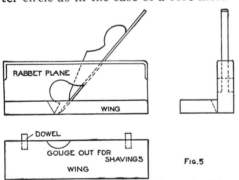

The Core-Box Plane with an Attachment for Using It as a Rabbet Plane

ing or a large fillet with thick edges, it will be necessary to provide some means for holding the piece to be planed and something for the plane to run on. This is accomplished as shown in Fig. 3.

To plane ogee guttering, which is usually somewhat less than a semicircle on the inside, strips should be tacked to the face to raise the plane the required height, as shown in Fig. 4.

The plane can be used as a rabbet plane by making an attachment, as shown in Fig. 5.—Contributed by J. A. Shelly, Brooklyn, N. Y.

Hints on Hardening Steel

The earliest hardening apparatus consisted of a fire and a pail of water; even now the cases are legion where nothing better is at hand and with them continued successful hardening and tempering is dependent upon the skill of the workman. Should it be desired to adopt better methods, methods which will permit the employment of less skilled labor, greater uniformity and increased production on duplicate work, which are inexpensive and almost crude in their simplicity and calling for materials that are obtainable in isolated situations, then the instructions which follow may be of service, as most blacksmiths have heard of or made use of them, although they may have long been forgotten.

For hardening tools, warm water is safer to use than cold. On steel of unknown grades it is safest to try this way, the first time at least, for the danger of cracking is less. Any good steel will harden in warm water except in rare cases. Some prefer boiling water. The same instructions apply to the use of oil. Oil-tempered is a synonym for well-tempered or tough-tempered. If fish oil is not available, any oil will do as well to a certain extent. Oil poured on the surface of the water in the barrel is good. The tool must first pass through the oil before reaching the water bath and it is hardened slowly. As a general rule the temperature of the work must be greater when it is to be quenched in oil than in water.

If a quantity of small parts are to be heated, a pot of hot lead is the best way to obtain uniform temperature. Any cast-iron pot will do for a small quantity—even a ladle—but the most lasting pot is the one with a thick bottom. A thin cast-iron shell soon burns through. For drawing the temper on a quantity of articles use a cast-iron pot with heavy steam-cylinder oil. A thermometer reading to 600 or 700 deg. F. is necessary for this bath. These pots can be placed on the blacksmith's fire and the coals built up around the sides to hold the heat within.

A scale, showing the temperature at which different classes of tools should be temper-drawn, also their color at that temperature, is of much value for temper-drawing with oil or by color.

Concealed Fasteners on Drawer Corners

A fastening especially adapted for drawer corners, but one that can be used for other purposes as well, is shown in the sketch. The corners are cut mitering, then glued, after which holes are bored at a 60-deg. angle from both sides and dowels driven in to force the parts together. Corners so fastened are much better than dovetailed, as they will never come apart.

Before boring the holes a sliver can be raised with a sharp chisel, which can be glued back in place after the dowels are inserted to make the work concealed. The corners can then be

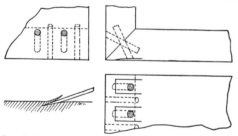

Interlocking and Concealed Dowels Hold a Mitered Corner Much Better Than a Dovetail Joint

rounded, if desired, to make a fancy drawer or box.—Contributed by Edwin E. Hahn, Philadelphia, Pa.

❡After a piece of furniture has been fumed with ammonia, another color effect may be given to it by applying equal parts of raw linseed oil and turpentine. This will make the color slightly darker and richer.

Chisel Point for Driving Steel Sheet Piling

In driving a line of steel piling through the structure of an old log dam, which was partly covered with a mat of concrete, a specially constructed chisel - point driver head had to be used, says a correspondent of Engineering Record. The concrete was worked out with wedges and points.

Chisel-Point Driver for Placing Steel Sheet Piling through a Log Dam

The timber work encountered below ran to such a depth, and the old work carried so much water that it was not feasible to dig it out, wherefore it became necessary to devise some scheme for clearing the way for the sheet piling. The chisel point was built up entirely of steel plates, from the cutting edge to the end of the section of piling. The cutting edge was welded. The section of piling was filled out with oak to fit the side plates which ran continuously from the point.

Transparent Paint for Glass

A transparent paint for glass may be made by tinting white shellac varnish with an aniline dye of the desired color. The glass should be warmed before applying the coating if possible. If a pane of glass or other object is to be coated, separate it from the frame, pour on the shellac and drain it off at a corner. This will give a smoother surface than if applied with a brush.

Pattern for a Tee Joint

Where it is necessary to make a side outlet for a straight pipe, or what is called a tee joint, the pattern for the

Space the lines A and B into equal divisions the same width as those on the half circles. Number these lines, as shown, beginning with 1 at the ends and in the center.

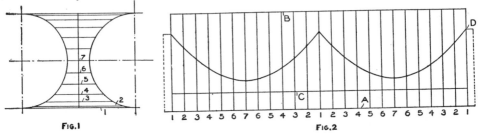

FIG.1   FIG.2

Manner of Laying Out the Stretchout of a Pattern for a Tee Joint in a Pipe Line

part attached to the straight pipe is laid out as follows:

Draw two half circles, as shown in Fig. 1, with sufficient space between them to provide for enough metal in the finished piece to hold its shape, and divide them into 12, 16, 20, or 24 parts, depending on the size of the pipe. Never divide them into 10, 14 or 18 parts. Draw a vertical line and number the lines, beginning with 1 at the edge.

Draw two parallel lines, A and B, Fig. 2, with sufficient space between them for the part to be made, also a parallel line, C, a distance from the line A equal to the width of the throat.

Set the divider points on the vertical center line and the end of line 1, Fig. 1, and step off this distance on all the lines marked 1 in the stretchout, from the line C upward, as shown at D, Fig. 2. Proceed in the same manner with the lines 2, 3, etc., Fig. 1, marking off the respective distances on lines 2, 3, etc., Fig. 2, until all of them are marked. Connect the points stepped off and cut out the pattern.—Contributed by S. C. Shipman, St. Petersburg, Fla.

❐A very small compression leak will reduce the power of a motor considerably.

Forced Gasoline Supply for an Automobile

With automobiles, depending on gravitation for the gasoline feed, trouble is often experienced on a hill  climb by not having enough gasoline in the tank to feed properly to the carburetor. The engine exhausts a few times and then stops. Sometimes this will happen when there is 1 in. or more of gasoline in the tank, for the reason that the grade is so steep that the carburetor stands higher than the level of the gasoline. Natur-

ally, the first thing an experienced motorist would do in such an instance would be to back downhill, turn the car around and back up the hill. This will put the tank higher than the carburetor and gravitation will do the rest.

But if far from home, this is a tiresome and laborious method. A motorist has found a way to make this unnecessary, by adopting the following scheme: A valve stem was procured from an old inner tube and the upper part, which contains the core or check valve, was sawed off. Then a hole was drilled in the brass plug of the gasoline tank, large enough to admit the valve stem so that the upper end projected through the plug, the

stem being then soldered in place. A
gasket was cut for the tank plug so
that it could be screwed down to make
it air-tight, and the job was complete.
Under ordinary conditions, the little
check valve is removed from the valve
stem so that air is admitted through
the opening.

When stalled on a hill, the little
check valve is screwed into place, connected with an air pump and a little
pressure applied in the tank. This
will force the gasoline feed and make
it possible to travel 6 or 8 miles on
a small supply of gasoline.

Parallel Vise Jaws

The gripping portion on the jaws of
a vise never holds the work solidly unless their surfaces come together paral-

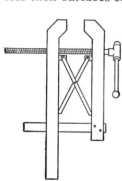

lel. The ordi-
nary carpenter's
vise is usually
adjusted at the
lower end with
a pin inserted in
holes or a ratch-
et bar and pawl,
but either is an
unhandy ar-
rangement at the
best. I rigged
up my vise with
a device similar
to lazy tongs, the two upper ends being fastened near the screw and the
lower ends bearing against the inside
surfaces of the jaws. The turning of
the screw to open the jaws forces the
lower parts open at the same time, and
in closing them the lower ends are held
apart the same distance as that between the jaws. The connecting pieces
at the top must be attached to make
the space occupied by the parallel device equal to that between the gripping
parts.—Contributed by Chas. Root,
Home, Kansas.

⸿A few small teeth filed in the back
edge of a carpenter's saw are very
handy for cutting off nails when repairing old work.

A Burr-Removing Tool

Several thousand slots were punched
in steel strips, one of which is shown
in the sketch at A. The burr at the
ends of the slots, though slight, was

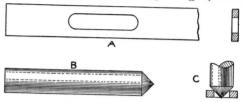

Tool for Removing the Burred Edges on a Slot
Punched in a Metal Strip

objectionable and it was desirable to
have the edges slightly rounded. To
take off the offending sharpness a piece
of drill rod, B, was beveled on the end
to 45 deg., then the beveled end was
ground on a coarse emery wheel while
the drill rod was rotated. This produced small cutting edges on the
roughened surface, which, when hardened, proved very lasting. The cutter was placed in a fast-running drill,
the slotted steel strips, held in the
hands, were pressed lightly against the
revolving tool C and moved lengthwise. The burr and sharp corners were
thus effectively removed.—Contributed by Donald A. Hampson, Middletown, N. Y.

Holding Countersunk Screws to
Thread Up to the Head

The device illustrated was made by
a correspondent of American Machinist for holding countersunk screws so
that they could be threaded up to the
head. It consists of a body, A, drilled
and tapped to receive the plug B, which
is a trifle larger than the head of the

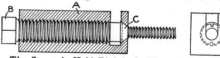

The Screw is Held Tightly in Place So That the
Threads can be Cut Close to the Head

screw to be threaded. The hole C is
countersunk for the screw, and then
slotted to permit the head of the screw
to be slipped out by slightly loosening
the plug.

Locomotive-Drawbar Truck

Locomotive drawbars are, at best, unwieldy pieces to handle. Owing to their irregular shape and weight it

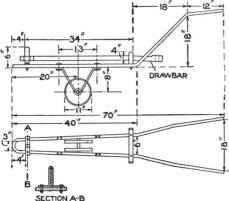

Details Showing the Construction of a Locomotive-Drawbar Truck Made of Pipe

is difficult to balance and carry them, even on a heavy shop truck, and when necessary to move them from shop to shop, the task is indeed tiresome.

The sketch shows a drawbar truck that can be made of 1-in. iron pipe and two light cast or wrought-iron wheels. One of the drawbar-pin holes in the bar is dropped over the horn at the front of the truck, and the remaining length of the bar is held by the U-shaped piece at the rear of the truck. The bar, being balanced in this manner, is very easy to wheel, one man transporting the heaviest bar with but little effort.

Transmitting an Engine's Operating Sound to a Distance

The operator of an isolated, stationary power plant where an explosive engine is used will appreciate the device described as follows for learning the performance of the engine without visiting the plant.

The device is a simple telephone working on the principle of the first telephones, that is dependent upon the property of the remarkable conductivity of sound by bodies whose elasticity is very great, such as wood, metal, etc. The transmitting and receiving in-

struments are of the same form and can be easily and efficiently constructed by fastening a thin circular metal disk over a hole cut in one side of a box— an empty cigar box will do. The opening must be made slightly smaller than the area of the metal disk and the latter should be fastened at its edge to the inner side of the box. Opposite this opening another hole is bored, through which the sound passes to the ear. The line wire is soldered to the center of the metal disk.

Such a telephone, which is of no use for the transmission of speech, will carry the sounds of the engine's explosions very audibly over considerable distances. These telephones have the advantage of great reliability, one line wire which may be any metallic line, such as a car-line rail or a fence wire, being used and care being taken at all points not to retard the intensity of the sound vibrations. These phones have transmitted the sound of an explosive engine for a distance of one mile.—Contributed by Grant Linton, Whitby, Ont.

Self-Closing Iron-Pipe Gate

This gate is made of five pieces of 2-in. pipe, two 2-in. elbows, two 2-in. tees, one piece of 1½-in. pipe, one 1½-in. nipple, one 1½-in. elbow, one 1½-in. flange, one 2-in. flange, and one ½-in.

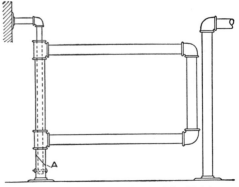

The Gate will Close by Means of Its Weight and the Sloping Cut in the Pipe

bolt. The 1½-in. pipe is connected as shown and extends through and almost to the bottom of the 2-in. pipe end of the gate where it is fastened with the bolt. The 2-in. pipe and connections are put together as shown, and the bottom pipe on the gate end is cut sloping, as shown at A. When the gate is pushed either way it rises on account of the sloping parts, and when released its weight will cause it to close for the same reason.—Contributed by Otto H. Von Fischer, Buffalo, N. Y.

Boring Holes in the End Grain of Wood

The ordinary carpenter's bit will not cut in the end grain of all kinds of wood and for this reason a correspondent of the Wood-Worker made a bit especially for this class of work from

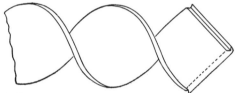

A Bit with Cutting Edges That will Bore in the End Grain of Any Kind of Wood

an old worn-out bit, but a machine bit will do if it is reground in the manner shown. The face, or cutting edge, is ground flat, then a V-groove made on each face side. A round groove will do, but a V-groove will make a better cutting edge as the chips will be broken up, and this prevents clogging.

Removing a Manhole Cover

In taking out the machinery in a mill preparatory to remodeling and starting work again, it was necessary to repair and inspect the boilers. These had been idle for some years and, previous to that, had been in service for a decade. The boilers were of the water-tube variety with extra large mud drums at the bottom. The manhole covers had to be removed from the heads of these drums to get inside to roll the ends of the water tubes. But the covers were tightly rusted besides being a good fit in their places. Jacks, bars, and levers were tried to no avail, and the job was about given up when

the superintendent conceived the idea of a battering ram.

To carry out the idea a runway was made by blocking up with ties and put-

A Tightly Fitted and Rusted-In Manhole Cover being Removed by the Use of a Battering Ram

ting 6 by 12-in. timber on top of them. Then an old length of $3\frac{7}{16}$-in. shafting was brought in and placed on the timber with rollers under it. Guides, not shown in the drawing, confined the travel of the shaft sideways. Three strong laborers were put on the job, and, taking a run of about 3 ft. soon knocked the first manhole cover to the inside of the drum. With the confidence born of experience the other covers were quickly removed by this old-fashioned method.

Channel Insert for Concrete Walls

When building concrete basement walls some means must be provided for holding shelves, hooks, and the like for provisions and storage. A correspondent of American Carpenter and Builder solved this problem in a satisfactory manner by forming a galvanized channel in the shape shown and

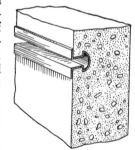

inserting it in the plastic concrete at the proper location before the concrete had set. This makes a T-slot similar to the slots on lathe and drill faceplates and on planer beds. A T-head bolt or hook may be inserted and fastened anywhere in the channel.

¶A clogged muffler will cause an engine to lose power. Give the muffler a thorough cleaning occasionally.

Double Handle for a Handsaw

The ordinary crosscut and rip hand-saws can be used as bucksaws where a large amount of work is to be done,

The Double Handle as It is Applied to the Handle of an Ordinary Handsaw

or for sawing timbers and posts, by attaching a double handle. This consists of two crosspieces clamped to the saw handle and having a hand hold at each end. The handle on the front or cutting edge of the saw is made to turn so that a straight or spade handle can be used as desired.—Contributed by A. S. Thomas, Gordon, Can.

A Crank-Handle Screwdriver

The construction of this screwdriver provides a crank action to the handle, which makes a rapid tool for small work. The handle has a metal sleeve

In Revolving the Screwdriver the Handle Has the Action of a Crank

in which the stem of the screwdriver revolves. The bend in the screwdriver shank should be so shaped as to make the outer end of the handle center the straight part of the screwdriver.—Contributed by Conrad Jung, Huntington, Indiana.

Removing an Insect from the Ear

This unfortunate accident has happened many times and it is a peculiarly painful condition for the patient to have an insect with its hooked claws scratching the tender ear drum. The remedy is a simple one and the intruding insect will be driven out immediately. Prepare an ointment as follows:

Vaseline	1 oz.
Coryfin	1 dr.
Menthol	10 gr.

This is well mixed together and can be kept ready for use at any time.

Wrap a little absorbent cotton around a small probe, the blunt end of a toothpick or similar instrument, and dip it into the ointment, then carefully introduce it into the ear. The fumes of the menthol will drive any live insect from within.

Any person lying on the ground is apt to get an insect in the ear and sometimes a bedbug is liable to enter while one is sleeping.—Contributed by Dr. R. W. Battles, Erie, Pa.

Pipe Supports in the Place of Decayed Wood

In making a quick repair on a portion of a wagon I found I could not conveniently use a piece of wood to re-

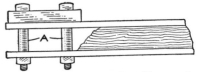

Pieces of Pipe Supporting the Iron Plates on the End of a Decayed Piece of Wood

place a section that had rotted out between two iron plates through which the bolts passed. I cut short pieces of iron pipe, A, to fit between the plates and slipped the bolts through these to prevent the plates from bending when the bolts were tightened.—Contributed by James M. Kane, Doylestown, Pa.

Rule for a Field-Note Book

When making a survey and taking field notes, a small metal rule is very useful, but if the ordinary steel rule is used and placed between the pages of the notebook, it is continually slipping out and becoming lost.

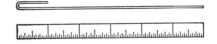

The Hooked End of the Rule can be Shaped So That Several Pages are Gripped at a Time

If a piece of brass with some spring to it, about 7 in. long, $\frac{1}{16}$ in. thick and $\frac{1}{2}$ in. wide, is bent in the shape shown, it may be placed at any page of the book without slipping out. The bent-over end is about 1 in. long, and the spring of the metal will make it grip the leaves of the book. The brass may be graduated as desired.—Contributed by Charles Motton, Toronto, Can.

Setting Flat-Bottomed Stones in Jewelry

The necessary tools for setting small flat-bottomed stones, such as halves of pearls, opals and turquoises, in mount-ings without prongs are the so-called pearl drills, one of which is shown at A, Fig. 1, and a set of beading tools, one being shown at B, says the Key-stone. A drill will cut a seat for the stone, as shown in the cross section, and the beading tool is used in the man-ner of a graver to form a projection of metal into a hemispherical shape, as shown in Fig. 3.

To make a star-shaped setting, as shown at A, Fig. 2, cut a seat with a pearl drill, the same width as the diam-eter of the stone to be set. Set one point of a steel divider in the center of the seat and draw a circle lightly around the seat as far out as the points of the star are desired to be. Divide the circle into five equal parts and, from the points so marked, cut the lines straight toward the center of the circle with the graver point. Cut the star

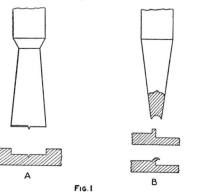

FIG. I

A Pearl Drill and a Beading Tool for Use in Setting Flat-Bottomed Stones

points as shown at B, making the cuts wide and shallow, and finish with a polished graver so as to leave the cuts

bright. Leave small portions of the metal next to the stone seat, opposite

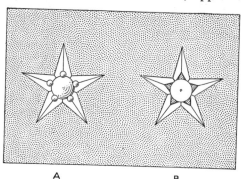

FIG. 2

The Star as It is Cut in the Metal and the Beads for Holding the Stone

each star point, to be shaped into beads for holding the stone.

Place the stone in the seat and put the beading tool against one of the projections which were left when the star points were cut. Press the tool down with considerable force and, at the same time, slightly revolve the

FIG. 3

Cross Section of the Metal and the Stone Showing the Shape of the Holding Beads

handle, "swinging" its top. The tool should be inclined a little so as to push the metal toward the stone. This oper-ation will result in the formation of a bead overlapping the stone, and clamp-ing it into the seat. Form the remain-ing beads in a similar manner. It may be found that some surplus metal has been squeezed out around the bottom of the bead. If noticeable, this should be carefully cut away with the graver point. A workman with good judg-ment and experience can generally leave the metal projection of such a size as to be just sufficient to form the bead, necessitating no further work in trimming.

¶Aluminum bronze does not do well applied over white-lead paint, as the lead affects the bronze. Hence it is better to use zinc white or lithopone, as they are neutral.

Belting a High-Speed Fan

A fan requiring a high speed and running in the opposite direction of the line shaft caused considerable trouble in wearing and burning out the cross

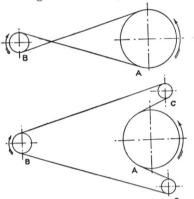

Idler Pulleys Used to Make the Drive Belt Run Straight Instead of Crossed

belt that drove it. The usual manner of belting the fan is shown in the first sketch, in which A is the driving pulley and B the fan pulley. The belt expense was greatly reduced by changing the drive as shown in the second sketch. The two idler pulleys, CC, permitted the belt to run straight, yet the reverse direction of the fan pulley B was obtained.—Contributed by Joseph Flood, Philadelphia, Pa.

Applying Cement to Rubber Patches

The holder shown in the illustration eliminates all the trouble experienced in the curling of rubber patches. The patch must be thoroughly cleaned with some abrasive, such as fine sandpaper or emery cloth, before applying a coat of cement, and the first coat of cement

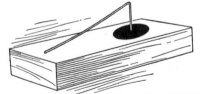

A Block of Wood with a Spring Clip Attached for Holding Rubber Patches

is allowed to dry before a second coat is applied. In these operations the patch will tend to curl and one edge is apt to stick to the other, thus destroying the adhesive.

The holder will keep the patch from curling until it is ready to apply on the puncture. The device consists of a block of wood to which a round wire spring is attached, as shown, the end pressing on the center of the patch.

Fastening Disks in a Wood Lathe for Turning

The old method of fastening small disks, from 6 to 14 in. in diameter, to a wood-lathe faceplate with screws takes considerable time, and where a large number of disks are to be turned, they can be attached and detached much quicker by using the following device.

A wood disk, A, is fastened to the faceplate B of the lathe, turned on the edge and faced off true. Three screws are turned through the wood disk from the back, at equal distances apart, allowing them to project $\frac{3}{16}$ in. on the face, the ends being then filed to sharp

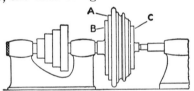

The Disks are Placed in a Lathe and Centered Much Quicker Than by Fastening Them with Screws

points. Another wood disk, C, is turned up in a similar manner and fitted to the tailstock spindle. Three screws are turned through this disk and the ends filed to a point as described.

The tailstock disk is placed on the material to be turned, centered and the points of the screws imbedded into the wood with light blows of a hammer. The disk with the work is then placed in the tailstock spindle which is screwed up against the faceplate on the headstock, and the work is ready to be turned.—Contributed by Chas. M. Allen, Knoxville, Tenn.

¶A flock of ducks will clean a potato patch of bugs and their eggs without harming the plants, as ducks do not scratch.

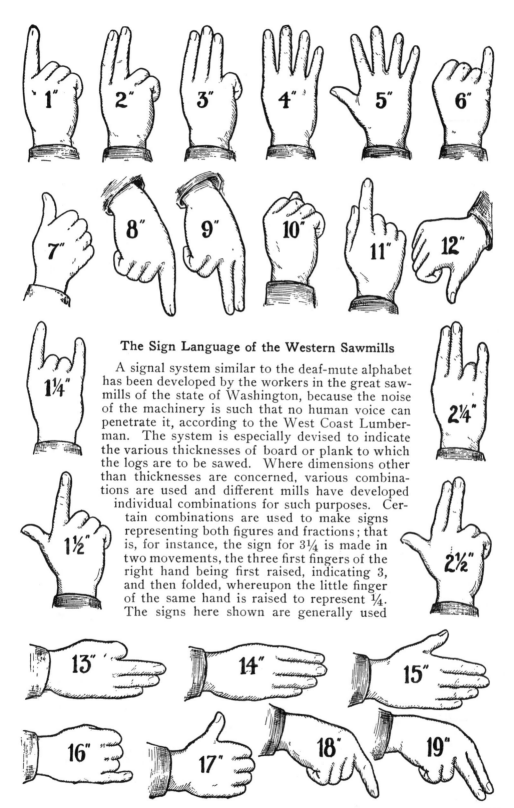

The Sign Language of the Western Sawmills

A signal system similar to the deaf-mute alphabet has been developed by the workers in the great sawmills of the state of Washington, because the noise of the machinery is such that no human voice can penetrate it, according to the West Coast Lumberman. The system is especially devised to indicate the various thicknesses of board or plank to which the logs are to be sawed. Where dimensions other than thicknesses are concerned, various combinations are used and different mills have developed individual combinations for such purposes. Certain combinations are used to make signs representing both figures and fractions; that is, for instance, the sign for 3¼ is made in two movements, the three first fingers of the right hand being first raised, indicating 3, and then folded, whereupon the little finger of the same hand is raised to represent ¼. The signs here shown are generally used

2125

and are thoroughly understood by the workmen and the signs up to and including 12 are given with the hand stationary. From 12 to 19 they are made by placing the hand in a horizontal position and drawing it across the body from left to right.

Reversed Action of Oars

The ordinary oar of a rowboat makes the rower sit facing astern with the back toward the way the boat is traveling. The inconvenience of not being able to see in the direction the boat is going is similar to walking backward. In striving to overcome this difficulty I constructed the device shown in the illustration to give a reversed action to the oars.

The apparatus consists of two wood segments of circles A and B, cut from material 2 in. thick with a radius of 8 or 10 in. The oar C and handle D are attached as shown. Around the two segments, and almost making a figure 8, is a 1-in. leather strap, E, fastened with a buckle, F. This single belt passes around both segments, crossing over itself at the point where the segments touch. The action is similar to a reversed belt connecting two pulleys with their faces close together, but in this case the leather is nailed down on the flat side of each segment. This forces the segments to move closely together without the slightest slip, producing the same effect as a pair of perfectly constructed cog wheels. The connecting or cross strips, G

give the up-and-down motion to the oar.

The oars are used in exactly the same manner as in ordinary rowing, and as the leather is quite flexible and there are only two pivots there is little friction. If the leather stretches, it can be taken up with the buckle which is on the slack side. The entire arrangement can be lifted out as an ordinary oar, and it has the additional advantage that it may be folded up, as shown.—Contributed by Sam Gluck, New York City.

Preserving Ox Gall

Users of ox gall in the paper-ruling trades find that, two or three days after dissolving the deodorized ox gall in hot water, it will turn to slime, which will render its further use impossible. For a number of years I have been throwing this mixture away, making a fresh one, but by experiment I put in a teaspoonful of liquid ammonia to each quart of mixture and was surprised to see it clear almost instantly. The ammonia seems to increase its efficiency rather than to be harmful.—Contributed by Rudolph I. Wilson, St. John, Can.

Mending Broken Oilstones

A broken oilstone can be repaired so that it will last until the stone wears out, in the following manner: The pieces are first heated on an iron plate to remove all oil, then thoroughly cleaned. The surfaces to be joined

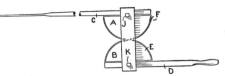

Arrangement of the Parts to Give a Reversed Action to the Oar, Permitting the Rower to Sit in the Boat Facing the Direction of Travel

and H, are made of hard wood. The bolts, J and K, hold the crosspieces and each makes a bearing for one segment. These bolts should be long enough to have extending ends which fit into holes bored in the gunwale and of a size to receive them loosely. This will

are well dusted with powdered shellac, which is melted by heating in the same manner. The parts are then placed together and tightly clamped until they become cool. The joints thus made will not interfere with the cutting surface.

Locating a Broken Line in an Igniting Cable

To find a wire broken inside the insulation in a cable is a very difficult job when one does not know how to go about it. Such breaks can be easily located, however, in the following manner: Procure a cheap pocket compass, draw each wire out at some point, separate it from the others and turn a current through it, at the same time holding the compass about ½ in. from the wire. If the current flows through, the needle of the compass will be deflected from normal in one direction or the other, but a broken wire will have no effect on the needle.—Contributed by John McDermott, Turtle Creek, Pa.

Adapting Gas Fixtures for Inverted Lights

When fitting inverted gas lights on certain kinds of fixtures, instead of using goosenecks, use the arms and attach lights as shown in Fig. 1. This will make a better-appearing job than the gooseneck method, as shown in

FIG. 1   FIG. 2

Reversing the Arms of a Gas Fixture to Adapt It for Use of Inverted Lights

Fig. 2. The arms should be adjusted so that there will be no leakage of gas in the joints.

❈The surface of cement floors may be cleaned of oil for making repairs by a few applications of muriatic acid.

Automobile Lights Directed by the Travel of the Wheel

Being compelled to use my motor truck a great deal at night over roads that were none too good, I devised a

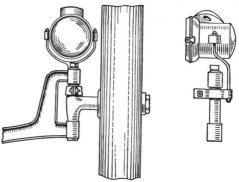

Lamp Brackets Attached to the Wheel-Axle Stub so That the Light will Follow the Wheel's Travel

way to attach the gas lamps so that their light would be directed in the line of the front wheels' travel at all times. The Y-shaped brackets which served to hold the lamps were removed from their original position and were lengthened by means of a piece of strap iron, welded to them at the junction of the forks. A clamp of strap iron was then made to fit around the upper portion of the spindle on which the steering stub turns, and to this clamp the lower end of the enlarged bracket was riveted. The clamp was then put in position and the bolt drawn tight, whereupon the bracket was marked and taken off to be bent so that the turning point of the lamp coincided approximately with the axis of the spindle.

The diameter of the lamp was such that it was necessary to revolve the clamp slightly when it was finally put in place to prevent any part of the device from coming in contact with the wheel. Naturally, with this arrangement, it is advisable to use lamps of small diameter and weight, not because of limited space alone, but because the location is such that they are subjected to very severe vibration.—Contributed by E. F. Hallock, New York City.

Forced Draft for a Kitchen Stove

Having considerable difficulty with the kitchen stove on account of floor draft, I put a few additional lengths of

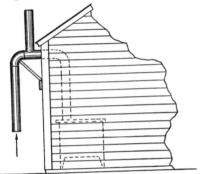

The Open End of the Pipe Extending Downward Admits Air That Causes a Draft in the Main Pipe

pipe on the main chimney without any marked improvement. I then hit upon the plan shown in the sketch, and it worked so well that the damper in the stove must be used frequently. The additional pipe was placed downward with an open end at the bottom, the upper end being connected with a T-joint, as shown, in the main pipe.—Contributed by W. A. Jaquythe, San Diego, Cal.

Cutting Thin Tubing

Cutting tubing of brass or steel with a hand hacksaw is very hard on the saw blades. Special blades are made for this work, and are commonly called "tubing saws," in which the teeth are so fine that the section of the metal being cut cannot slip up between successive teeth and break them. However, these tubing saws are not always to be had when one wants them. Instead of them, drive a piece of wood inside the tube, completely filling the

hole and the piece can be cut with safety with almost any saw blade. Hard wood is better than soft wood for this work. If a whole length of tubing is to be cut into short pieces, fill the tube with lead, and it can be easily knocked out of the sections after they are cut.

Thin brass tubing or sheet brass may also be cut in another way. Reverse the blade in the frame and begin to saw with the back of the blade. The blade will soon pick up particles of metal and thus roughens up enough to cut quite well. It cuts somewhat on the principle of the friction saw, so commonly used where power is available. It is not a speedy cutter, but where there is only one saw blade to complete a job it is a trick well worth knowing.

Gauge for Cutting Hedges

A great deal of difficulty is usually encountered when cutting hedges and it is almost an impossibility to get a straight line. The attachment for a wheelbarrow, shown in the illustration, makes the cutting a very simple matter. The attachment consists of two uprights, about 2 in. square and 3 ft. long, graduated in inches on one of their surfaces, and an adjustable crossbar. A ¼-in. hole is bored in the center of each piece on each mark. The uprights are fastened to the sides of the wheelbarrow with bolts having thumb nuts, as shown at A A. The crossbar is a piece of material, 1 in. thick, 2 in.

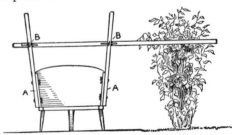

The Crossbar may be of Any Shape to Make a Guide for Cutting the Hedge Tops

wide, and about 4 ft. long. Two slots, ¼ in. wide and about 8 in. long, are cut in this piece, as shown at BB. This is to provide for the slant of the uprights. Two bolts with thumb nuts can be used to hold the guide to the uprights.

When cutting the hedge the guide is set at the desired height and the top of the hedge can be clipped off evenly, the wheelbarrow being moved forward as the clipping proceeds. The advantages are evident. The guide is adjustable, and the clipped tops can be thrown into the wheelbarrow. Any shape of guide may be used, which makes it possible to obtain any variety of fancy shapes on the hedge.

Blank-Tag Holder

Although a great many tags are used in our store we have never had a good place to keep them, and usually they  were placed loose in a box and were not easily found. One day I strung several on a cord and tied a knot in one end and the other end to a nail. The knot was small enough to allow the tag to slip off when pulled and yet large enough to keep them from slipping off by their own weight. —Contributed by Geo. B. Wright, Norwalk, Conn.

A Gauge Siphon

The gauge siphon, as its name suggests, is simply a siphon which enables the operator to determine at all times exactly the location of the end of the tube with respect to the bottom of the tank. A simple sketch of the apparatus is shown. The siphon consists of two rubber corks and a glass rod bent to form an ordinary U-tube, to which a rubber hose is attached.

The cork A simply acts as a bearing on the edge of the tank and a support for the U-tube. The cork B is simply put on the tube to take up the side thrust of the tube, due to its own

weight and the weight of the rubber hose. This cork may be used on either

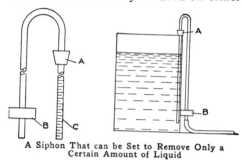

A Siphon That can be Set to Remove Only a Certain Amount of Liquid

tube according to the direction of this side thrust.

A scale, C, might be etched on the tube and a direct reading of the tube's immersion taken. This apparatus will be found practical for use in sieve tests where the residue in the bottom of the tank must not be disturbed, also in oil-storage tanks where it is desired to draw off only the clear oil.

An Emergency Split Pulley

An emergency split pulley can be easily cut from a plank, and if great width is necessary, several planks can be placed side by side. A circle is drawn on the plank the size of the pulley. If the plank is not wide enough place two of them with their edges together. Draw another circle for the width of the rim and cut out the inside, leaving a crosspiece on one side of the diameter or center line. The saw is run into the part to be cut out on the line A. The shaft hole is cut out to fit snugly on the shaft and two holes bored through the spokes for bolts. A

Wood Split Pulley as It is Cut from a Plank for an Emergency Case

pulley can be quickly made in this manner, and it will answer the purpose as well as an expensive pulley.—Contributed by E. Leslie McFarlane, Nashwaaksis, Can.

Bending U-Bolts

The bending of U-bolts is easily accomplished with the tool shown in the illustration. The shank of the tool A

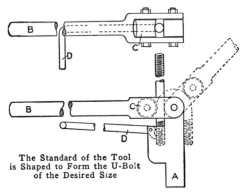

The Standard of the Tool is Shaped to Form the U-Bolt of the Desired Size

is made to fit the square hole in the anvil, and the lever B carries a roller, C, in a semicircular course over the upper end of the support. The lever D holds the threaded stock and prevents its being drawn out of the tool by the action of the bending lever B.

The tool must be made for a special size of stock and for a certain bend and cannot be used to make any other sizes. Sometimes it is necessary to make a large quantity of the U-bolts of one size and then it will save time and expense to make the bending tool.—Contributed by Roy H. Poston, Flat River, Mo.

A Hammock Swing

This hammock swing consists of a frame made of gas pipe and fittings and covered with canvas. The size of the

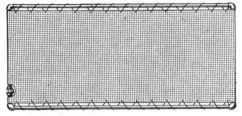

The Frame is Strongly Made of Gas Pipe and the Canvas Stretched Tightly on It

pipe used was ¾ in. in diameter, the two side bars being 74 in. long and the end pieces 30 in. long. The corners were connected with ¾-in. els, and one end piece built up of two parts and one union.

The canvas is 1 yd. wide with a 3-in. hem, the ends lapping over the gas pipe and the sides being fastened as shown.

The hammock is hung with ropes or chains of light steel as desired. A pair of hangers for each end will be required. The chains are used by fastening the ends of one chain in the pair to the corners of the hammock, then the other chain in the center and to the beam above, adjusting it to the height desired.—Contributed by Mrs. J. V. Moore, Seattle, Wash.

Fuel Storage for a Motorcycle

Having a clear glass carboy handy and desiring a receptacle to store several gallons of gasoline for my motorcycle I arranged the carboy as follows: A wood stopper was made for the neck, two holes bored in it, one large enough to pour in the gasoline and the other of a size to admit a piece of copper tubing, about 3½ ft. long.

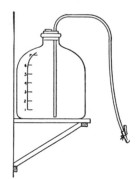

The stopper was placed in the neck of the carboy and the copper tubing was inserted into the small hole so that the end almost touched the bottom. The tubing on the outside was then bent over until the end extended below the bottom of the carboy. A small length of rubber tubing was fastened to this end.

The gasoline was poured in through the large hole with the aid of a funnel and the siphon started by drawing out the air until the gasoline began to flow, then the rubber tubing was doubled and tied with a bit of string to keep the liquid from flowing until it was necessary to fill the motorcycle tank. The carboy was kept on a shelf at the right height. When filling the carboy the level for each gallon of gasoline was marked on the outside, so that I could determine the amount of gasoline on hand at any time.—Contributed by J. A. Hart, Philadelphia, Pa.

A Stud Driver

The driver consists of a piece of hexagon bar stock drilled and tapped to fit the threads cut on the stud, and a short pin having a flat surface filed tapering from one end to the other and fitted in a hole drilled through two parallel sides of the threaded piece.

In use, the driver is turned on the stud until the flat side of the pin strikes the top end of the stud. The pin is

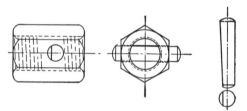

A Driver That is Quickly Attached to a Stud for Turning It into Place

then tapped lightly with a hammer on the large end, causing it to tighten against the end of the stud. A socket wrench of the right size is used for turning it. To remove the driver from the stud, tap the small end of the pin lightly with a hammer and turn the driver in the reverse direction.—Contributed by C. E. Bradley, Fall River, Massachusetts.

Clamps to Hold Picture Frames

An effective way to glue and clamp a picture frame is to use four narrow strips, two of which are shown in the sketch at A, with their ends notched for the clamps. This will bring equal pressure on all corners. — Contributed by J. M. Adamson, Carey, Idaho.

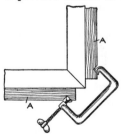

Block to Assist Hammer in Pulling Long Nails

The pulling of a long nail with a carpenter's hammer requires a block to

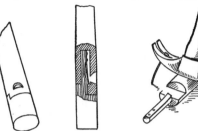

Block Attachment for a Hammer to be Used in Pulling Long Nails from Wood

raise the center of the hammer high enough to draw the nail straight at the end. A block not always being at hand, I put one on the handle of my hammer and found it very convenient. The block constitutes the end of the hammer handle and is fastened with a spring clip, as shown, which can be pressed with the thumb when the block is to be taken from the handle and used for pulling a nail.—Contributed by A. S. Thomas, Gordon, Can.

Electric Lighting of Bubble Glasses in a Level

Bore a hole in the end of the level opposite the plumb bubble, large enough to receive a dry cell of battery such as used for flash lamps. Mortise

When the Level is Used in a Dark Place, the Light can be Flashed on the Bubble Glass

a space under each bubble glass large enough to receive a small electric globe, and bore two holes for push buttons. The lines for the wires are shown plainly in the sketch. A hole bored through lengthwise will provide a place for the wires. The bubbles can be lighted when the level is used in dark places.—Contributed by Chas. C. Bradley, W. Toledo, Ohio.

❡Old paint worn too thin to burn off may be removed by applying a coat of linseed oil before using the burner.

Locking a Cork in a Bottle

The bottle-locking device shown in the illustration is for use on bottles

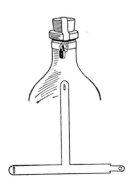

containing poisons or other fluids that might prove dangerous to anyone not familiar with their nature. A clasp is made of thin metal, as shown by the diagram, which is bent around the bottle neck and over the cork, the tongue end with the round hole being inserted through the slots in the other ends and a small padlock attached in the round hole. The size of the clasp will depend on the size of the bottle.—Contributed by Jos. J. Kolar, Maywood, Ill.

A Paint-Can Hook

The hook is shaped from a piece of round iron, ¼ in. in diameter and

about 16 in. long. The bend in the center which forms the hook part is welded together and the upper end flattened to slip under the siding while the lower end is pointed and made sharp to stick into the wood. The flattened part prevents the

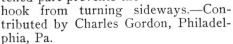

hook from turning sideways.—Contributed by Charles Gordon, Philadelphia, Pa.

Remedy for Swelling Feet and Enlarged Pores

Persons who work in boiler rooms or in shops where steam is present are often troubled with swelling feet or enlarged pores. A good solution to be applied which will prevent this as well as the odors of perspiration can be made in the following manner: Mix to-

gether 60 parts alum; 10 parts tannic acid; 5 parts salicylic acid; 20 parts starch and 5 parts talcum; add enough water to dissolve them and make a preparation thin enough to apply easily. The solution is harmless and inexpensive. — Contributed by Loren Ward, Des Moines, Iowa.

Oil Spout Formed in a Bottle Stopper

Having occasion to use an oilcan when none was at hand, I constructed a substitute by forming a spout in the stopper of a bottle. An ordinary bottle of the smaller size was selected and

a wood stick, about 4 in. long, was whittled to fit in the neck of the bottle. The outer end of the wood was cut pointed, and a V-shaped groove cut in the side from the pointed end to the base. The oil will run along the groove and can be dropped into a bearing as well as with an ordinary oilcan. —Contributed by Arthur Koeppner, Cleveland, Ohio.

Starting a Bolt in a Difficult Place

Recently, while working on an automobile, I found it difficult to get a bolt started in its place, and when I had

about decided to remove other parts to enter the bolt, I hit upon the following scheme of overcoming the difficulty. A

piece of wire was procured and one end lightly soldered to the bolt head. This served as a handle for placing the bolt and was easily removed by giving the wire a few turns. The same means can be used to enter bolts and pins in places not easily accessible, the time of preparation being small as compared with the practical value of the device. —Contributed by Wm. A. Murry, Cold Spring, N. Y.

How to Make an Engineer's Kerosene Torch

By F. W. BENTLEY, Jr.

A compact, light and strongly built brass hand torch is the pride of the engineer who owns it. However, in the construction of many torches the maker is forced to combat with a few difficulties coincident with the necessary use of kerosene, that sometimes discourages an extra outlay of time and expense in its construction. In the first place the soiling nature of kerosene will prevent the average torch from being placed in a grip or suitcase with overalls or clothing. In the second place, the construction of many torches of this kind is such that the process of filling the oil chamber necessitates a withdrawal of the large wick, which in itself makes the torch only an objectionable necessity.

In the accompanying sketches the construction of a brass torch is explained which will eliminate almost all of the serious drawbacks generally encountered in the use of a kerosene torch. In addition to other merits of its construction, the most important feature is the small expense of making one. Referring to Fig. 1, the shell or body is of 2-in. brass tubing, which can be purchased for about 10 cents per foot. The top piece can be turned out of a piece of 2½-in. brass rod. The bottom piece is also made with but few operations on the lathe out of a piece of 3½-in. brass rod. The part for the wick, and the base are simply sweated to the tubing.

The throat nipple, containing the tin wick casing, is shown in Fig. 2. The wick casing can be either sweated or riveted into the nipple. A small round-nose chisel should be used to puncture the casing in a number of places, the raised tin portions pointing upward on the inside of the casing. This will enable the wick to be drawn upward, but at the same time will prevent it from dropping down into the torch in case the same is accidentally dropped, or receives a sudden jar. The end of the nipple, holding the wick casing, is screwed firmly into the upper

portion of the torch, and is taken out only for the renewal of the wick.

The cap covering the upper portion of the nipple when the torch is not in

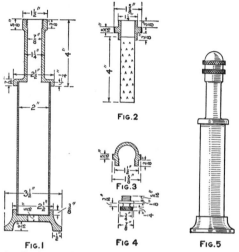

FIG.2

FIG.3

FIG.1 FIG 4 FIG.5

An Engineer's Torch That can be Stored in a Tool Chest or with Clothing without Leakage of Oil

use, is shown in Fig. 3. This covering permits the torch to be placed in contact with anything without danger of soiling it. The filling of the torch is accomplished by the removal of the filling plug in the cupped portion of the lower, or bottom, piece. The details of the plug are shown in Fig. 4. The concave portion of the bottom enables the torch to be filled without spilling and splashing oil. A sketch of the torch assembled, showing its neat exterior appearance, is given in Fig. 5. Of course, the sizes of the several pieces can be varied to suit the requirements of the person for whom it is made, but in the line of a portable torch, using kerosene oil, the points of its construction for durability, cleanliness and inexpensive manufacture will be found hard to excel.

⁋If an ignition cable becomes frayed at the ends, one or more strands are likely to come in contact with the metal parts of the magneto, the coil or the car, and cause trouble.

A Pencil and Compass Holder

Carpenters and other workmen have occasion to use compasses in their work and often need to strike a circular line with a pencil. If no other device is at hand, one can be made in a few minutes from a piece of tin,

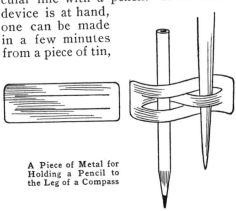

A Piece of Metal for Holding a Pencil to the Leg of a Compass

sheet copper or brass. Take a piece of the metal, ½ by 1¼ in., and make two slits in it, then bend the center piece in an S-shape and the two outside pieces also in an S-shape, but in the opposite direction, and the holder is complete. A compass leg is slipped in one loop and a pencil in the other, and the result is a device that cannot be beaten for utility. The spring of the metal holds the inserted pieces very firmly.

Cutting Eccentric Slots on a Lathe

The method of cutting two eccentric slots in a cam plate on a lathe is shown in the sketch. Two circles are drawn concentric with their respective slots on the cam plate and the slots laid out

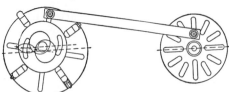

Manner of Oscillating the Chuck of a Lathe so That Eccentric Slots can be Cut

and roughly drilled. The plate is then clamped in a lathe chuck so that the center of one circle runs true. A connecting bar is fastened to a stud on the faceplate of a smaller lathe, set in line, so that the other end of the bar can be connected to a stud set in the chuck holding the plate.

The smaller lathe is started and the connecting bar gives a rocking motion to the chuck holding the plate. The adjustment of the studs holding the connecting bar limits the length of the rocking motion. It is only necessary to use an ordinary boring tool to cut the sides of the slot accurately.—Contributed by James H. Rodgers, Hamilton, Ont.

Transferring Photographs to Watchcases

Instructions for making a picture on a watchcase, watch dial, or other similar object, are often sold at a high price and most of them turn out to be a simple carbon transfer, or a process of sensitizing metal which is difficult to carry out. The method herewith given is extremely simple, and with it anyone can do good work from the start, without experience in photography. It makes a perfect, transparent film that appears as if the photograph were taken directly on the watchcase or dial.

First prepare the following mixture: Collodion, 4 oz.; Vence turpentine, 1 dr.; camphor spirits, 10 drops, and 95-per-cent alcohol, 1 oz. Flow this solution over the photograph that is to be transferred and carefully lay it aside to dry for 15 minutes, or longer, then paste the print, face down, on a smooth piece of plain glass, using ordinary library paste. Allow it to dry for at least one hour, then, with the bowl of a spoon, or a finger, rub the picture from the center out, wetting with cold water until all the paper backing is removed, and place the glass with the picture into a bowl of hot water. The composition will free itself from the glass.

Place the film on a piece of ordinary paper and cut it to the desired size. It is usually best to cut it in the shape of a disk to fit the watchcase. Place this disk back into the warm water, and the film will soon float while the paper sinks to the bottom. With a solution of gum acacia, grease the case that is to receive the picture, then very carefully place the picture in the right position and attach it firmly by pressing with a silk cloth. The best place to put the picture is either on the inside of the cover or on the dial. If placed on the dial, the picture will show up in every detail, yet the figures can be seen through the picture.—Contributed by J. G. Allshouse, Avonsmore, Pennsylvania.

Piston-Ring Closer

When replacing a piston in the cylinder of a gas engine, it is rather difficult to close the three or four rings so

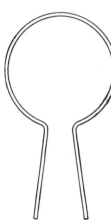

that they will enter the bore. The mouth of most cylinders is countersunk or beveled to facilitate starting the rings, but without assistance, this will be of little help if the rings are new and stiff. Some mechanics tie the rings closed with light copper wire which is removed as each ring starts into the bore.

A time and labor-saving tool can be made for this work that will pay for itself in the work on one engine. Secure a piece of metal, $\frac{3}{16}$ in. thick and 1 in. wide, and bend it to the circle of the piston—for a 4-in. piston, the ring should have a 4-in. inside diameter—leaving a gap of about 1 in. and bending both ends back to form handles as shown. With this clamp one man can easily replace cylinder pistons alone and in a short time.

❈A filler for ebony is made of lampblack and plaster of Paris mixed in a paste by using gold size or japan.

An Inexpensive Post Pipe Vise

A pipe vise of any size suitable for holding pipe up to 3 in. in diameter is an expensive and a heavy tool, and,

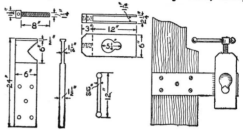

Flat Construction of a Pipe Vise That can be Quickly Attached to a Post

in a great many instances where pipe work of a light nature necessitates only the use of a small pipe vise, a heavy bench or rigging must be carried along to attach the vise to, or a temporary bench must be erected.

A vise that can be very inexpensively constructed and quickly bolted to a post or wall corner of sufficient rigidity to stand the strain of work is shown in the sketch. Its manufacture requires only a few hours' work on the lathe and shaper. Owing to its construction the vise is able to stand a great deal more abuse and heavy usage in rough and hurried work than the finer machine vises intended for use only on the shop bench.

A Rivet Clamp

Rivets that are placed through holes in square or circular sheet-metal work must be held by the protruding end while the stake or mandrel is placed on the head. A clamping device for holding the rivets can be easily made from a cotter that is of suitable size for

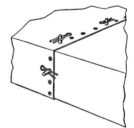

the rivet. The legs of the cotter are bent to fit the rivet as shown. Several cotters can be shaped to hold as many rivets. — Contributed by Lorin A. Brown, Washington, D. C.

A Paint-Can Opener

A very handy paint-can opener can be made on the small or upper end of the paint-brush handle. The small end

The End of the Paint-Brush Handle is Shaped to Insert under the Cover Edge

is cut off where it will be large enough not to break easily, and then it is cut wedge-shaped. This is used as a lifting bar to pry off the cover.—Contributed by J. A. Nolan, Woodside, Cal.

Handhold for a T-Square

A large portion of the dirt and smut that accumulates on a drawing comes from handling of the T-square by the blade. One way to avoid the dirt is to fasten a cleat to the top of the T-square blade for a handhold. This will prevent the fingers from coming in

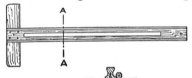

The Handhold as It is Attached to the Top of a T-Square Blade

contact with the drawing, and provides a place for pencils and instruments, as shown in the cross section.—Contributed by W. E. Crane, Cleveland, Ohio.

Starting Holder for a Nut

The holder is made of sheet metal, rolled into a tube. A nut is then inserted in one end and the metal hammered to the shape of the nut. Any

The Holder Made of Sheet Metal Grips a Nut to Start It on the Threads

length of metal can be used, as desired. In use, the shaped end of the metal is slipped over a nut and a slight pres-

sure on the other end will hold the nut so that it can be turned on the threads of a bolt in otherwise inaccessible places.—Contributed by John E. Hollarbush, Huron, S. D.

An Adjustable File Handle

The handle is constructed of round machine steel, ¼ or ⅜ in. in diameter and about 15 in. long, which, when bent over in the shape shown, will leave the handle part about 5 in. long. Before making the bend the ends are threaded with a small die, having the same number of threads as those cut in a ¾-in. nut. The steel is then bent in the shape

The Tapering Portions of the Threaded Ends are Easily Clamped on the Tool Shank with the Nut

shown, and the inside portion of the threaded ends are filed flat to admit the shank of the tool. A ¾-in. nut is used on the threads.

The tapering shank on most hand tools can be inserted between the two ends, and the sloping parts are easily clamped on it by turning the nut.—Contributed by G. H. Holter, Jasper, Minnesota.

Sawing the Edge of Timbers Straight

In cutting a piece of timber both edges of which are crooked or jagged, attach a straightedge, A, on one edge

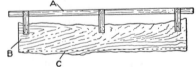

A Straightedge Nailed to One Edge of a Timber to Guide the Other Edge on the Saw

of the timber, B, and the piece can be more easily run through the ripsaw to cut on the line C.—Contributed by Joseph Flood, Philadelphia, Pa.

❡The priming coat of paint should be put on a building before the plasterer begins his work.

How to Test a Storage Battery with Cadmium Contacts

The amateur, in building storage batteries, will often be unable to get the desired results, although the color of the positive and negative plates may be correct and a voltmeter connected across the cell may give the proper indication of the condition of the cell, due to the fact that the plates are not properly formed. When the above conditions exist, it is quite necessary to test each plate separately, which may be done by means of a pair of cadmium contact pieces and a low-reading voltmeter.

These contact pieces, according to Lyndon, should be made as follows: Take a piece of 1/4-in. hard copper wire and force it into a hole drilled in the end of a 3/8-in. piece of cadmium. The ends of the pieces of cadmium and copper should now be pointed and a small hole, A, Fig. 1, drilled for the lead to the voltmeter. The center portion of the contact pieces should then be taped to prevent the likelihood of accidental contact with the battery plates. Two such contact pieces are shown in the sketches, but it is not imperative to have two of them, as a piece of copper will serve for one, and a piece of cadmium for the other and they may be interchanged, if the voltmeter readings are reversed.

The total or resultant voltage of the cell may be obtained by placing the copper ends in contact with the positive and negative terminals of the battery. Further readings may be taken as follows: Place the cadmium contact B in the acid and the copper, C, in contact with the positive terminal of the cell, as shown in Fig. 2. If the cell is fully charged the voltmeter should read about 2.30 volts. Now change the copper over to the negative terminal of the cell and the voltmeter needle will go the wrong way, indicating a negative reading; change the connection so that they correspond to those given in Fig. 3, and the voltmeter needle will deflect the right way and give a reading of about .2. The

sum of these two readings is then the voltage of the cell which should be 2.50, when the cell is fully charged. When the reading between the cadmium and the negative plate is less than .10, the

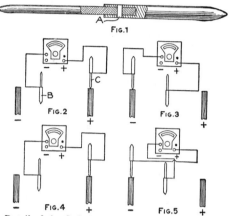

Detail of the Cadmium Contact and the Manner of Making the Test on a Storage Cell

cell is not fully charged and the charging should be continued until the proper value is reached.

Readings on a discharged cell may be taken as follows: The potential of the cadmium with respect to both plates is the same and the resultant is found by subtracting one reading from the other. The connections should be made, as shown in Figs. 4 and 5. When connections are made as shown in Fig. 4, the voltmeter should read about 2.05 and when made as shown in Fig. 5 about .25. The voltage between plates then is about 1.8 volts. The cell should never be discharged beyond this point.

Drying Blueprints

A factory where a large number of blueprints are used dries the prints quickly with an electric iron. A table is provided for this purpose, which is covered with a piece of oilcloth, cotton batting, and cheesecloth, in the order named. The iron must not be too hot, as this will ruin the print. This drying method, used in connection with an electric printing machine, makes it possible to turn out a print in about three minutes.—Contributed by J. S. Bray, Indianapolis, Ind.

Protecting the Edges of Concrete Curbing

The edges of concrete curbing may be protected against chipping by means of iron rods or tubing placed in posi-

FIG.1   **FIG.2**

The Edge of the Curb is Protected with a Piece of Pipe Anchored in the Concrete

tion as shown in the sketch. The anchoring wires are shown in Fig. 1, A being the twisted type and B the hairpin anchor. The rods are held in the forms while the concrete is being poured with wires CC, which are cut close when the forms are removed. The finished curb is shown in Fig. 2.—Contributed by James M. Kane, Doylestown, Pa.

Cup-Valve Extractor

An extractor for removing carbonized cup valves from an air compressor may be made from a piece of wood, as shown in the sketch. Procure a piece of hard wood, about 12 in. long, 2½ in.

The Ends of the Wood Expand on the Cup in the Manner of the Lathe Chuck

in diameter on the large end and 1¾ in. in diameter on the small end. The size of diameter depends somewhat on the size of the valves. A hole, $\frac{7}{16}$ in. in diameter, is bored lengthwise through the center to admit a ⅜-in. bolt, 12 in. long, with 3 in. of thread on each end. Both ends are bored out tapering as indicated. These are to receive round, tapering wedges of iron or brass which are threaded to fit the bolt. Two saw cuts are taken through the center of each end, at right angles to each other, to prevent splitting the wood when the wedges are drawn in place.

The end that fits the valve is in-

serted, then the bolt adjusted to expand it. The wood gives ample hand hold to work the valves loose. The bolt and wedges can be reversed as desired to use either end of the stick.—Contributed by A. H. Harrison, Los Angeles, Cal.

Pointing Pickets

The easiest and quickest way to point small lots of pickets is described by a correspondent of the Wood-Worker. The method is to cut out the shape of a picket from a board and nail on a side and end strip for a stop as shown in the sketch. Drive two brads through from

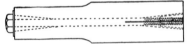

Pattern Form to Hold Pickets While Pointing Them on the Cutter of a Shaper

the under side and sharpen the points. These will help the stops to hold the piece in the pattern. The pattern and picket is run on a straight-wing cutter on a shaper, allowing the pattern edge to run against the collar.

Removing Tin Roofing

Having a large amount of tin roofing to remove, I made a tool, as shown in the sketch, to cut the metal at the seams, thus allowing the sheets to be taken off in sections. The tool is shaped like an ordinary can opener, except that it is a little larger and the handle longer. A wire and cross handle are attached so that a boy can draw the tool while a man guides it through the tin. The cutter is made of tool steel, and hardened. The tool can

The Cutter is Made Similar to and Used in the Same Manner as a Can Opener

be used for cutting stovepipes, for furnace jobs and on many other kinds of tin-shop work.—Contributed by E. S. Sites, Muncie, Ind.

An Elbow Pattern

By J. A. SHELLEY

Elbow patterns are considered by pattern makers generally as rather a mean job; this is particularly so when, for reasons of economy, it is not deemed best to turn them, and they must be finished by hand with a spokeshave. To make an elbow pattern with the least outlay of physical energy requires extreme accuracy in building. The segments should be carefully

fastening the heads securely to this surface and then put on the segments. For the inside, or shorter radii, these may be in one piece, but for the outside it will be more economical to divide the alternate courses into twos and threes.

In getting out the heads and segments, be sure to have enough for both halves, and dowel the end heads together with two pins in each. The

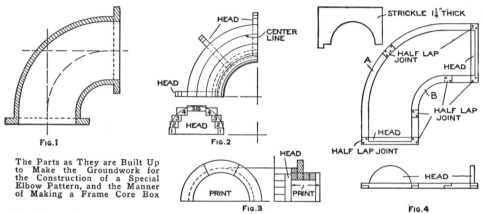

The Parts as They are Built Up to Make the Groundwork for the Construction of a Special Elbow Pattern, and the Manner of Making a Frame Core Box

planed to the proper thickness and sawn to the exact radii so that, when the circles indicating the diameter are laid out on the ends, there will be no excess of stock.

A study of the layout for the 18-in. special elbow, illustrated in Fig. 1, will disclose several interesting constructive features. The end view of the head, Fig. 2, shows all the segments in place, numbered from 1 to 5 and starting at the bottom, or joint, on each side. It will be seen that No. 5 is made in two pieces, sawn exactly on the center line, and fits between the segments marked 4. This prevents the destruction of the center line and eliminates the feather edges that would result if No. 5 were glued on top of No. 4. The plan shows the segments to the left of the center segment removed and the location of the three heads to which the segments are nailed and glued. It is well to have a good straight surface on which to build the first half. Start by

second half is, of course, built on the joint of the first. The prints are built up of segments, as shown in the sectional view of one end of the pattern, Fig. 3, and fastened to the heads with glue and screws. The flanges, with the straight part of the pattern, are built up and turned together and fitted over the prints, to which they are fastened with screws from the inside.

The constructive details of the frame core box are fully shown in Fig. 4. The outer curve A is made in two pieces, fastened together with a half lap joint, and the inner B, in three pieces, which are fastened in the same way. The crosspieces at the ends are halved into these, and the heads fastened to them with screws.

White marks on mahogany caused by dampness may be removed by rubbing the surface with a soft cloth moistened in a little sweet oil. Rub it in well.

An Auxiliary Air Valve for Gasoline Engine

An auxiliary air valve for increasing the power and decreasing the gas consumption of a gasoline engine can be made of an ordinary grease cup, and it will do the work as well as an expensive valve. Procure a 1¼-in. hard-grease cup  and cut the slots AA, allowing about one and a half thread intact at the bottom. The slots BB in the upper part can be cut deeper, but in either case each pair of slots should be exactly the same depth. The connecting bar C is riveted to the back of the grease cover D, for turning it.

The end of the lower part is screwed into the carburetor intake pipe just below where it branches off to the various cylinders, and its position can be arranged as desired by tightening or loosening it a little. Upon acquiring a traveling speed of, say, 15 miles an hour, with the valve closed, the traveling speed may be increased in varying degree by opening the valve more or less.—Contributed by Frank C. Barks, Denver, Colo.

Inclosing a Valve Action

Many owners of old automobiles would be glad to know of a way to silence the open-valve action on the 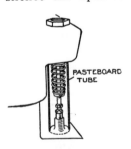 motors and prevent the dust and dirt from entering. One of these owners, a correspondent of the Automobile, effectively accomplished this by using a paper tube slipped over the valve stem and spring, as shown in the sketch. The tube may be a piece of one used for mailing drawings, blueprints or calendars, cut to the right length to make a tight fit lengthwise, and then split for its full length, whereupon it is sprung around the stem and spring. A light hose clamp will hold it in place. The tube may be painted black or covered with aluminum paint, after it is thoroughly coated, inside and out, with shellac varnish to make it waterproof.

How to Find a Crack in Metal

Clean the surface of the metal, turn on a small quantity of kerosene and allow it to stand for a minute or two, then wipe off the oil and strike the piece a sharp blow with a hammer. The oil will show along the outline of the crack. The jar caused by the blow of the hammer will drive the oil out of the crack to the surface of the metal.—Contributed by J. F. R., Bethel, Vermont.

Repairing a Broken Bicycle Crank

Having broken the locking part on the two-piece crank of my bicycle I decided to fix it rather than buy a new one. Both ends of the shaft part having the locking device were  cut off about ¼ in. from the end and slotted as shown. A piece of round steel with a projection on each end to fit into the slots was cut to make the shaft part of the hanger of the right length when the piece was in place. A hole was drilled through the center of the piece to admit the holding bolt. The notches in the ends of the shaft should receive the projecting ends of the center piece snugly so that the three pieces will turn as one.—Contributed by J. E. Nyberg, Jacksonville, Fla.

¶In painting a smokestack with the use of regular oil paint and not asphaltum varnish it would be well to thin the paint with fish (menhaden) oil, which possesses considerable drying quality and withstands considerable heat.

Power-Driven Catamaran

The catamaran shown was constructed especially for use in the waters at a sawmill. The construction permits the shaft and propeller to be lifted out of the water at a moment's notice without stopping the engine. The floats being made of solid cedar logs, there is no danger in running into sunken logs, rocks, or on a beach. These features are of great advantage where the catamaran is used.

The logs are 18 ft. long, cut from dry cedar timber, the bark being first removed and the large end sharpened and smoothed so that they offer the least resistance. Larger logs could be used to make a catamaran that would carry more freight or a larger engine. The logs are placed 5 ft. apart and crosspieces bolted on their upper sides. A platform is built on the crosspieces as shown in the illustration, leaving an open space in the center for the driving shaft.

The engine is placed on an oak rol-ler, 4½ in. in diameter, being set so that the center of gravity will be over the center of the roller when on a level. The engine is bolted to the roller and the roller is free to turn in sockets on either end, that is, to slightly revolve when the driving shaft is raised, otherwise it is secure. There is one stuffing box used at a point about 18 in. ahead of the propeller, and this box is fastened to the lower end of a vertical rack that slides through a slot and is controlled with a pinion driven by rods, gears and a handwheel at the seat. This construction permits the propeller to be quickly raised clear of

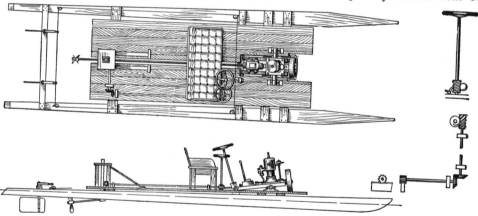

An Engine-Propelled Catamaran for Use in Shallow Water Where There are Numerous Submerged Obstructions That would Injure an Ordinary Boat and Soon Ruin Its Propeller

used to make a catamaran that would carry more freight or a larger engine. The logs are placed 5 ft. apart and crosspieces bolted on their upper sides. A platform is built on the crosspieces as shown in the illustration, leaving an open space in the center for the driving shaft.

The engine is placed on an oak rol-

the water or lowered to a depth of 18 inches.

The engine, steering and shaft control are all operated from the seat. The rudders are twin, both responding to the same wheel. There is no rail, but one could be placed around the platform to make it quite safe.

The conditions of the body of water

are suited to the craft. It is a lake with narrow shores with a great many curves on the line, suggesting a large river. It is impossible for a heavy sea in a storm. The lake is 10 miles long and has been used for driving logs for at least 20 years and, consequently, there are numerous sunken logs with their ends at or near the surface. Many times these logs cannot be seen until one is near them. An ordinary boat could not stand these conditions.

The catamaran was inexpensive outside of the engine, as the parts were taken from discarded machinery. The boat would be of no use on a large body of water, as a heavy sea would wash over it and a large wave would tend to capsize it, but for use on inland waters it is worth while to make it.— Contributed by Clifford W. Johnston, Parry Sound, Can.

Shingling to Produce a Diamond Shape

There are many carpenters that do not know how to lay shingles in a gable or between windows on side walls in diamond shape. This is very easily accomplished if the shingles are laid as shown in the sketch. It will require but little more time than

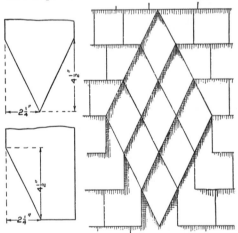

Method of Cutting Shingles so That When Placed They will Make a Diamond Shape

plain shingling. All the joints are broken as in regular shingling. The diamond shingles should be sized, that is, as wide as the courses are laid. The

sketch illustrates a course, 4½ in. to the weather. These shingles are placed in the courses until the required width is obtained. The other shingles joining the diamond are beveled on one side.—Contributed by Ernest S. Yawger, Ithaca, N. Y.

An Alarm for a Lathe Boring Tool

After the boring tool on my lathe had run into the faceplate several times, I devised an attachment that would not only prevent this, but also give an alarm when the tool was almost through the work. I first fastened a small piece of metal, about ¼ in. thick and 1 in. wide, with a bolt having a wing nut to the bed of the lathe just ahead of the carriage, and a like piece of metal on the carriage. I procured the hard rubber stem from a discarded tobacco pipe and fastened a piece of this to each of the pieces of metal. The rubber pieces served as insulators on which the ends of insulated wire were attached, and were bored so that a contact would be made when the two came together. Two dry cells and an electric bell were attached in the circuit.

When the metal clip was adjusted to the right location on the bed of the lathe, the metal clip on the carriage would make the contact when the tool in the tool post would be almost through the work, and the bell would sound the alarm.—Contributed by D. G. Hardy, Milltown, Mont.

Reducing the Glare of an Automobile Lamp

The disagreeable glare of the electric headlights on automobiles may be eliminated by covering the upper half of the glass with a cream metal polish and allowing it to dry. When dry, it gives the appearance of frosted glass. To make an even line across the center of the glass, a small piece of cardboard with a straight edge should be held tightly against the surface when applying the substance. Of course, the coating should be applied to the inner surface of the glass so that it will not be washed off in a rain. This treatment does not in the least affect the amount of light cast upon the road.—Contributed by E. K. Marshall, Oak Park, Illinois.

Setting Bolts in Concrete to Hold a Machine

When anchoring bolts in a concrete pier, I found that the location of the bolts could be more easily determined with a piece of soft pine placed on the bolts of the machine and struck with a hammer than with a rule. Holes were bored at the location of the dents made by the bolt ends and a skeleton base made as shown. This kept the bolts in their right places while pouring the concrete. If this is done in the man-

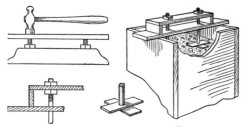

A Skeleton Base for Holding the Bolts in Their Right Places Until the Concrete Sets

ner illustrated, the machine will fit on the bolts perfectly.—Contributed by James M. Kane, Doylestown, Pa.

A Fence-Post Puller

The lower portion of a wooden fence post after it has been in the ground for a long time becomes so set that it is almost an impossibility to draw it out, necessitating the use of a spade or shovel to remove it. When it is necessary to withdraw a considerable number of posts, the usual method is extremely laborious and expensive.

The sketches in general detail illustrate an excellent and simple jig for instantly and easily pulling the posts from the ground, no matter how securely time may have set them into the earth.

A hitch is taken on the post near the ground by means of a small chain, the free end passing over a fulcrum stick, A, to the doubletree behind a team of horses. The point of bearing, or axis,

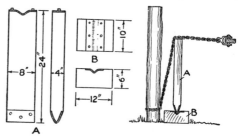

A Fulcrum Stick Used to Draw Out Firmly Set Fence Posts with a Chain

of the stick is supported by the base block B, which is easily thrown with the fulcrum stick from post to post as the work progresses along the fence. A moderate pull on the chain will draw out any post.

Combination Tool Holder and Steady Rest

A tool of the kind shown in the sketch is very handy for turning small and long bars of steel or brass. The steady-rest part is offset from the part that holds the tool. The shank of the tool is set in the tool post so that the steady-rest part is central with the centers on the lathe. The tool is adjusted with a screw in the end of the shank.

The tool is set and a cut taken to reduce the stock to the desired diameter on the end of the bar, then the screws on the steady rest are adjusted on the turned part and the feed of the

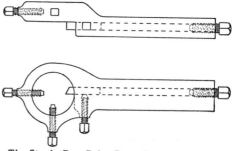

The Steady Rest Being Part of the Tool Holder, Prevents the Stock from Springing

lathe started. It is obvious how the tool works.—Contributed by Chas. Homewood, Cedar Rapids, Iowa.

Homemade Skirt Marker

Procure a piece of ¾-in. gas pipe, 6 in. long with a thread on each end, and two flanges, A and B, to fit on

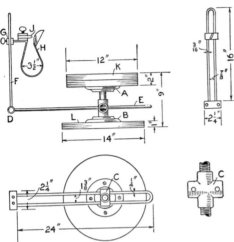

Homemade Skirt Marker for Making a Line on the Goods Encircling the Lower Edge

the threads of the pipe, as shown. Remove the threads from a ¾-in. cross, C, so that it will slip on the ¾-in. pipe. Bore two ¼-in. holes through the ends of one way of the cross, allowing 1¾-in. space between them. A piece of ¼-in. round iron is bent into U-shape and the ends are run through the holes drilled in the cross. A ⅜-in. round end piece, D, is drilled to receive both ends of the U-shaped horizontal piece E, also the U-shaped upright piece F, which is made of ³⁄₁₆-in. round iron, and all four ends are riveted in the piece D. Make a clamp, G, with a setscrew to hold the marking device H at any desired position. The marking device consists of a round disk of brass and a chalk holder, J. Two disks are cut from wood, 1 in. thick, the upper, K, 12 in. in diameter and the lower, L, 14 in. in diameter.

The horizontal rods E move through the cross from right to left while the cross turns on the ¾-in. pipe standard. The clamp G holds the adjustment vertically.

The one being fitted with a skirt stands on the upper disk K, and the lower edge of the skirt is placed between the chalk and the brass disk, so that by taking hold of the chalk with one hand and the skirt with the other and turning the rods E, a line is marked on the outside of the goods at the bottom.—Contributed by Mrs. Harriet M. S. Kerbaugh, Allentown, Pennsylvania.

Cutting Miters on a Band Saw

Where a number of pieces are to be mitered and there is no power-driven miter saw in the shop, the band saw will do the work, if the machine is supplied with an attachment for holding the pieces at right angles while the cut is being made. The attachment consists of a holder made of two pieces of hard wood, each 1⅜ in. thick, 3 in. wide and 14 in. long. A shoulder is cut on each piece, as shown in Fig. 1, and then they are joined together to make a right angle, as shown in Fig. 2. Adjusting screws are placed in the inside edges of the pieces, as shown at A. Ordinary wood screws are used and they are allowed to project about ¼ inch.

The material to be mitered is laid out with a miter square, as shown by the dotted lines in Fig. 3, then it is cut roughly on these lines. The pieces are then placed in the holder, as shown in Fig. 4. The material is sawed two or more times, each time closing the pieces together on the point. It makes no difference if the cut is not straight, the joint will be a perfect fit.

To aid in holding the stock when pushing the holders back and forth on the saw table, two strips, A A, ¼ in.

Form for Holding Pieces to be Cut for a Miter Joint on a Band Saw

thick and ½ in. wide, are nailed to the top surfaces of the holder sides. Each pair, as mitered, should be kept together. When finished, they are nailed together with corrugated fasteners and the halves are placed together, as shown in Fig. 5. These are placed in the holder and jointed in the same manner. In roughing out the material, the joints may not fit perfectly and there is apt to be an opening either at the outer or the inner edges. Always start this opening on the saw when cutting the joint on the two halves.

This same principle can be applied when getting out segments for circles to be turned for patterns, or caps and bases for columns. Dress the material on both sides to make it the desired thickness and mark each segment, as shown in Fig. 6. Cut out the segments on the band saw, place the miters of each pair together and cut through the joint, as shown in Fig. 7. Both sides at the joint are then fastened with corrugated staples. After all the segments are jointed and fastened in pairs, two

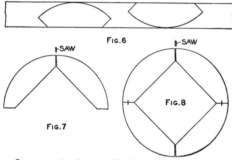

Segments for Pattern Work or Porch Columns can be Mitered in a Similar Manner

halves are placed together and the joints cut on the band saw, as shown in Fig. 8. When fastened together they are ready for turning.

Repairing Magneto Arm

A magneto that is used quite extensively on automobiles has an extending arm for retarding or advancing the spark, and this arm was broken accidentally. Instead of waiting for a new part the old one was repaired quickly and in such a way that a new piece was unnecessary. The break in the arm was as shown at A. The parts were joined closely and held with a piece of ⅛-in. brass, as shown at B. The brass was cut to fit over the extension on

the hub and fitted to the curve of the larger circle. Holes were drilled and tapped for two screws, and holes were

Repairs on a Magneto Arm That Saved Time and the Cost of a New Piece

also drilled and pins inserted to hold the parts together.—Contributed by Donald A. Hompson, Middletown, New York.

Greased Plates Used for Unloading Automobiles

The loading of automobiles into box cars, or unloading of them, is a very difficult job for those inexperienced in handling the large machines, especially where two are placed in together. The turning of a long-wheel-base car will not permit it to pass through the freight-car door, and the ordinary process is to lift it with a force of men or block and tackle. A very easy method is to place sheets of metal—these are usually found about freight houses—on the floor of the freight car where the automobile wheels will run on them, as shown in the diagram. Before running the wheels on the sheets, smear hard grease over their surfaces, and one person can easily push that end of the car over so that it will pass out of the freight-car door, the wheels sliding easily on the grease. Longer wheel

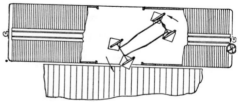

Manner of Placing Greased Plates on a Freight-Car Floor for Sliding Automobile Wheels

bases may require plates placed also under the rear wheels so that they may be slid over in like manner.

Hanger for a Lathe Chuck

One of the best methods of caring for a lathe chuck is to arrange a hanger for holding it when not in use An

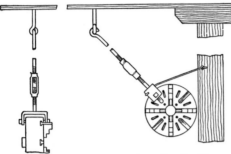

The Chuck is Easily Taken from One Position to the Other as Occasion Demands

eyebolt fastened in an overhead cross-beam or joist, a turnbuckle, and a clevis, or a U-shaped piece of metal with a bolt, to fit over the chuck, not only constitute a hanger for holding the chuck when not in use, but provide an easy means of swinging it into position on the lathe spindle. The illustration clearly shows the hanger as it is used.—Contributed by J. Harger, Honolulu, H. I.

Homemade Micrometer

Desiring to have something a little different in the way of tools from other mechanics, I constructed a very useful measuring device that takes the place of a micrometer. The jaw A is made of $\frac{3}{16}$-in. square, cold-rolled steel, heated and bent as shown. This is slotted on one side to admit a piece of scale, B, $1\frac{3}{16}$ in. long. Before slotting

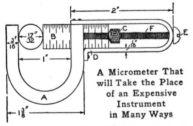

A Micrometer That will Take the Place of an Expensive Instrument in Many Ways

the jaw a hole is drilled centrally in the location of the slot and tapped for a 10-32 machine screw, F. A ⅛-in. hole is drilled through the entire

length of the screw in the center and it is also slotted $1\frac{3}{16}$ in. to receive the scale. The head end of the screw is supported by a yoke, D, made of $\frac{1}{16}$-in. steel, $\frac{3}{16}$ in. wide and fastened with rivets to the jaw A. The knurled nut C is used for adjustment. A small closed spring made of .013 spring wire, wound on a rod measuring .085 in. in diameter, is inserted in the ⅛-in. hole in the screw and fastened at one end to the scale and at the other with a pin, E, in the slot of the screw head. This provides a tension on the scale to keep it against the knurled nut C. The measurement is read on the scale between the outside surface of the jaw A and the nut C.—Contributed by J. J. Kolar, Maywood, Ill.

Box-Cover Fasteners for Parcel-Post Packages

Many kinds of packing cases and boxes have been invented for use in the mails after the parcel-post law went into effect. When packages must be examined it requires no little time, in most cases, to undo the fastenings. The illustration shows a cover that can be quickly detached and replaced. The cover is slotted at its edges to admit the nails on one side of the box, and screw hooks are used at the other side. In making the examination, it is only necessary to turn the screw hooks so that their ends will pass through the slots and then slide the cover off.—Contributed by D. L. Merrill, Battle Creek, Mich.

Cleaning the Hands of Aniline Stain

To clean the hands after handling aniline stain or dye, first wash them with a little bleaching powder, then with alcohol, and follow with a good soap, such as sand or pumice-stone.

Air Circulation in Furnace Heating

The many faults of a hot-air furnace for residence heating usually arise from an inefficient layout, or lacking study of the conditions concerning the house to be heated due to incompetence of the one installing the plant. A few things must be considered in regard to the location of the furnace as well as the circulation of the air currents. One of the most frequent errors is that the fresh-air supply is not adequate, so that the rooms will become over-heated with dead air, producing a stuffy atmosphere.

An insufficient air outlet will cause the same trouble. As much heated air must be admitted to a room as that which passes out, whether through leakage around the windows and doors or through an opening provided for its free circulation.

If a hot-air duct has a register opening into a room without other air outlet than cracks at window and door openings, only little air will be in circulation, as shown in Fig. 1. One method of arranging the inlet and outlet is shown in Fig. 2. While this method causes a complete circulation of air, it does not admit fresh, pure air from the outside.

One of the best arrangements to pro-

center, while the return air passes back around the outside of the register, as shown in Fig. 3. The returning cold air will be partly heated as it passes over the jacket of the hot-air space in the furnace. In this method the air currents will take the course shown by the arrows. This method, however, while causing free circulation of the air, does not supply fresh air.

Those desiring pure, fresh air in a residence, or, especially, in halls and schoolrooms which are occupied by many people at a time, must provide some means to supply a continuous circulation of air, taken from the outside, heated, delivered to the rooms through ducts, and then expelled to the outside. While this may be an expensive method, it produces an atmosphere in the room equal to that outdoors on a summer day. Such a system may be modified where fewer persons are concerned, only a small portion of the air being taken from the outside, or a sufficient amount to keep pure heated air inside. This system is shown in Fig. 4. The inlet duct A should have the same area as the combined areas of the ducts delivering heated air to the rooms, or even larger. The warm-air ducts B should enter the

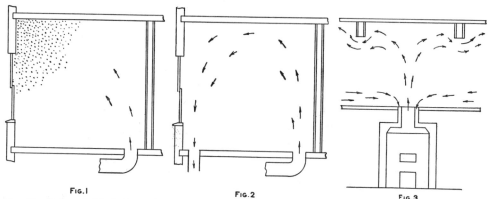

FIG. 1   FIG. 2   FIG. 3

The Circulation of Air is Impeded by Not Having a Cold-Air Outlet, the Free Circulation being Obtained by a Proper Outlet, Which is Further Aided with Proper Arrangements for Receiving Cold Air Back into the Furnace

vide a good circulation is to construct a furnace so that the heated air will pass into the room, or rooms, from the

rooms at a height above the average person's head, and the dead or cold, spent air should be expelled through small registers, C, in the baseboard, into ducts leading to a chimney. This chimney may be one provided for the

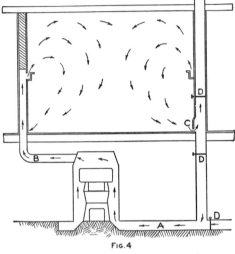

FIG. 4

The Passage of Either Outside or Inside Air, or a Part of Both, through the Furnace is Controlled with Dampers

purpose, but it is better to use a division in the smoke chimney.

The opening into the rooms for the heated air may be made more or less invisible by having them long and narrow, and hiding them with a plate rail or paneling. If the same method is used at the baseboard, nothing will show the presence of the apparatus in the building.

To use only a part of the fresh air from the outside and a part of the cold from within, it is only necessary to have several return ducts from the openings C, to pass the air back to the furnace, and provide dampers, D, to control both the incoming air and the return air.

The outside opening should be located where no high wind can blow into it, and so that the eddies of air will have no tendency to draw the air out of the duct rather than let it pass in freely without being blown in.

❏Be sure to wipe out a tire casing thoroughly with a damp cloth to remove any grains of sharp sand, as these will scratch and score the inner tube and sometimes cause a leak.

Rubber Cement Used for Pasting Papers

Rubber-patching cement will be found very useful for pasting papers where it is desired to avoid wrinkling or curling, the method being very simple. Use thin rubber-patching cement, which can be further diluted with gasoline or benzine, giving each part to be pasted one or two coats and, when the cement is thoroughly dry, pressing the parts firmly together. It is not necessary to be careful about smearing over the edge, as the dry cement forms a thin film that can be readily removed by rubbing lightly with the fingers.

In making corrections on thin-paper tracings, cut out the part to be changed and fill in with a patch of thin tracing paper, using about 1¼-in. lap. The patch will only show slightly in the finished blueprint. Temporary patches can be removed by moistening with gasoline.—Contributed by H. M. Warren, East Orange, N. J.

An Oil-Hole Cleaner

The gummed and caked oil that plugs an oil hole is not easily removed, and sometimes a bearing runs hot because no oil reaches the moving surfaces. A cleaner for the purpose, much better than an awl, is one having a revolving spindle with an awl or screw point, which can be made as follows: The handle consists of a large file handle to which is attached a spring lever carrying an arc cut from an old egg-beater cog. The spindle revolves in the handle and is kept in place by a washer soldered to it at a point where it will fit

Revolving Spindle will Quickly Loosen and Remove Any Dirt or Caked Oil in a Hole

under another washer fastened to the end of the handle.

The small cog, also taken from the egg beater, is attached to the spindle where it will mesh into the cogs on the arc. The spring to which the arc is attached is fastened, as shown, in a slot cut in the handle. This allows the arc of the cogwheel to be moved back and forth by finger pressure, and it is readily seen how easily and quickly caked oil can be removed from an oil hole with this cleaner.—Contributed by Roy Kauffman, Goshen, Ind.

A Burring Tool for Brass Tubing

In cutting a large quantity of brass tubing, a bur was formed on the ends which had to be removed and a slight bevel cut with sharp edges. The cutting of this bevel required a special tool, which was made in the following manner: A piece of round cold-rolled steel, 4 in. long, was procured, a $\frac{1}{16}$-in. slot milled in its center, as shown, and a piece of $\frac{1}{16}$-in. tool steel was then fitted to it as a cutting tool. The steel had a notch filed in it to shape the end of the tube as desired.

The tool was placed in the chuck of a drill press which was run very fast.

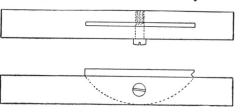

Tool Used for Removing Burs Formed by Cutting Tubing with a Roller Cutter

The pieces of tubing were pushed on over the end of the cold-rolled steel and up against the rapidly revolving tool which removed the bur and beveled the edges.

Boring Holes in Wood at an Angle

The hole to be bored is located by squared lines as in ordinary work, then the jig is made, the thickness A being twice the size of the bit, the other sides depending on the angle, which is cut as required. Lines are drawn on the faces of the block so that it can be readily set on the work where it is fastened with nails.

The device can be used repeatedly, if a dowel point, about ½ in., is inserted in the longest face and cut off at the correct angle. The dowel holds the block while the bit starts into

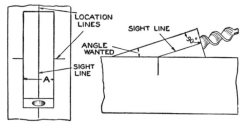

An Angle Block for Holding a Bit to Bore a Slanting Hole in Wood

the work.—Contributed by Edwin E. Hahn, Philadelphia, Pa.

A Support for a Breast Drill

It often occurs that the drill point of a breast drill breaks, especially if it is small, and hard material is worked. This difficulty seems to be effectively overcome by attaching to the drill the device shown herewith. It consists of a clamp having in its upper flattened end a slot through which the handle of the drill is inserted and screwed tightly, and at a lower point a screw clamp fitting just above the drill chuck. In a sleeve, in one piece with or otherwise attached to the clamp, slides a rod, the movement of the latter being controlled by a spring within the sleeve. This rod forms a second support for the drill and as the latter penetrates into the material, the rod is backed up into the sleeve, while the spring, acting contrary to this motion, holds its end firmly against the work or

The Support on a Breast Drill for Preventing the Breaking of Small Drills

some surface beside it. The vibration of the drill bit, which is the cause of breakage, is eliminated by this double support.

¶A 5-gal. can with a tapering top and the bottom removed makes an excellent funnel for filling automobile tanks.

A Pneumatic-Tire Vulcanizer

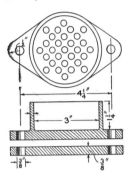

The base of the vulcanizer can be made of a piece of iron, about ⅜ in. thick, but it is best to make a pattern and have one cast so that it will finish to the dimensions given. After being machined, 29 holes, each 3/16 in. in diameter, are drilled in the base of the cup as nearly equidistant as possible. Pins are inserted tightly in these holes with their upper ends flush with the top. Make a plate, the same size as the base of the cup, and drill holes to match those in the ends of the cup base so that this and the plate can be clamped together with the tube or tire between them. Fill the cup with gasoline and light it, and the heat generated will vulcanize the rubber nicely.—Contributed by G. Crawford, Jr., Schenectady, N. Y.

Temporary Repair on a Broken Valve Spindle

The breaking of a brass valve spindle is of no uncommon occurrence and the break invariably takes place at or near the top of the shoulder that secures the valve seat, or disk, to the spindle. When such a break happens on a piece of machinery far from a repair shop the repair can be made on the spot, as taps and drills of some kind are almost invariably to be found in the engine room, and with these tools it is a simple matter to temporarily repair the spindles.

File off the lower end of the broken spindle squarely and remove the part remaining on the shoulder plate. Center the two pieces and drill a hole, for the size of tap to be used, through the plate and a short distance into the spindle. Tap both holes and connect the parts with the threaded end of a common machine bolt, and cut it off to allow sufficient end for beading over a small portion against the shoulder plate. This method will often permit a valve to give efficient service until a new spindle can be made.—Contributed by F. W. Bently, Milwaukee, Wis.

Grease Cup for Wagon Wheels

Drill a hole, 21/32 in. in diameter, in the center of each axle and connect it with a hole of the same size just back of the shoulder on the spindle and on the under side of the axle. This is the right size hole to tap for ½-in. fittings. The center of the spindle is drilled with a ⅜-in. drill to make a hole intersecting the horizontal one.

A ½-in. plug is turned into the end of the hole, and a grease cup fitted on

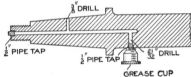

The Grease Cup as It is Attached to the Skein of a Wagon

the under side, as shown. In greasing the wheel, turn the cup down sufficient to force the grease into the axle. —Contributed by W. E. Crane, Cleveland, O.

A Preventive of Grimy Hands

A thorough scrubbing will not remove the grime and dirt that seem to work right into the skin on the hands when handling some makes of electric wires or working about machines that are covered with oil and dirt. A correspondent of Electrical Review uses a coating thoroughly rubbed on the hands before starting to work which prevents the grime from entering the pores of the skin. The preventive consists of 4 oz. of grain alcohol, 3 oz. of glycerin and 3 oz. of water. The mixture quickly dries on the skin, and after work a washing with soap and water will quickly remove all the dirt.

A Windmill

By WINTON BALL

A windmill, or motor, that will run in any direction of the wind, and one that requires only ordinary mechanical skill to construct, may be built as hereafter described and, if properly constructed, will prove efficient for all purposes for which a windmill may be used.

Make two semicircular disks of strong boards with a radius one-third of the size of the wheel wanted. Cleat them together securely so that one point of each half will touch at the center of the other, as shown in Fig. 1, the points A, B, C, and D being equal distances apart. The center E is located exactly midway between points A and D, and, consequently, also between B and C. The mill will require four such parts, two of which are fitted with cast-iron flanges with holes to fit on the shaft to be used. One of the flanges is shown in position at F. The remaining two wood parts are bolted together at right angles to each other, as shown in Fig. 2. These two parts can also be fitted with a flange, if desired.

Place the two single parts, one on either side of the double one, allowing a space of about 2 ft. between them,

Fasten them together with ceiling boards, or preferably sheet iron, nailed

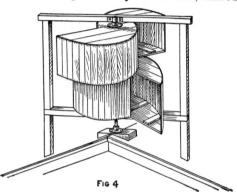

FIG 4

The Mill, being Built on the Turbine Principle, can be Run in Any Air Current

to the periphery of the disks. Good canvas may be used if a flange is fastened to the center part, so that the three parts of the frame can be securely fastened to the shaft.

The straight sides are left open for the air currents to pass through the S-shaped openings, thereby counterbalancing almost all the back pressure on the returning side of the wheel, as shown by the arrows in Fig. 3. The construction of the wheel makes two S-shaped chambers at right angles to

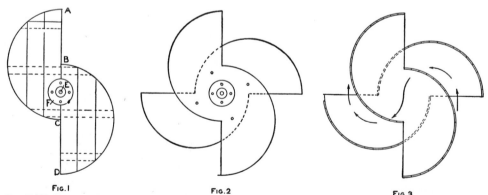

FIG.1   FIG.2   FIG.3

Detail of the Parts to Construct Air Chamber That Directs the Outgoing Air against the Inner Surfaces of the Part Returning toward the Wind, thus Counteracting the Back Pressure on the Outside

with all the arcs corresponding. The distance these parts are separated will vary according to the size of the wheel.

each other. A large wheel must be assembled on the tower. The windmill complete is shown in Fig. 4.

Scribing a Line Encircling Round Stock

In cutting pieces ½ in. long from round bar stock with a hand hacksaw, it was almost impossible to cut them off squarely, but  I found that I could follow a line with the saw blade if it was scribed straight, encircling the bar. This I accomplished with the aid of a visiting or postal card, wrapped on the bar so that one edge was at the right place, and by using a scriber against it as with a straightedge.—Contributed by Robert Adams, Philadelphia, Pa.

Clamps to Hold Rugs While Beating Them

The clamp shown in the sketch is for holding a rug straight on a lawn 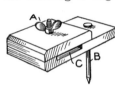 while beating it. One clamp is used at each corner of the rug. Each clamp consists of two blocks of wood, one spike and a bolt with a thumb nut. The thicker part of the rug at the edge is placed into the notch C, and the bolt A is tightened on the clamp. The spike B is easily pushed into the ground when the rug is laid out flat.—Contributed by H. W. Hahn, Chicago, Ill.

Tile-Outlet Cover

A great deal of trouble is caused by small animals entering the tile at the outlet of drainage systems where they  are apt to get stuck in the narrow opening and stop the flow of water. It is very difficult to locate the point of obstruction and much expense is often incurred in finding it. The trouble may be prevented very easily by attaching a wood frame over the outlet and hinging a wood door to it at the upper edge. This door will be held open by the outflowing water and, while not obstructing the flow, prevent any animal from entering. When there is no flow of water the door covers the outlet completely.—Contributed by Thos. L. Parker, Wibaux, Mont.

Making Section Lines for Patent-Office Drawings

When making drawings for the patent office the conventional symbols and cross-section lines must be closely followed. One of the rules that must be carried out is the wavy line showing earth, and a  correspondent of American Machinist draws these lines rapidly by using a piece of bristol board the straight edge of which is nicked with the thumb nail. This is used as a ruler, which draws wavy lines as shown in the sketch.

A Gold Front Sight for a Rifle

The salt spray present in the air along our coasts is ruinous to metal gun sights, but an efficient and inexpensive gold-crowned front sight may be made as follows: The top of the plain front sight 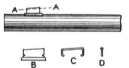 is filed down about $\frac{1}{64}$ in., as shown by the line AA in the sketch. Two notches are cut in the base of the sight, as shown at B. Using a heavily plated nose piece of a pair of eyeglasses, a bracket, C, is formed to fit the prepared sight snugly. Solder is applied to the ends only. This will prevent any discoloration on top of the sight. A good bead effect is obtained by cutting off the sides of the bracket, as shown at D.—Contributed by C. F. Heizer, Falfurrias, Tex.

Cleaner for Aluminum Ware

The following formula will be found useful in making a solution for removing the tarnish from the inside of aluminum pots and pans: Dissolve 2 oz. of lump ammonia in 1 qt. of water; 2 oz. of salts of tartar in 1 qt. of water, and a 10-cent can of potash in 2 qt. of water, while boiling. Add to the latter solution the ammonia, then the salts-of-tartar solutions, in order named, and boil the whole mixture for 30 minutes. This solution is kept in jars for use at any time.

Place a small quantity of the solution in the vessel to be cleaned, set it on a fire and allow it to boil, but be careful not to let it boil over on the polished surface. Keep it boiling for about two minutes, then rinse out and use any good cleaner to scour the surface. This will restore the satin finish as when new.—Contributed by Nellie Dempsey, New York City.

Preventing Needles from Rusting

Workmen repairing sails or doing similar work outside can prevent their needles from rusting in the following manner: Fill a brass shotgun shell with a thick grease that will not run and insert the needles in it. If a 12-gauge shell is used, a cover can be made of a 10-gauge shell.—Contributed by Forrest Clark, Coronado, Cal.

Electric-Lamp Tester

Where a large number of incandescent lamps are used a great deal of time is consumed in turning the lamps into and out of an ordinary socket for testing the filaments to see that they are not broken. The following device eliminates the disadvantages of the threaded socket and effects a great saving in time.

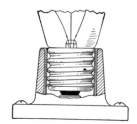

The device consists simply of an ordinary porcelain lamp socket, that has had the inner screw shell removed and the threads hammered out on a piece of ⅝-in. pipe and then replaced. The inside diameter of the shell after it is hammered out should be large enough to permit the threaded base of the lamp to slip into it. Lamps may be rapidly tested by sliding them into this socket and there is no more likelihood of a short being produced on the line than there was before the socket was changed. A partial cross section of such a socket is shown in the accompanying sketch.

❡Beeswax or soap placed in a screw slot will make it stick to the screwdriver blade for starting.

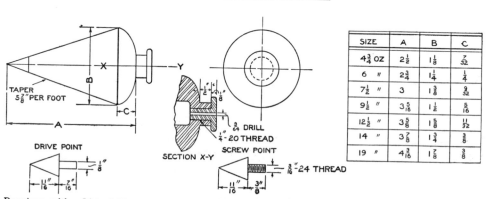

Drawings, with a List of Dimensions, for Making a Series of Plumb Bobs, Each of Which Has the Right Proportion for Its Size and Weight

SIZE	A	B	C
4¾ oz	2½	1⅛	7/32
6 "	2¾	1¼	¼
7½ "	3	1⅜	9/32
9½ "	3 5/16	1½	5/16
12½ "	3⅝	1⅝	11/32
14 "	3⅞	1¾	⅜
19 "	4 3/16	1⅞	⅜

How to Remove Large Chucks from Machines

An easy and convenient way to remove a chuck from a turret lathe, or other machine, is to form a sling of belt lacing to hold it with one hand while the other turns the spindle by the belt.

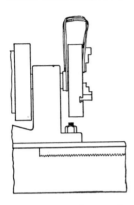

In the ordinary way one has to hold the chuck while turning the belt. This lets the chuck fall when it comes loose and sometimes results in cutting or bruising the hand.

It is much better and quicker to take two lengths of belt lacing and tie the ends together to form an endless piece. Place one loop around under the flange of the chuck and the other under one jaw. This forms a sling which can be taken in one hand over the chuck while the other pulls the belt to turn the machine spindle to unscrew it from the threads.—Contributed by Chas. A. Thissell, Beverly, Mass.

A Hose Clamp

The hose clamp illustrated herewith will hold high-pressure hose securely. It is easy to construct, being made of seamless brass tubing, about $1\frac{1}{2}$ times the diameter of the hose. The wall of the tube should be about $\frac{1}{16}$ in. thick. A section

is cut from the tubing about 1 in. long for ordinary sizes and placed on the hose, then bent to fit the latter loosely, making the shape similar to a figure 8. A hole is drilled through both walls of the metal, at the narrowest part, to admit a large stove bolt loosely. The hose is placed in the larger opening and a piece of rod in the smaller one. The clamping is done in the ordinary manner. I have used such a clamp on pressures up to 200 lb. without a single failure.—Contributed by Wm. G. Toplis, Philadelphia, Pa.

Repairing a Worn Plunger

A pitted or corroded plunger or rod may be repaired by cleaning out the corroded portions and filling them with solder, babbitt metal, or block tin a little higher than the surface of the rod. The uneven portions can then be filed or turned down in a lathe to a level with the surface of the rod. A brass rod can be repaired easier than one of iron, as the solder adheres to it more readily.

Pole-End Clasp for Handling Ceiling Globes

The incandescent globes, comprising a rigid ceiling cluster, or the individual light, are often located at a height from the floor which renders them inaccessible for removal without the aid of a stepladder or scaffolding of some kind.

The sketch shows a simple device by means of which lights, located at almost any distance from the floor, can be easily and readily removed. The four grip fingers are of $\frac{1}{16}$-in.

spring steel and are bolted at their lower ends to a 1-in. pipe coupling. Their upper ends are wrapped with tape, which gives a strong frictional grip on the glass so that the lamp can be turned from its socket in spite even of corrosion which often covers the coarse thread of the screw.

The handle can be made in sections, if necessary, to reach a ceiling of any height. With the assistance of this simple and inexpensive device the removal and application of incandescent globes in any overhead location is an easy task.

Number Holder for Automobiles

A number holder can be cut from a piece of hard wood that will serve the purpose as well as one made of metal, and the work can be done with ordinary tools. The shape of the holder is shown in the sketch, the distance A being the length of the number plate and the distance B wide enough to allow the plate to hang in front of the radiator when the holder is fastened to the radiator neck. A hole, C, is bored through the wood to fit the radiator neck and the wood sawed in two on the dotted line. Bolts, D, are used in

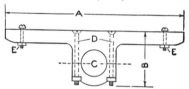

A Number-Plate Holder Made of Hard Wood and Fastened to the Radiator Neck

clamping the parts on the neck. Small bolts, E E, are used to fasten the number plate on the holder.—Contributed by Earl R. Hastings, Corinth, Vt.

Holding Pearls While Drilling Them

Hollow out the end of a piece of peg wood and fill the cavity with gum shellac. Imbed the pearl in the cement as shown in the sketch and, after filing a

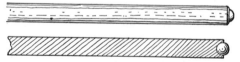

The Pearl is Securely Held in the End of the Wood While Drilling the Hole

little to make a flat surface, the drill is easily started.—Contributed by Wm. A. Jones, Raleigh, N. C.

A Wood-Breaking Block

Firewood, such as scraps of boards, is often more easily broken up into stove wood than if sawn or cut with an ax. I rigged up a block, about 15 in. high, and cut a notch about 8 in. deep, tapering from 2 in. in width at the outside to ¾ in. at the bottom. By plac-

ing the firewood into the notch, as shown, the pieces are easily broken with an ax or hammer. The block

Block for Holding Firewood for Breaking It Up into Stove Lengths

should be fastened solidly.—Contributed by John V. Loeffler, Evansville, Indiana.

A Wood Scraper

A useful wood scraper and stencil-mark remover can be made by attaching a handle of the desired shape to a discarded safety-razor blade. The tool will be found very handy in a cabinet shop. The opening for the blade should be a close fit, so that a new one can be

The Handles may be of Any Shape Suitable for the Work at Hand

easily inserted when necessary.—Contributed by W. A. Jaquythe, San Diego, Cal.

Soft Faces for a Hammer

The head of the hammer is made of soft steel with threaded ferrules, A A, to hold the soft faces B B. The ferrules are knurled to make them easily turned with the fingers. Any kind

Any Kind of Soft Metal Face can be Used on the Hammer Head

of a soft face made of fiber, leather, copper, or brass can be turned up and kept on hand for different work.

An Automatic Pressure-Gauge Alarm

Any ordinary pressure gauge may be easily equipped with a simple, home-made contact device operated by the needle on the gauge, which may be

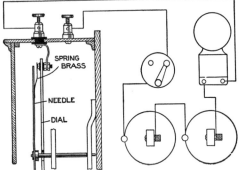

Contact Points as They are Attached to a Gauge for Closing a Bell Circuit

connected in series with a vibrating bell and battery, so that the combination will serve as an automatic alarm, giving the engineer an audible signal when the pressure has exceeded or dropped below a previously determined value. A contact device for this purpose may be constructed as follows:

Carefully remove the glass front of the gauge, and then the needle from its spindle. The end of the shaft upon which the needle or pointer is mounted is usually tapered and the needle simply forced on, so that great care should be exercised in removing the needle to make sure the shaft is not bent, nor its bearings or other parts of the gauge injured. Then, on the under side and at the outer end of the pointed end of the needle, fasten a very light piece of spring brass that is to wipe over a contact to be mounted on the face of the instrument. This contact is fastened on the face in such a position that the spring on the needle is in contact with it, when the needle indicates a pressure corresponding to the value at which the alarm is to be given; and it should, of course, be insulated from the dial and in turn connected to a binding post mounted on the outside of the frame, or containing case, of the gauge and insulated from it. A second binding post is mounted

on the case and electrically connected to it. These two posts form the terminals of the contact device and are connected in series with the bell battery and a small single-pole switch.

In remounting the needle make sure that it occupies the same position on the dial when there is no pressure acting on the gauge that it did before it was removed. The spring on the under side of the needle should be very light and flexible, and so adjusted that it will wipe over the contact on the dial with a minimum friction. It would, no doubt, be best to mount a small piece of platinum both on the end of the spring and on the contact where they touch each other, to reduce the trouble due to corrosion and arcing.

A diagrammatic sketch of the contact device and circuit is shown herewith. One or more additional contacts may be mounted on the dial and connected to other binding posts, which in turn may be connected in series with bells of different tones. If two contacts are used, one may indicate an excessive pressure and the other a reduced pressure.

A Bench Stool on Wheels

In my regular work, consisting in repairing electric fans, smoothing irons and other small appliances, I find that walking back and forth in front of a 22-ft. bench to get certain tools and materials required for the particular work in hand becomes more tiresome than the work itself. To remedy this, I conceived the idea of putting my stool on small flanged wheels to roll on a hardwood track laid on the floor in front of the bench. It is now an easy matter to reach the test set, at one end of the bench, or the vise, at the other, without leaving my seat. To insure steadiness and permit rapid rolling, the wheel base should be about 3 ft. long.—Contributed by Chas. K. Theobald, Vicksburg, Miss.

❢Never rub a polished varnished surface with a dry chamois skin, as it will surely scratch it.

An Inexpensive Electric Blueprinter

A large glass bottle with a mouth that will admit a 100-watt tungsten electric globe makes a good substitute for the cylindrical blueprinting machine. The drawing, together with the blueprint paper, is wrapped around the outside of the bottle and the electric globe suspended within. The tracing and paper may be held in close contact on the glass with large rubber bands and a sheet of cardboard as a backing. When only a few prints are to be made, the only spare time being at night, this arrangement will prove quite satisfactory.

Lock for a Bench Drawer

The bench drawer can be easily supplied with a lock that will answer the purpose and protect the workman's tools from the borrowing mechanic. The lock consists of a piece of ⅛-in. flat steel that will fit loosely in a vertical position in the drawer. About one-third of the way from one end drill a hole in the piece and fasten it with a nail or screw on the inside surface of the front part of the drawer. Another screw, A, is turned in where it will catch the longer end of the metal, and when the latch is turned over on this screw it will be out of the way. A

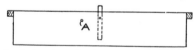

The Lock Consists of a Strip of Metal Attached to the Inside of the Drawer Front

scale or piece of flat steel inserted between the bench top and drawer will turn the latch so that the drawer can be pulled out.

Nonrusting Soldering Flux

Dissolve small pieces of zinc in hydrochloric acid in the usual manner and, after it has been allowed to stand for some time, remove the undissolved zinc, and filter. Mix with one-third its volume of chemically pure ammonia and dilute as necessary for the work

An Automatic Closing Stanchion

A practical stanchion that will close automatically by the action of the beast when placing its head through the bars is shown in the sketch. The stanchion is made in the ordinary manner except that it is equipped with the self-closing parts. When turning the stock out, the bar A must be thrown to one side and to set the stanchion after

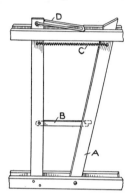

this is done, it is only necessary to place the piece B as shown, so that the coil spring C will hold it in position. When the beast enters, its movement of the head downward trips the piece B, the spring locks the bar A under the loop D, and the stanchion is securely closed.—Contributed by Ralph Crane, Ypsilanti, Mich.

Setting a Band Saw

In setting a band saw one is liable to have the first few teeth set a little too wide. To overcome this and have the teeth all in line I use the following method: When putting the band saw on the wheels I put it on upside down, so that the teeth will point upward. Then it is tightened until the saw set is drawn to the right width, whereupon the wheels are turned slowly by hand until the saw has made one complete turn. This will put any teeth in line that were out and save the trouble of using the set to draw them back a little.—Contributed by Ernest J. Dickert, Niagara Falls, N. Y.

℃Vitriol etching fluid will settle and stick to the bottle, but by placing a few very small pebbles in the solution it is easy to loosen up the settlings and cause them to dissolve again.

Gauge for Sawing Wedges

The gauge is for use in connection with the gauge on the circular-saw table. The saw gauge is set the width

Gauge to Hold Stock on a Saw Table to Cut Wedges for Stair Building

of the wedge gauge plus the thickness of the wedge at the small end. The stock is cut to the length of the wedges and reversed each time a wedge is cut, to keep the grain of the wedge running straight.

The gauge will aid in cutting wedges of all kinds, but it is specially adapted for cutting them for stair construction of the housed-in type.—Contributed by Ernest S. Yawger, Ithaca, N. Y.

Repair Joint for Large Pipe Lines

The joint illustrated is one that I have used for some time in making repairs on pipe lines of various sizes and under all kinds of conditions. The band surrounding the joint is made of metal, about No. 14 gauge, the diameter being 2 in. larger than the pipe. If the metal band is not over No. 14 gauge, it can be sprung around the pipe and forced back to the size with a chain. Holes are punched along the edges for a double row of rivets which are put in and hammered down, using a 1½-in. bar of steel as a dolly. The

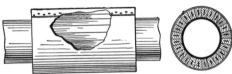

A Joint Made in a Pipe Line by a Band Filled in with Wood Strips and Wedged

bar will easily slip in between the band and the pipe.

When the band is in place and riveted over the joint, make some wood strips, ⅞ in. thick by 1 in. wide and as long as the band, the length of which

will depend on the joint being covered. The strips should be sawed on a bevel as shown, so as to fill the space between the band and the pipe as closely as possible. After the strips are driven in, split the ends of each strip slightly with a chisel and start wedges in the splits all around, but do not drive them in tightly. Then drive each wedge equally until the strips are all tightly wedged together. Wedge the other end in the same manner, then slightly split the ends of the strips in the opposite direction or at right angles to the other split and across the wedge. Drive wedges in these splits in the same manner, to close up any space between the wood and the metal. Do not drive any wedges between the strips, or between them and the metal.

If heavy band metal must be used for a large pipe, make the band in halves and offset the joint so that the inside surface is smooth. I have used these repairs under 1,000-ft. head without a leak. Also on a long line of pipe drawn apart for a considerable distance, a long band was used and a perfect joint made. Care should be taken to secure straight-grained wood for the strips. I find a repair of this kind can be made where the water cannot be taken out long enough to make a lead joint, and where no supplies are available.—Contributed by Geo. A. Nihell, Goodyears Bar, Cal.

Remedy for a Kicking Cow

Provide two straps similar to a hame strap and buckle each one just above the cow's hoof. Slip a small ring over each strap before they are buckled in place. These will do no harm to the cow if they are left in place all the time. At the milking place have a strap, 12 or 15 in. long, with a snap in each end and fasten it to the rings in the straps on the cow's feet. The cow cannot raise either foot in an effort to make a kick. This only takes a moment's time to attach, and it saves a bruised bucket or the skin of the milker.—Contributed by R. C. Bowden, Magazine, Ark.

How to Attach False Centers

A piece of hardened steel having no centers cannot be ground perfectly by holding it in a chuck. False centers, that will provide a way to grind the surface for the full length, may be attached as follows:

If a piece of hardened steel, 6 in. long and $1\frac{1}{64}$ in. in diameter, is to be ground, proceed to polish each end, then solder a piece of cold-rolled steel on this polished surface, as shown in the sketch. Place the steel in a steady rest on the lathe and center each end

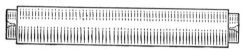

Soft-Steel Ends Soldered to a Hardened Piece of Steel to Provide Centers

in the usual way. These centers serve to hold the steel while grinding the surface, and then they can be removed by striking them with a hammer.—Contributed by Chas. Homewood, Cedar Rapids, Iowa.

How to Make a Pair of Fiber Pliers

A pair of pliers, that will be found to be very useful to anyone that is called upon to handle "live" wires, replace "blown" cartridge fuses in difficult places, such as behind switchboards, or in "live" circuits where there is no switch to open the circuit while replacing the fuse, may be constructed from some heavy sheet fiber. The general appearance of such a pair of pliers

The Parts Forming the Handles and Jaws of the Pliers are Made of Heavy Sheet Fiber

is shown in the accompanying sketch. Grooves may be cut in the jaws so that the object to be handled may be easily held.

℄Ordinary calcimine may be made somewhat waterproof by the addition of a little phosphate of soda.

Spring on a Faceplate Clamp

The ordinary clamp for holding work on a faceplate may be easily fixed to lift its jaw automatically from the work

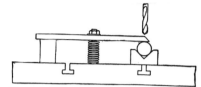

The Clamp Jaw is Raised from Its Holding Position by a Coiled Spring around the Bolt

when the nut of the bolt is loosened. All that is necessary to make this possible is to place a coil spring over the bolt beneath the jaw, as shown in the illustration. The spring also keeps the jaw from turning or changing its position when the nut is released.—Contributed by N. C. Danielson, Moline, Illinois.

Motorcycle Cleaner

No doubt all riders desire a clean motorcycle, but unless the machine is frequently cleaned of dirt and grease, these are apt to accumulate to an extent that discourages further endeavor in this direction. A correspondent of Motorcycling describes a

cleaner made by filling a tin can with a coil of lamp wicking which may be used without soiling the hands. The wicking is soaked in kerosene. When not in use the lid is placed on the can to keep it clean until required.

Plug-Cock Lubricant

A good lubricating mixture that will prevent leakage, for use on plug cocks, is made of 1 lb. of suet and $\frac{1}{2}$ lb. of beeswax, melted together. Mix thoroughly while hot, then strain and set away to cool.

℄A well cleaned talcum-powder can makes a good receptacle for flour of emery.

Block for Setting Castings in a Lathe Chuck

Having a quantity of flange castings to face on one side, true with the back, it was necessary to provide some quick

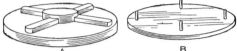

Backing Piece for Rapidly Adjusting Castings to be Turned in the Chuck on a Lathe

way of setting them in the lathe chuck. The back side of the casting, with the four lugs, is shown at A in the sketch. A universal chuck was used on the lathe, in which, of course, a single turn of the wrench would tighten and loosen the grip. To level them up by the back, a disk ⅛ in. less in diameter than the flanges was cut out of a ⅜-in. maple board and four ¼-in. pins were driven in, as shown at B, all being of the same length. These pins projected through the back of the board a trifle and were brought to a common level by fitting on a surface plate. The block fitted loosely in the chuck jaws and between the chuck face and the pieces to be trued up. All that was necessary to set up a flange was to place it in the chuck and tap it back against the pins.—Contributed by Donald A. Hampson, Middletown, New York.

An Extension Carpenter's Bit

When doing plumbing work or electric installation it is sometimes necessary to use an extension bit and many times the workman does not have one of the proper size at hand, says Electrical Review. A temporary affair can

Pipe Connection Used to Make Any Length of Extensions for an Ordinary Carpenter's Bit

be made in emergency cases from a piece of ¼-in. pipe, a ⅜ to ¼-in. reducing coupling, and a ⅜-in. bushing. The thread on the pipe is cut quite long so that the end will extend slightly into the coupling. The end is then squared to receive the end of the bit. The bushing is cut in halves and placed over the shank of the bit, which, when tightened, will hold the bit solidly in the coupling. Any length of pipe may be used, also any size of bit, which makes this extension very desirable.

Keyway-Cutting Tool for the Drill Press

Chipping and filing keyways in holes, ⅝ in. in diameter and under, is slow and unsatisfactory work without machinery or special tools. A simple tool for the drill press can be made to do this work far better than by hand. The tool consists of a piece of cold-rolled steel to be held in the drill chuck, one end of which is drilled and tapped for the cutting tool and its setscrew. The lever on the drill press is used to force

Tool to be Placed in a Drill-Press Chuck and Used for Cutting Keyways

it down through the work. After each cut the tool is driven out a little until the desired depth of the keyway is cut.

A White Paint for Boats

A government formula for a white paint to use on the outside of a boat is as follows: The proportions of the pigment and fluids are varied to suit the requirements. The formula is given for the first coat, which is the thickest. White lead in oil, 7 lb.; zinc white in oil, 7 lb.; raw linseed oil, 2 qt.; turpentine, 2 gills, and japan drier, 1 gill. This will make 1 gal. of paint. If too thin, add more lead and zinc, and if too thick, add more liquids.

Hose Clamp Used on a Small Hose

An ordinary hose clamp of usual dimensions can be used on pressure hose of much smaller diameter, if a piece of garden hose is forced on the end of the smaller hose. The clamp can then be drawn up on both so that there will be no leak.

Template Guide for Lathe Work

Forming dies, balls, ball hollows, and similar work, may be easily accomplished in an ordinary lathe with the

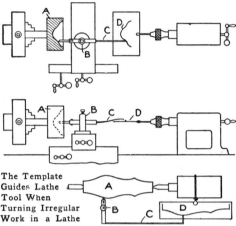

The Template Guides Lathe Tool When Turning Irregular Work in a Lathe

use of the attachments shown in the sketch. The work to be turned is shown at A in the different sketches, and the ordinary toolholder B is guided by a pointer, C, which is kept on the template D. It is obvious that if the pointer C follows the outline of a drawing on the template, it will cause the tool to cut the same shape into or on the work being turned.—Contributed by V. Verpeut, Jersey City, N. J.

Open-Air Swinging Bed

The best way to avoid the discomfort of a stuffy bedroom on a hot night is to prepare an outside swinging bed in the manner shown in the illustration. Procure an old bed spring and suspend

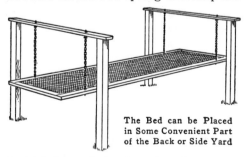

The Bed can be Placed in Some Convenient Part of the Back or Side Yard

it with four chains hanging from eyebolts fastened in crosspieces on four posts. With an old carpet and a cou-

ple of blankets, this makes a comfortable place to sleep. A canvas can be thrown over the top to protect it from the sun's rays if the occupant desires to use it for an afternoon's nap.— Contributed by T. Canary, Chicago.

Broken Wires in the Insulation

It is a common occurrence for an electric wire on the igniting system of an automobile to become broken within the insulation. This will cause no end of trouble, and the kind that is not easily found. It is best to look for these hidden breaks before taking the engine apart to locate the cause of the trouble.

To Avoid Stucco Leaks

Very frequently roof work in connection with stucco walls develops leaks which are hard to locate. The leaks are usually not the fault of the roofer.

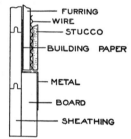

To eliminate all danger, the construction should be as shown in the sketch. The leaks in the stucco will be caught by the metal flashing which carries the water to the surface on the outside. This method also gives a shoulder for the stucco work to rest upon and helps to keep it from cracking. The board used should be as thick as the combined thickness of the furring, mesh and stucco, and should be 5 in. high, so that it will be flush with the outside of the stucco when finished. When properly installed the upright portion of the metal must be back of the entire construction, even to the building felt or paper ordinarily used on stucco work, the down turn serving as a counter flashing under which any other flashing, such as is used with tile, tin or slag roofs, can be slipped.—Contributed by Ward Mosher, New York City.

A Hot-Bearing Alarm

The following simple alarm is **very effective** in giving an audible signal to an engineer or attendant in charge of

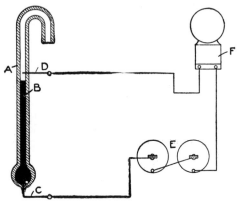

The Mercury Tube and Its Connection in an Electric Circuit for Ringing a Bell

machinery when any of the bearings or other parts, reach a temperature greater than some previously determined value for which the alarm is adjusted.

The alarm consists of an ordinary vibrating bell and battery connected in series with a special switch. This special switch consists of a small glass tube that has a bulb formed on one end and two pieces of platinum wire fastened in its wall. One of these pieces of wire is located at the lower end of the tube and the other a short distance from the lower or bulb end. Their ends extend a short distance inside the glass wall so that they can make electrical contact with a quantity of mercury that is placed in the tube. The quantity of mercury should be such that it barely makes electrical connection with the upper platinum wire when the temperature of the mercury corresponds to the temperature of the bearing at which the alarm is to be sounded. For all temperatures below the above value the two platinum wires will not be connected by the mercury, and since they are connected in series in the bell circuit, the circuit will be open. A diagrammatic arrangement of the circuit and tube containing the mercury is shown in the sketch, in

which A represents the glass tube; B, the mercury; C and D, the platinum wires; E, the battery, and F, the vibrating bell.

A number of tubes or switches may be connected in parallel and any one of them will cause the bell to ring. In such an arrangement it is necessary for the attendant to examine all the bearings whose switches are connected in parallel, in order to determine which has an excessive temperature, but this objection can be easily overcome by using an ordinary annunciator and assigning to each bearing, or group when a large number are equipped, a separate indicator, in which case inspection of all the bearings is not necessary.

The inside diameter of the glass tube should be comparatively small and the bulb on the end relatively large, as this arrangement makes the switch much more sensitive, because the column of mercury will then change more in height for any given change in temperature. The upper end of the tube can be bent over and its end turned down, which will prevent, to a certain extent, foreign matter accumulating on top of the mercury. These tubes should all be mounted as near the bearing, or part of the machine they are to guard, as possible. They may be easily mounted mechanically, but they will not perform properly unless they are influenced in the right way by the temperature they are to govern. A small wad of asbestos wool may be placed over the bulb when it is in contact with the outer surface of the bearing which will prevent undue radiation and cause the temperature of the mercury to correspond very nearly to that of the bearing.

Short pieces of platinum wire that will serve the purpose can be obtained from the base of an old incandescent lamp. Platinum is used because it does not corrode and it expands and contracts the same amount as glass with a change in temperature, which gives a perfect seal between the glass and platinum at all times.

⁋A cork placed on the sharp point of a bill file keeps it harmless until needed.

Preparing a Plastered Wall for Paint

The usual method of preparing a plastered wall for painting is to fill all cracks with plaster of Paris, or a mixture of the plaster and whiting, but a better way is to add some plaster of Paris to some of the paint and make a putty of it with which to fill the cracks. This will not absorb the paint as plaster alone will do. Very large cracks must be filled with plaster of Paris and whiting, to which some glue size has been added.

Bracing a Corner Post with Concrete

Dig the hole in the usual manner, then in the directions opposite to the pull of the wires dig trenches, 10 in. wide and 2 ft. long. Put in some broken stones or brick and pour cement over it, first a layer of stone, then some cement, and so on until the trenches are filled. The trenches, of course, connect with the post hole and are filled as the post is being held in place by a temporary brace. After the filling is done, a better brace cannot

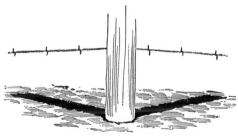

The Concrete around the Base of the Post Has Two Connecting Concrete Extensions

be had, and the unsightly corner brace is not needed.—Contributed by Harriette I. Lockwood, Philadelphia, Pa.

A Safety Stepladder

The ordinary factory-made stepladder may be considered a complete and ready-to-use product, but it is so in ap-

The Strips Hinged to the Back-Support Sides Prevent the Ladder from Tipping Over Sideways

pearance only. Anyone who has had experience with a stepladder knows that, while working on its top, it has a decided tendency to tip over, especially when one is leaning too far to one side or the other.

The sketch herewith shows a very simple appliance to render a stepladder safe. As shown, two strips of wood are fastened by means of hinges to the sides of the back supports. Blocks are fastened to the supports at the ends of these strips to prevent them from spreading too far. These will hold the ladder quite rigid and keep it from tipping when the load becomes top-heavy.

As the sides of the back support are usually about 6 or 8 in. shorter than the front when the ladder is closed, the strips will come about even with the front sides when they are closed against the back support. The blocks should not be put on until after the strips and hinges are in place.—Contributed by James E. Cooley, Hartford, Conn.

Automatic Water Supply to a Coffee Boiler

A useful method of keeping the water in coffee boilers at a constant level is shown in the diagram. The

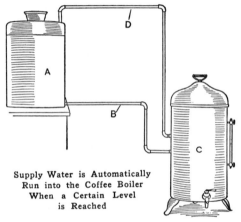

Supply Water is Automatically Run into the Coffee Boiler When a Certain Level is Reached

supply tank A is filled with water and securely corked. The water flows through the pipe B into the boiler C. When the water rises in the boiler to the opening of the pipe D it cuts off the air, causing a vacuum in the tank A. This prevents the water from flowing into the boiler. When the water boils down below the end of the pipe D, a fresh charge of water is automatically admitted to the boiler.—Contributed by F. E. Purser, Winnipeg, Canada.

Rear-End Signals on Trains

The adoption of the double-track system which has become almost universal on the railroad highways has reduced collisions to the rear-end class only. Automatic block systems, the employment of rear flagmen, and a sharp lookout by the engineer of the rear train constitute about all the pro-

tection now in use. A large percentage of the serious accidents are rear-end collisions. Block systems occasionally fail and men are not infallible; hence a need for better protection if possible.

Many accidents could be avoided by automatic means other than the block system, one of which is as follows: On the rear end of each train carry a tank of acetylene gas and connect it to a double searchlight, one directing a pencil, or ray, of light vertically and the other horizontally to the rear. The light, or jet, is regulated by a valve operated by a centrifugal governor, which in turn is run from an idler that can be dropped on the axle of the rear car at will. The governor is adjusted so that when the speed of the train falls below a certain fixed value the valve controlling the flow of acetylene gas will open. The valve is of the kind allowing a small flow of gas at all times when in service, thus acting as a pilot light.

The minor construction details of this device are so simple that any good mechanic can easily install it without further description.—Contributed by F. B. Lambert, Chicago, Ill.

A Fountain Scrub Broom

A very serviceable scrub broom can be made by attaching the brush to a piece of bamboo pole for a handle and forcing water through it with a hose connection. As the joints of the bamboo are closed, a hole must be bored through them all. The brush is attached to the end of the pole in the same manner as it is fastened to

Clean Water is Applied to the Broom with Regulated Pressure from a Faucet

the ordinary handle, or the handle of the broom may be cut off close to the brush and a hole bored through the stub, in which the bamboo is attached. A hose connection is fastened to the other end.—Contributed by Leroy Bradley, Lorain, O.

Cleaner for a Soldering Copper

To keep the point end of a soldering copper clean use a 1-in. pipe cap for a cup and fill it a little above the rim with No. 0 steel wool for a wiper. The threads in the cap will hold the wool in place, and by drawing the hot copper over it, the point will always be bright and clean. After the exposed part of the wool becomes matted down, it can be taken out and turned over. A hole can be bored in the center of the cap for fastening it to the bench.—Contributed by A. R. Cunning, West New Brighton, N. Y.

A Flexible Finger-Ring Gauge

Roll a tapering tube around the regular jewelers' ring gauge, using Manila paper, and glue the edges together to give it the form shown at A. Cut off the ends and slip on different-sized

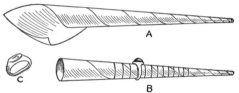

The Gauge being Flexible, Rings Bent Out of Shape can be Accurately Measured

rings, friction-tight, marking the places for each size and half size plainly in ink as shown at B. Rings bent out of shape, as shown at C, can be accurately gauged on the paper taper.

To Clean Articles of Steel

An excellent method of cleaning steel articles which have become rusted or oxidized, consists in rubbing the surfaces with pure sweet, or olive, oil, applying several coats, then laying them aside for several days, after which they are thoroughly rubbed with unslaked lime.—Contributed by Ralph W. Jones, St. Louis, Mo.

Isinglass, or mica, in stoves can be cleaned by soaking and washing it in vinegar.

A Detachable Overflow for a Tank

Deeming it unnecessary to add an overflow to a barrel section which I had fitted up for a tank and not car-

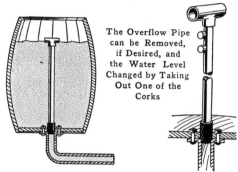

The Overflow Pipe can be Removed, if Desired, and the Water Level Changed by Taking Out One of the Corks

ing to remove any of the attached pipes, I slipped a piece of rubber tubing over the end of a piece of pipe so as to make a water-tight fit, and inserted it in the outlet in the manner shown. Holes were drilled in the pipe at intervals and plugged with corks. The water can be made to overflow at any height by removing a cork in the pipe at that level. The rubber tubing can be discarded and the pipe threaded to fit into the waste nut at the bottom.—Contributed by James M. Kane, Doylestown, Pa.

A Compression Pressure Gauge

Desiring to test the compression, to find the trouble in a two-cylinder engine, and being unable to secure a pressure gauge, I made one as shown in the sketch, which is nothing more than the lower part of an old spark plug, with the core taken out and a

A Compression Gauge Made of a Tire Gauge, an Old Spark Plug, and a Tire Valve

bicycle clamp valve soldered in the place of it.

The plug is screwed into the cylinder and any tire-pressure gauge used to test the compression.—Contributed by S. J. Pearson, Bennettsville, S. C.

Block for a Sliding Gate

The most commonly used gate is that which slides on a crosspiece nailed between two posts set diagonally with

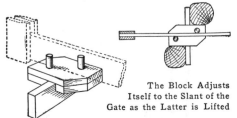

The Block Adjusts Itself to the Slant of the Gate as the Latter is Lifted

the line of the fence. Such a gate can be handled very well, but the sliding may be greatly improved by placing a block, shaped as shown, on the crosspiece. A little grease applied from time to time will make the gate work almost as easily as if it were on rollers.—Contributed by A. S. Thomas, Gordon, Canada.

Cutting Liners for Babbitted Bearings

One of the most difficult things about babbitting bearings is the cutting of the liners, especially if it is desired to have them very thin for fine adjustment. The cutting of the liners can be easily done in the following manner: Lay a piece of paper on the bearing face and press it down firmly with the fingers around the edge, also around the holes for the bolts or studs. This will leave an exact impression of the bearing face which can be traced with a lead pencil. This makes the pattern.

Two boards, A and B, are cut a little larger than the pattern, and an old magazine or other paper, having leaves that lie evenly and flat, is placed between

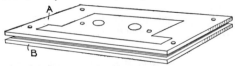

The Boards Hold the Paper Leaves Together While They are Cut to the Right Shape

the boards. The pattern is placed on top of the board A, and a few small nails are driven through the pattern, paper, and boards, to hold them together. A band or scroll saw is used to

cut around the edge of the pattern. The holes for the bolts can be bored to the right size with an ordinary bit. The edges can be finished with a coarse file or sandpaper. The liners will come out neatly cut to shape and in a pile that can be roughly handled.—Contributed by H. F. Hopkins, N. Girard, Pa.

A Self-Contained Gasoline Soldering Torch

The handle of the torch constitutes the reservoir for the gasoline. It is made of a piece of 1-in. gas pipe, 6 in. long, fitted with a cap on each end. The cap on the rear end is drilled centrally and tapped for an ordinary bicycle-tire valve. A heavy leather gasket should be placed in this cap so that the joint will hold air and gasoline without being turned up tightly. The cap at the other end is put on after filling the threads with glycerin and litharge.

An ordinary soldering-copper end

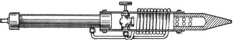

This Soldering Iron is Exceptionally Good for Use in the Wind on Roofs

is bored out, leaving the walls about $\frac{3}{16}$ in. thick, and $\frac{1}{8}$-in. holes are drilled through the walls for vents. The connection for holding the copper to the handle consists of two pieces of strap iron, each $\frac{1}{8}$ in. thick, $\frac{3}{4}$ in. wide, and $4\frac{1}{2}$ in. long. One end of each piece is hammered concave so that it will fit over the outside of the cap. Holes are drilled in both ends of each piece to admit $\frac{5}{32}$-in. machine screws, and corresponding holes are drilled opposite each other on the circumference of the cap and copper and tapped to fit the screws. The parts are then put together as shown.

A $\frac{1}{8}$-in. needle valve is fitted between the two pieces of strap iron, as shown, and connected to the reservoir with an 18-in. length of $\frac{1}{8}$-in. copper tubing such as is used on an automobile carburetor. Small unions are soldered to the ends of the tubing which make connections with two short nipples, one soldered into a hole drilled in the pipe and the other turned into the needle valve. The tubing is given several coils around the two pieces of strap iron where they will be near the flame that comes from the vent holes in the copper.

Fill the handle about two-thirds full, with gasoline, replace the cap and attach a bicycle hand pump to the valve and pump up a fairly good pressure. Pour a little gasoline in a pan and ignite it and hold the coil over the flame, or place the coil in the flame of a lamp for about one minute, then open the needle valve.—Contributed by A. H. Waychoff, Lyons, Colo.

A Disk Cutter

The cutter is made similar to a pair of dividers—in fact, it can be used as dividers and as a bevel protractor—from sheet steel, $\frac{3}{32}$ in. thick. The parts are cut to the proper shape, and to make them rigid, a part of the metal is turned over, as shown, into an L-shape.

The thumbnut and bolt, at A, holds the arms

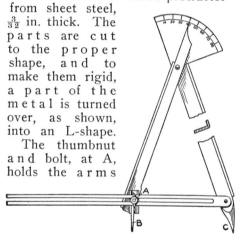

A Disk Cutter That can be Used Also as Dividers or as a Bevel Protractor

firmly for heavy work and will also hold the cutter B, which can be set at any angle. The end C is filed to a sharp point. A protractor scale is laid out and marked with a sharp-pointed tool.

The tool I made had 9-in. arms and a connecting slot bar, 6 in. long. It cuts disks or washers from cardboard, leather and wood boards of soft pine or poplar.—Contributed by John V. Loeffler, Evansville, Ind.

Painting Small Stakes

Having a large number of pieces to paint, for use in staking out a newly platted addition to a city, I found that

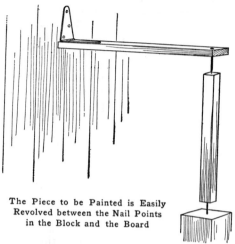

The Piece to be Painted is Easily Revolved between the Nail Points in the Block and the Board

the device shown in the sketch saved considerable time and made it much easier to do the work. A piece of board was fastened to the side of a building, at a convenient height, with a strap hinge. A nail was placed in the end of the board so that its point projected on the under side, then a block was set firmly in the earth with a nail projecting upward in its upper end. Each piece to be painted was placed between the two nails as shown, and in painting the stick could be revolved.—Contributed by P. F. Noyes, Ft. Myers, Fla.

Preparing a Cracked Wall for Painting or Papering

When a plaster wall or ceiling is so badly cracked that it will not do to paint or even paper the surface, cover it with strong muslin or light canvas. Use a strong paste made of flour in the ordinary way with a little glue added to give it stronger holding qualities. Press out any air bubbles that may occur and make the surface quite smooth. Either water or oil colors, as well as paper, may be applied to this surface, and it will make a very smooth and a sure job.

Telephone-Receiver Holder

Finding it necessary to devise something that would accommodate a one-armed salesman in receiving orders over a telephone I devised the stand shown, which consists of an old ceiling plate procured from a discarded gas chandelier, and pieces of brass pipe. The ceiling plate was 3¾ in. in diameter and 2¾ in. high. A piece of ½-in. brass pipe was cut 10 in. long, and a cap was fastened to one end, the other being inserted through the hole in the plate from the under side. The plate was then filled, two-thirds full, with solder, covering the cap. When the solder had hardened I bent the upper end of the pipe and cut it to straddle a piece of pipe of equal size. Then another piece of pipe was cut 3¼ in. long; two ¼-in. holes, 2¾ in. apart, were drilled through it, and two pieces of ¼-in. wire inserted in the holes, the ends of the wires being then bent upward to fit the receiver snugly. The short piece of pipe was soldered to the upper, bent end of the upright.

This device proved to be very satisfactory, inasmuch as it not only served the purpose mentioned, but was also very handy for those with two hands, since they could write and talk at the same time and refer to catalogs without delaying the customers.—Contributed by Jno. F. Gleaser, Cincinnati, O.

Silver Paste for Coating Brass Articles

The marks and figures on scale beams, scales for thermometers, steam gauges, etc., can be finished in the following manner: Fill the marks and numbers in the brass with japan and clean the surface to be finished, after which the article is placed in an oven to bake the japan.

The surface of the metal is thoroughly cleaned with a fine grade of emery cloth and a paste, made as follows, then applied and well rubbed on the metal: Mix ½ oz. of chloride of silver, 5 lb. of ordinary salt and ¼ lb. of cream of tartar thoroughly in a dry state, then add enough cold water to make a paste. Do not add too much water. As light affects the silver, the mixture should be kept in a dark place or in a covered earthen vessel. After thoroughly rubbing this paste on the metal surface this will take on a dirty yellow tinge. It is brightened by again rubbing the surface with a mixture, in a dry state, of ¼ lb. of cream of tartar and 5 lb. of salt. When this is finished, the metal is thoroughly washed to remove any trace of salt, then dried and lacquered.

Repairing a Split in a Water Pipe

A lead pipe burst one Sunday noon leaving a split about 1½ in. in length. This required a wipe joint, but we

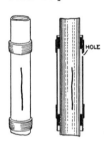

could not get a plumber at that time and would have been without water if repairs had not been made that were intended at the time to be temporary only.

Having dried the pipe well and cleaned it, I wrapped the pipe with adhesive tape, about 5 turns each, above and below the split. Then I placed a piece of stiff paper around the pipe on the two bands of tape so that the paper was held a little distance from the pipe. The ends of the paper were held with another turn of tape. A hole was stabbed in the paper near the top and the space filled with hot lead. After removing the paper and lead it left a neat-looking job which has proved to be as good as a wiped joint.—Contributed by Chas. H. Richards, Toronto, Can.

Handling Large Chucks on Lathes

A chuck on a large lathe, almost the full size of the swing, can be easily handled with the use of a piece of

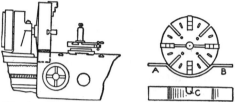

The Chuck Rests on the Metal Which is Supported on the Lathe Ways

metal on the ways, as shown. The flattened ends, A and B, rest on the ways, and the center part is bent to fit the edge of the chuck. If the chuck jaws project, a slot is cut in the metal, as shown at C, to receive one jaw end. The chuck can be easily slipped along on the ways when turning it from the threads of the spindle.—Contributed by J. Harger, Honolulu, H. I.

Screwdriver Made of a Bicycle Pedal

The screwdriver illustrated was constructed especially for turning in loose screws and nipples on bicycle spokes. It can be used for a great variety of work, however, where machine screws

A Crank-Type Screwdriver with a Ball-Bearing Shaft for Light Work

are used. The screwdriver is made of an ordinary hub of a bicycle pedal. The frame part is removed and the threaded shank of the pin is cut off, then drilled centrally and tapped to receive the end of the screwdriver blade. The blade is made of steel wire bent as shown.—Contributed by W. E. Nolan, San Francisco, Cal.

❡Crossing the belt that runs the radiator fan on an automobile will reverse its motion and force the warm air from the engine through the radiator and prevent freezing in severe cold weather.

Truck Wheel on a Grindstone Frame

A very convenient way of moving an ordinary grindstone from place to place is to make a small frame at the bottom of the posts and attach a small wheel, similar to a wheelbarrow wheel, with the lower part slightly above the surface of the ground. This will easily touch the ground when the other end of the frame is raised, and the stone can be pushed about in wheelbarrow fashion.

Care of Striping Pencils

Striping pencils, used by wagon painters and decorators, should always be thoroughly cleaned and greased with tallow after being used. A match box, or a similar box, cut as shown,

A Holder Made of a Match Box to Provide a Place for Keeping Striping Brushes

makes a good receptacle for these articles and also makes it easier to find them when wanted.—Contributed by James M. Kane, Doylestown, Pa.

Guard Attachment for a Long Ladder

The ladder attachment shown in the sketch serves as a guard for gutters and will enable the painter to paint back of the ladder. It can also be used on the roof of a building as a roof ladder. The attachment consists of two hardwood arms, 1 in. thick, 2 in. wide, and about 1 ft. long, fastened to the ladder stringers and joined together with a board nailed on their top edges. The board serves to hold the paint pot. When not in use the attachment folds against the ladder.—Contributed by J. V. Loeffler, Evansville, Indiana.

Loading Barrels in a Wagon Box

A barrel loaded in a wagon box is apt to roll about unless pieces are placed under the edges, but even then,

The Curved Parts Cut into the Pieces Keep the Barrel from Rolling About

if the barrel is a large one and full, the pieces will not hold it. A simple device for keeping the barrel from rolling is made of two pieces of 2 by 4-in. wood, about 3½ ft. long, with a concaved place cut out near the center, as shown, and the ends cut to a point so that the barrel may be easily rolled up on them. Join the pieces together with strong pins. Roll the barrel into the notches and it will remain there until ready to unload.

For hauling a number of barrels, remove the wagon box, make the pieces of heavy timbers extending from one bolster to the other and cut as many notches as there are barrels to be hauled.—Contributed by J. G. Allshouse, Avonmore, Pa.

A Floating Mooring

By making a boat fast to a loose collar of wood placed about a conveniently located pile, the boatman will always find the knot in the end of the painter upon the surface of the water instead of submerged to a depth of several feet, which often happens when the rope is tied to the pile itself. The collar of wood can be

made of material 2 in. thick and 4 in. wide, and of such a size that it will easily slip over a pile. The joints should be securely fastened with bolts. —Contributed by Forrest Clark, Coronado, Cal.

A Built-Up Crankshaft

In making a crankshaft for a twin-cylinder engine I was fully aware of the difficulty in making a built-up shaft to secure a perfect alinement as well as having the parts equally spaced. I overcame the difficulty in the following manner:

The engine being a small one, the crank webs, or arms, were made of a cold-rolled steel bar, ⅜ by 1 in., and two pairs were marked off on this material, a line being scribed through the center of one face on each piece with a gauge, whereupon the location for the holes was center-punched. All eight holes were then drilled in a lathe

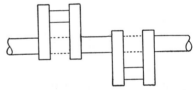

After the Pieces are Located and Fastened the Unnecessary Parts are Sawn Out

for a ⅜-in. shaft; the pieces were piled one on the other and a perfectly straight piece of ⅜-in. steel rod was inserted through the holes in the ends to be used for the crankpins, thus adjusting this series of holes in perfect alinement. The holes in the other ends, being ⅜ in. in size, had to be enlarged to ½ in. or the size of the shaft. This is where the wisdom of the scheme became apparent, for, in spite of careful laying out, marking and drilling, when the holes at one end were in perfect alinement, those at the other end showed such variation as to make proper and accurate assembling out of the question. The next step was to bolt the stack of four pieces to a slotted faceplate, after first soldering along each joint as a temporary binder, and centering the hole in the outer piece as true as possible, then boring all holes to the ½-in. size in the manner of ordinary boring on a lathe.

After removing the pieces from the faceplate and separating them, they were mounted on the shaft in the proper locations; the rod for the crankpins was inserted, and both crankpins and shaft pieces were fastened as desired with screws or pins, driven, soldered or brazed. The portions of the shaft shown by the dotted lines are sawn out and the parts filed and polished.—Contributed by Harry F. Lowe, Washington, D. C.

Repairing a Break in a Suction Line

A serious break that occurred in a 14-in. suction line to a condenser, and also the clamp that was made for temporarily repairing the pipe, are shown in the sketch, which is redrawn from the Southern Engineer. The clamp was made of iron, 2½ in. wide, with holes in the lugs for ¾-in. bolts. The clamp was made 16½ in. inside diameter.

About 5 lb. of white lead was procured and thinned down a little with gasoline. A quantity of asbestos wicking was unraveled and pulled apart. The asbestos was mixed with the white lead so as to form a putty, which was put around the pipe in a layer about 3 in. thick, over the crack. The clamp was then put on and drawn up tightly.

A vacuum was maintained for two weeks without any trouble, and when the clamp was finally removed, to put

The Break in the Pipe and the Construction of the Clamp for Holding the Special Packing

in a new suction pipe, the putty was found to be firm and perfectly tight, and doubtless would have remained so indefinitely.

❡A grape-juice or milk bottle will serve admirably as a rolling pin or potato masher.

Collet for a Vertical-Shaft Milling Machine

The illustration shows a simple form of collet which can be fitted to the spindle of any ordinary vertical mill-

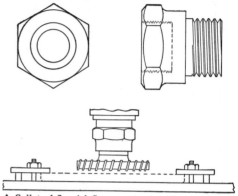

A Collet of Special Construction for Holding Cutters in Vertical-Spindle Milling Machines

ing machine. The collet is made from a machine-steel forging, machined hexagon in shape so that a large wrench may be used to tighten it in place.

The inside thread of the collet is cut to fit the thread of the spindle on which it is to be used. The outside thread is cut to fit that of the milling cutter used. Due care should be used in cutting the threads, as a good fit to both spindle and cutter is necessary.

In machine shops where several makes of vertical milling machines, each having a different size of spindle, are in use, a standard cutter might be employed if the machines are equipped with a collet of this kind, each having the same size outside thread, thereby making a saving in the cost of cutters.—Contributed by C. E. Bradley, Fall River, Mass.

To Keep Varnish in Jars

Dip the cover, rubber, and top of a screw-top fruit jar in melted paraffin, then pour the varnish, left over from a finishing job, into the jar and seal tightly. The paraffin will prevent the cover from sticking and, by excluding the air, preserve the varnish indefinitely.—Contributed by Alice M. Smith, Tacoma, Wash.

An Adjustable Stock Holder

In handling considerable work that required bars of stock to be held horizontally as they were fed into the machines, one of the men devised a holder that was suspended from the ceiling and adjustable for height to suit different classes and sizes of stock.

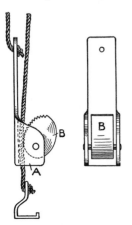

This holder is shown in the illustration. A piece of flat steel with two wings bent at right angles to the back is formed as shown at A. At its upper end a length of sash cord passes through a hole and is knotted. The free end runs up and through an eye fastened in the ceiling and back down again where it passes between the wings and down to the foot of the holder which is an L-shaped piece in which the stock is laid. To prevent slipping a toothed roller, B, is inserted between the wings. This roller is drilled eccentrically as shown and permits the passage of the cord when it is in one position and holds the cord when in another position. The notches help to hold the cord, and as the weight increases the grip will be greater.

Paint for Steam-Gauge Hands

Steam and other gauges placed in dark places are very hard to read correctly. This trouble can be overcome to some extent by painting the hands with a coat of brilliant aluminum powder mixed with good, clear varnish to the thickness of syrup. The varnish will protect the bright surface and prevent it from becoming soiled or dirty. The hand can be seen in a very dark place when coated with this paint.—Contributed by C. R. Dreese, Kansas City, Kan.

Cleaning a Gun of Lead

There is nothing that will keep a gun or other steel or iron articles in so good a condition as mercurial ointment. It has been used for years by surgeons to prevent their instruments from rusting. Do not grease the article, simply wipe it with a cloth saturated with the ointment.

In caring for a gun, wipe it out well, then run a wiper through saturated with the ointment, and there will be no rusting whatever. Neither will the outside of the gun rust if the ointment is applied there. The ointment will not only prevent rust, but will also loosen any lead in the barrel.

If a gun has become leaded and is wiped as described, it will appear to be full of rust or dirt after standing a few days. If wiped again, the wiper will be found covered with minute particles of lead which have been loosened by the mercury, and the barrel will be clean. The mercury has no affinity for iron, but has for lead.—Contributed by J. H. Beebee, Rochester, N. Y.

Cutting Bars on an Angle

On a job where a large number of bars were to be faced at an angle of 60 deg. and only a 30-deg. cutter was at hand, the work was accomplished in the manner shown in the sketch. A wood block was sawed at an angle of 30 deg., laid in the vise of the milling machine and

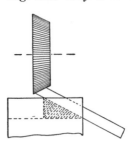

used as a guide against which the bars were clamped. The 30-deg. cutter was placed on the arbor of the machine, and the pieces were thus finished to the required angle.

⊄An earthenware cement can be made of 1 part powdered lime, 2 parts grated cheese, and the white of an egg mixed to form a paste.

To Strengthen Scaffold Boards

A simple and effective method of stiffening thin boards used for treads on scaffolding is shown in the sketch. Two pieces of timber, about 1 in. thick, 3 in wide, and as long as the boards are wide, are placed between them near the ends. The boards are then nailed together at their ends and the braces nailed between them. This

A Board Used on Scaffolding Strengthened to Prevent Sagging in the Center

will be found to make a stiffer tread than a single board of double thickness.—Contributed by C. K. Theobald, Vicksburg, Miss.

Repairing a Broken Connecting Rod

Owing to the construction of the ordinary two-bar connecting rod, shown in the illustration, the breakage of one of the rods is by no means an uncommon occurrence. The breaking of a rod, either the upper or lower, generally occurs at a point near the box, which makes almost any form of temporary repair an impossibility. However, a piece of pipe and a long rod threaded at both ends can be utilized in an efficient way to take the place of the broken bar of the rod.

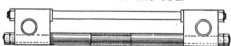

A Piece of Pipe and a Long Rod Taking the Place of a Broken Bar

The writer has seen one of this type of rods repaired in this manner which gave good service for a period of two years.—Contributed by F. W. Bently, Milwaukee, Wis.

Sleeve for a Marking Brush

It is necessary to have the bristles of a marking brush short and stiff, and in order to keep them uniform, one user fitted a sleeve on the brush that could be adjusted as the bristles became shorter by wear. The sleeve, as shown, slips over both brush and handle and is set for its different positions with a U-shaped wire spring having a projection at one end to en-

The Close-Fitting Sleeve Holds the Ends of the Bristles to Make Them Compact

ter a hole in the handle after passing through the sleeve. Several holes in the handle provide the range of positions for the sleeve.

Measuring Wire Diameters without a Gauge

A simple way of ascertaining the diameter of wires, when no wire gauge is at hand, and a method used by a German engineer, is to wind a number of coils close together around a lead pencil or other round object for 1 in., more or less, and divide the length of

A Simple Problem: Find the Wire Diameter When the Number of Coils and Length are Known

the wound part by the number of coils, thus obtaining the diameter of wire in fractions of 1 in. This method is applicable and gives quite reliable results for diameters as small as .005 in.

Fasteners for Small Metal Tubes

A handy fastener for small wires, copper and brass tubing can be formed by using links taken from a brass keyring chain. Each link is bent as shown and fastened with upholsterers' tacks or brass screws with round heads. This makes a neat fastener for bell wires and, if well insulated in the bend, can be used on wires carrying considerable current for experimental purposes.—Contributed by C. R. Dreese, Kansas City, Kansas.

Keeping Cork in a Bottle Away from Opening

When trying to extract a cork without the aid of a corkscrew it often happens that the cork is forced into 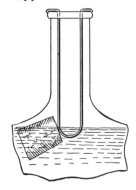 the bottle. The result is that every time the bottle is inverted the cork is drawn into the neck of the bottle and stops the liquid from running out. To prevent this, bend a piece of spring wire into the shape shown, and insert it in the bottle neck. The wire form should be long enough to extend slightly into the bottle. When the bottle is inverted the cork will be kept back from the neck and there will always be an opening, regardless of the position taken by the cork. Of course, this cannot be used in bottles containing corrosive liquids or acids. —Contributed by J. J. Kolar, Maywood, Ill.

Temporary Repair on a Governor Valve

The seats and valve of a well-known type of a governor had become so badly worn that throttling the engine down was an im- 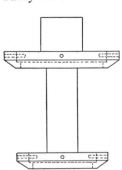 possibility. After facing the seats off in good shape the valve was too small, and in order to run the engine while a new valve was being procured it was decided to fix up the old one temporarily. Each flange was turned off to make a shoulder, as shown by the dotted lines in the sketch. Brass rings were made and pressed up to this shoulder, and

four small pins put in as shown. The valve was then ready to be turned off on a bevel to fit the newly dressed seats.—Contributed by Donald A. Hampson, Middletown, N. Y.

A Window Card

A novel window card may be made by painting one side of a double-strength piece of glass with black iron varnish and lettering the desired inscription with a sable brush, using ink made by mixing oxide of zinc and mucilage. This is much cheaper than cardboard, and the writing can be easily washed off and the glass used over and over again.—Contributed by T. F. Monaghan, Philadelphia, Pa.

To Make a Pattern Fillet Quickly

Having a hanger-bracket pattern to make in a hurry, I saved considerable time by making the fillets as follows: 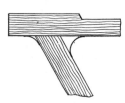 The fillets were on a 2½-in. radius and 2¾ in. wide. A tube was made of a tin piece, 15 in. long, rolled to a diameter of 5 in. This was cut into six equal parts and each part fastened into the corners of the patterns with small nails. The space between the tin and the wood was filled with old putty and waxed over the outside surface. As there were 16 corners to be filled in, I found that the time was reduced considerably by using this method instead of cutting the fillets from wood.—Contributed by E. A. Butler, Meriden, Conn.

Lifter for Opening Boxes

A simple tool to use in opening boxes is made by hammering one end of a short piece of ¾ or ½-in. pipe closed and smoothing the chisel end thus made on a grindstone. This tool serves all the purposes of a cold chisel in box opening and is inexpensive.

An Electric Cigar Lighter

By J. H. MILLER

One of the later electric heating devices is the electric cigar lighter, and for those who desire to make their own apparatus this description is given. The heating coil of the lighter is the important part and should be constructed and tested out before the handle is fitted to it.

The coil is made of the finest resistance wire that can be procured, No. 39 nichrome wire being used in the one described. About 30 in. of this wire is sufficient for a 110-volt circuit. Wind this wire on a mandrel, made of No. 14 gauge steel wire, slip the coil thus made from the mandrel and insert a piece of asbestos string that will fill the inside of the coil. Be sure to have all the turns separated from each other. The finished coil should be about 3 in. long.

A piece of transmitter asbestos board, $\frac{1}{4}$ in. thick, is procured, and a circular recess, $\frac{3}{4}$ in. in diameter, and $\frac{3}{32}$ in. deep, is cut into it with a small chisel. The outside is trimmed down to 1 in. in diameter, whereupon a small hole is drilled in the center, and one at the circumference. Insert one end of the coiled wire in the center hole and wind the coil spirally on itself with another asbestos cord between the turns. The coil should about fill the recess cut into the asbestos board. The other end of the coil is inserted through the small hole at the circumference. This brings the ends of the coil out on the back of the board. A piece of thin mica is fitted over the face of the coil, to hold it in place when the coil and board are fitted into the socket on the handle. A piece of wire, wrapped around the parts, will serve to hold them together temporarily and while making the tests.

Connect the leads to the supply from a 110-volt circuit. If the wire is the proper length, the coil will heat up sufficiently to char wood through the mica covering. If in doubt about the length of the wire, make it of plentiful length

so that, when testing, a little can be cut off at a time until the right heat is obtained.

The handle is made up as follows: Procure a small metal can, 1 in. in inside diameter, and cut it off $\frac{3}{4}$ in.

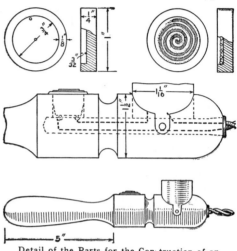

Detail of the Parts for the Construction of an Electric Cigar Lighter

long, making the cut on a curve so that it will fit snugly on the surface of a cylinder $1\frac{1}{2}$ in. in diameter. Cut a hole in the bottom of the can, $\frac{3}{4}$ in. in diameter, and place the coil with its base and mica covering into the can end. Fill in all unoccupied space with asbestos fiber, taking care to keep the leads to the coil well insulated from each other and from the box.

Turn up a handle, as shown. If there is no lathe at hand, this work can be done at a local shop, or by a person owning a lathe. A $\frac{1}{4}$-in. hole is bored centrally through the handle and a $1\frac{1}{16}$-in. hole bored to meet it from one side, over which the can part holding the coil is attached. Another hole is bored of such size as to admit a flush push button into the side of the handle, and on a line with the heating coil. The connections are made from the push button and the heater to the flexible lamp cord, as shown. Direct or alternating current can be used if it is 110 volts.

Stamping Fixture for Small Tools

The illustration shows a fixture designed to take care of the stamping of special drills, reamers, taps, etc. The

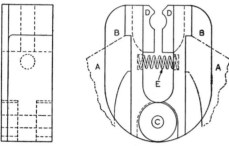

A Holder for Small Round-Shank Tools While Marking Them with Hand Stamps

jaws AA are those of a quick-action cam-and-lever vise, and BB are the two jaws of the fixture, which are held together by the hinge pin C and have a recess cut in their upper ends to take various-sized jaws, DD. The jaws are held apart for the insertion and removal of the work by the action of the spring E.

For stamping special taps, reamers, drills, and all round-shank tools, when only a few of a kind or size are made at one time, this method is quick, accurate and very efficient, as the operator soon learns to do a neat job in locating the stamps by hand.—Contributed by Chas. F. Scribner, Hartford, Conn.

A Homemade Oil Burner

The oil burner illustrated was designed by a correspondent of Power who claims that it gives very good re-

Detail of the Oil Burner Made Entirely of Pipe and Fittings for Use in Boilers

sults. The burner is constructed entirely of pipe and fittings. The manner of its construction is clearly shown. The inner pipe has slots cut in it with a hacksaw, the number of slots cut be-

ing governed by the amount of work required of the burner. A small hole is drilled in the plug at the end to make a miniature nozzle. The roughness caused by cutting the slots should be filed away and the edges peened down so that a flat jet of steam from each cut will strike the oil.

An opening is cut in the cap on the end of the outside pipe with a hacksaw. The size of this opening will be governed by the amount of fire required. For a small boiler, a coarse saw cut is sufficient with four cuts in the small inside pipe for the steam. For a larger boiler, make more cuts on the inner pipe and a larger opening on the outside cap. Use a needle valve on the oil-supply pipe and let the oil to the pipe under 40 or 50 lb. pressure at about 140 deg. temperature.

The burner is inserted through the fire doors where it will be near the center of the fire box. Do not let the blaze strike the boiler and keep a bright incandescent fire by applying the proper amount of steam and oil, and keep the stack damper almost closed. The ash-pit dampers should be left from 4 to 6 in. open, or sufficiently to feel a draft of air entering.

Removing Dents from Aluminum Ware

An aluminum coffee percolator had several dents in the sides which resulted from the natural wear in domestic use. With only a few simple tools at hand I was at a loss to know how to remove the dents. It finally occurred to me to pour a small ladleful of melted lead inside the pot, in a spot where the shape was perfect, after covering the surface of the metal with oil to prevent the lead from sticking to it.

This lead form was placed over the dent on the inside and the outside surface tapped lightly with a hammer until it assumed the original shape. The whole time taken was less than a half hour and the job proved a success.—Contributed by Edwin M. Davis, Philadelphia, Pa.

Painting Wood

By A. ASHMUN KELLEY

Painting wood is not the simple matter it was years ago. Then the wood was almost exclusively select white pine, and that is a wood very easy to paint. But now we have many kinds of wood to paint, such as cypress, redwood, hard pine, etc., and each of them requires a specific treatment.

Broadly speaking, all hard woods should be primed with a penetrating fluid, with little pigment. Linseed oil is penetrating enough on certain soft woods, but not so on hard woods. It will scarcely enter some. In this latter case the thinning fluid should be turpentine or benzol, with little or no oil. On some woods benzol does better than turpentine. Another feature of these liquids in the priming coat is that they, being antiseptics, will resist the attacks of the fungus called mildew. Mildewing occurs in the presence of dampness, or of linseed oil and pigments, being worse with some pigments, ocher for instance, than with others, such as white lead or zinc oxide. But observe that it will not do to add any benzol to the second or other succeeding coats, because benzol attacks oil as a solvent. A coat of benzol alone on cypress makes a good preparation for the priming coat of paint. A little benzol in the priming coat on shutters or blinds will prevent the mildewing of the chrome-green paint with which these fixtures are often painted. Cypress would be in better condition for receiving the priming coat of paint if left exposed to the weather for some months, because in running through the planer under great pressure it receives a hard glaze, through which paint can enter only with difficulty, and then only partly. If the surface cannot be weathered, go over it with water, to raise the grain, or add some water to the paint, and beat it well into the paint, which will help the paint to enter the wood; and as it afterward evaporates, it can do no harm. Redwood is rather easy to paint, and certainly much easier than cypress.

For barns and other country buildings, where the work is rather rough, nothing is better in the way of a protective paint than simple iron-oxide paint. It holds its color well, and if the trim is in some suitable color— even white will do, or dark sage green, but nothing gaudy—the brown will look sober and appropriate to the surroundings. An oxide is always a more durable paint material than a carbonate. For instance, iron oxide is almost unchangeable in color and wears extremely well, and so also zinc oxide, although the latter is rather too hard and brittle to stand without scaling or cracking, but it holds its oil and whiteness well. On the other hand, a carbonate, say, of lead, or of lime, which is whiting, will chalk and lose its color.

To paint a porch floor, what is called "dust color" is very good, as it will not show the dust as other colors will. It may be made from this formula: Zinc white, 21 lb.; best whiting, 8½ lb.; lampblack, 3 oz.; French yellow ocher, 1½ lb.; all dry colors. Mix thoroughly in the dry state. Add enough raw linseed oil to form a paste, then a little good varnish to act as a binder, thinning with turpentine, and adding driers enough to dry the paint in a few hours on a dry, warm day.

To paint an inside or room floor that must be used soon, mix some shellac varnish with the desired color, then thin down the mass with alcohol, the denatured article answering. Apply two coats, an hour between coats. If done in the evening, the floor will be dry and hard enough by morning. In fact, it will be hard enough to use in a few hours.

As a rule, painters use too little oil on outside work, and they also rub out too little. If sure that the oil is really boiled, all right, for it is better for second and last coats than raw oil. But it is difficult to get the genuine article oil, and the other kind is not desirable.

Prime cypress with white lead, well

thinned with turpentine or benzol, the latter preferred. About 20 per cent of the mass may be one of these fluids. Never guarantee a job of painting on cypress.

Linseed oil should never be used in the priming coat on redwood. Thin out white lead with turpentine. The addition of about 20 per cent of turpentine to the priming coat on exterior work is generally conceded to be better than all oil. Two coats of exterior paint, well brushed out, will wear better than two coats of paint not well brushed out. Two coats of heavy paint will not wear as well as two coats of thinner paint.

Imitation spirits of turpentine have not as strong a solvent action as the pure gum spirits. Turpentine from wood distillation is not as good in painting as gum-turpentine spirits. To test turpentine, place a few drops on white paper and expose to the air for a few minutes. If pure, it will leave no traces, but will leave some slight spot if adulterated.

It is best to prime a new frame building before the plasterer gets to work. He causes a great deal of moisture with his wet plaster, which acts on the wood before painting, while if primed beforehand, the moisture will have little or no effect on the woodwork.

To paint spruce siding, use white lead thinned with raw linseed oil and with little or no driers. If the wood is quite new, add a little water to the paint.

To find the number of gallons of paint that can be made from a mix of white lead in oil, say, 100 lb. of lead, consider that this weight of lead alone equals $2\frac{2}{3}$ gal. To this add the amount of oil, turpentine, driers, etc., mixed with it, and the result will be the total number of gallons of mixed paint.

Soldering a Setting without Removing the Stone

Sometimes it is impossible to remove a stone from a ring in order to solder a break near it. Bend a piece of No. 15

The Copper Clamp Cools Gradually, Preventing Any Sudden Change of Temperature in the Stone

gauge copper plate, 3 in. long, to the shape shown at A. Clamp the top lightly down on the stone, as at B, and heat the setting gradually until the solder flows. Stones break in heating on account of the sudden cooling. The copper strip retains the heat and keeps the stone from cracking.

This does not apply, of course, with pearls, opals, turquoise, jade, or similar soft stones. In heating diamonds do not allow anything to touch the stone while hot, and, in cooling, do not place it in a draft or move it.—Contributed by W. A. Jones, Raleigh, N. C.

Drill Jig for Making Oil Holes in Pulleys

An angle plate is used for the support on the drill-press table and a mandrel is attached to the vertical part and carries two cones having an angle of 30 deg. This makes it adjustable to the diameter of the bore on any pulley within reasonable dimensions. A pulley is clamped between the cones as shown, and the drill press table turned

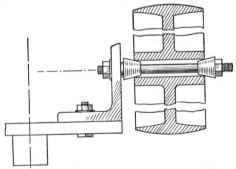

The Jig can be Quickly Attached to the Table of the Drill Press

to bring the right location for the hole directly under the drill point.—Contributed by G. Barrett, Hamilton, Ont.

A Pressure Cleaner for Greasy Machinery

Procure an ordinary length of garden hose and adjust the nozzle to a fine stream, then fill it with gasoline or distillate. Attach the hose to a faucet and turn on the water. This will make an excellent pressure cleaner. One hose full of gasoline is usually enough for one engine, but if not sufficient, repeat the filling after running the water out of the hose. As the water pressure is usually high enough in all cities, this method works to perfection.—Contributed by Carl H. Kaufmann, Santa Ana, Cal.

Dump Sides on a Wheelbarrow

The sides of the ordinary wheelbarrow are hinged at the bottom and the ends at the front are fitted with a piece of sheet metal cut on the arc of a circle. Holes are drilled in the sheet iron near the upper edge and corresponding ones in the front end of the wheelbarrow so that they will coincide when the sides are in an upright posi-

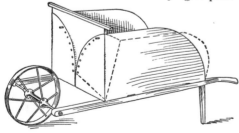

Each Side or Both of Them can be Lowered by Removing the Pins

tion. The sides can be set at any angle and a pin inserted in coinciding holes to hold them rigidly.—Contributed by Fred L. King, Islip, N. Y.

Protection for Building a Brick Stack in Cold Weather

As we were compelled to build a 40-ft. stack in zero weather some means had to be provided to protect the

Sections of the Stack were Built Up within the Inclosure Which could be Heated

workmen and to keep the mortar from freezing. We built a frame of 2 by 4-in. material and stretched chicken wire over the frame, then two thicknesses of canvas. The structure was built in sections, having four sides and a gable roof, and when the house was completed four men could lift it. A snatch block was provided at the top of the scaffolding at each corner. With two men on the ground and two men at the top the inclosure could be raised with ease when necessary.

Sections of the stack were built as high as the inclosure would permit, then it was raised and the staging built up to it. The workmen enjoyed the comforts of a heating stove and electric lights.—Contributed by J. A. Spiker, Pocatello, Idaho.

❡To put a new wick in any lamp burner carefully and quickly, first thread a needle, then run the thread across the wick and pass the needle through the burner.

Old and New Methods in Plumbing

The upper illustration shows the method of plumbing where tile connections and old-style soil basins are

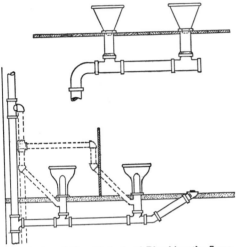

Old Style and New Methods of Plumbing the Same House, Showing How to Make It Sanitary

used without traps. This unsanitary arrangement endangered the health of those living in the house. The other part of the illustration shows how this same house was changed and modern plumbing used. Windows were put in to allow the light to flood the room. The dotted lines show the ventilating pipes which are attached under each soil basin to remove the foul air to the outside.—Contributed by Geo. C. Crowley, Jr., Newark, N. J.

Glass Cutter for Small Circular Work

Without the aid of any special machine the cutting of small circular pieces of glass for gauges and other

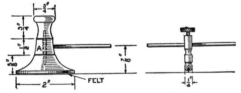

An Adjustable Cutter Holder to Make Small Circular Disks of Glass for Gauges

small work is sometimes a difficult and costly piece of work.

The sketch shows a light and inexpensive cutter that can be made with very little expense and labor. The wood parts can be turned quickly on any wood lathe, the only turned portion of metal being the piece A, and almost any other piece of metal in the form of a rod can be used. The arm is No. 10 gauge steel wire, as is also the pin holding the handle knob and the base together.

The cutter wheel, or disk, can be taken from any cheap glass cutter and is easily renewed by punching out the small pin holding it. The general construction of the holder is clearly shown. The radius for a cut is quickly adjusted by sliding the holder the proper distance from the center of the base. In almost any kind of repair shop this little device will be found quite serviceable.—Contributed by F. W. Bently, Milwaukee, Wis.

Protecting Gas Globes

Trouble is often experienced in the use of glassware on gaslights, especially those of the inverted type, due to the expansion of the holder, screws and globe when they become hot. This trouble in most cases can be entirely eliminated by inserting a ring of thin sheet asbestos under the rim

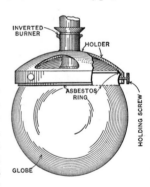

of the globe where the screws make a contact. It is desirable to have the ring of such width that no part of the globe holder can come into direct contact with the globe, although this is not so essential as to have the asbestos between the contact screws and the globe.—Contributed by A. P. Connor, Washington, D. C.

⟨Turpentine will remove varnish and paint stains from cloth.

Annealing High-Speed Steel

The most effective way to anneal high-speed steels so that they can be worked in any desired shape like soft machine steel is as follows:

Procure a piece of iron pipe, 5 or 6 in. inside diameter and 12 or 15 in. long, and place the steel inside, then fill the remaining space with cast-iron borings, taking care to have the steel in the center and well surrounded with the borings. This is placed in a forge and heated slowly until the whole is red hot, then, while in the fire, it is covered with ashes and fine coal and allowed to cool.—Contributed by J. W. Hornaday, Birmingham, Ala.

Protecting Tanks from Freezing Water

A great many water tanks are ruined each year by the expansion of the water when freezing in severe weather. A simple device to prevent this is to procure a good-sized copper bucket and suspend it in the water in an inverted position, allowing air to remain in the bucket. When the water freezes the extra pressure that would otherwise be exerted on the walls of the tank, instead acts on the air in the bucket which is compressed, and thus the tank is relieved. An iron or tin bucket would soon rust out in the water and,

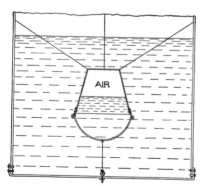

The Air in the Bucket Relieves the Pressure Caused by the Freezing Water

for this reason, it is best to use a copper bucket.—Contributed by Irl R. Hicks, Hallsville, Mo.

Graphite-Cup Filler

Since all modern steam pistons are lubricated with graphite, the graphite-cup filler shown will reduce the waste

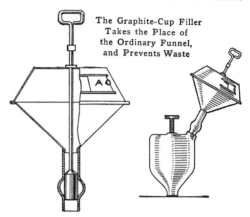

The Graphite-Cup Filler Takes the Place of the Ordinary Funnel, and Prevents Waste

caused by spilling or by a gust of wind. The body, or container, is made of sheet metal, attached to a brass casting which constitutes the feeding device. This has a piston, worked by a ¼-in. brass rod with a handle at the top. A piece of ¼-in. tubing is soldered to this rod, above and below the top of the container, at the right distances to prevent the valve from being moved too far up or down. The door A is large enough to receive the graphite easily. It is only necessary to turn the filler into the thread of the graphite cup and work the piston.—Contributed by R. J. Herold, San Francisco, Cal.

Hardening Crankpins on a Shaft

Desiring to have all the bearings hard on a crankshaft and the throws and couplings soft, I first copperplated the shaft, then turned up the crankpins and hardened them. I found that the pins were well tempered and the other parts soft. — Contributed by Stanley M. Zimmey, Harvey, Ill.

❡When sharpening a pencil stick the knife blade through a slip of paper and it will act as a guard to prevent the lead dust from soiling the fingers.

String-Cutting Attachment for a Finger Ring

This attachment can be easily made and will pay for the trouble of making in the time it saves the clerk or wrapper. The knife and holder is cut from a strip of sheet steel, about ¼ in. wide, its length depending on the width of the ring. The steel is cut almost halfway through, as shown at A, then fastened in a vise and bent down and sharpened to form the blade. The other part of the steel is bent as shown and attached to the ring with the end C, or it may be soldered, as desired. The corners and edges should be rounded with a file to prevent chafing the finger.—Contributed by J. V. Loeffler, Evansville, Ind.

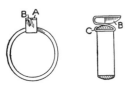

Combination Center and Circle Punch

After drawing the desired shape on blanking dies it is usually the custom to drill a series of holes inside of the line as close together as possible and then break out the scrap. In laying out the holes, I found the combination center and circle punch more convenient than the dividers. The drills most used for drilling the holes are ¼ in. in size, and to make the combination for this size, a ⅜-in. drill rod was turned down to ¼ in. on one end, whereupon a $\frac{1}{16}$-in. hole was drilled through its center and enlarged to ⅛ in. at the upper end, as shown. This prevented any interference with the burr caused by constant hammering on the punch.

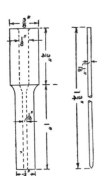

A piece of $\frac{1}{16}$-in. drill rod was placed in a lathe chuck and tapered on the end to the desired angle for the center punch. Then it was cut off so that it was about ¼ in. longer than the circle punch. Both punches were then hardened for about ½ in., on their working ends, and then drawn to a medium-dark straw color.

The circle punch was used to mark off the die, leaving the required distance from the die outline and enough space between each circle to prevent the drill from breaking out into the hole just drilled beside it. After punching the circles into the die blank, the punch is fitted into each circle and the center punch inserted and driven to mark the center of the hole.—Contributed by F. W. Shrier, Pittsfield, Mass.

Side Cutters on a Spade

Two sections of an old mower cutter, heated and bent at right angles and riveted on the sides of a spade about 2 in. from the cutting edge, will prove a great help in digging garden and small drains. The spade will make a clean cut, and it is not necessary to jab the sides of the cut to be taken.—Contributed by A. S. Thomas, Amherstburg, Ont.

How to Bore a Taper Hole in Metal

To bore a taper hole in a piece held in a lathe chuck, where neither a taper attachment nor a compound rest is supplied, is a task requiring no little skill. However, the work may be made easier as follows:

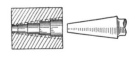

First drill a hole through the metal of a size slightly smaller than the small end of the desired taper, then by successive steps drill larger holes (always a little smaller than the finished size) until the piece takes the appearance shown in the cross section. A plug should then be turned, having the same end diameter as the hole to be bored and the same degree of taper. By trying it in the drilled hole, the high spots can be easily detected and taken off with a bottoming tool. This is continued until the hole is cut to the desired taper, but a little small and with its surface rough. Finish with a hand scraper, checking and fitting with the aid of red lead or Prussian blue. A very accurate job can be done in this way. A boring tool with a long, straight cutting edge is good to use in place of the hand tool, but it must be used with care and only a short length taken at a time.

Plugging the Bell End of a Soil Pipe

As it was necessary to stop up the open end of a section of soil pipe through which water flowed at intervals, I plugged the end as follows: In

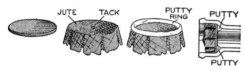

Series of Operations in Making the Parts to Plug the End of a Soil Pipe

the absence of a thick block of wood, I cut a disk out of a piece of white pine, ½ in. thick, smeared the face of it with thick paint and secured a piece of jute on the painted surface with a tack. A ring of putty was placed around the edge—on the jute which held better than the wood—the latter being driven into the pipe. The putty was forced into the shape shown, and made a water-tight joint. A cement plug could be easily built over the wood.—Contributed by J. M. Kane, Doylestown, Pa.

To Prevent a Machinist's Pocket from Sagging

It is customary to place a small hanging pocket in machinists' aprons and shop coats in which to carry a micrometer, or other small tools. It is almost impossible to accidentally spill anything out of the pocket, but most tools carried therein will hang out and away from the body, as shown in the first sketch, where it is liable to

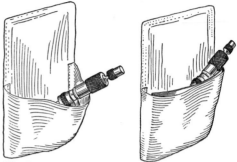

The Pasteboard Slip Placed in the Pocket will Keep It Straight and Prevent Sagging

be struck by a running lathe chuck or other moving part of a machine.

If a piece of pasteboard, the width and depth of the pocket, is placed within, as shown in the second sketch, the pocket will keep its shape and any tool will lie flat against the body where it cannot be broken.—Contributed by Henry J. Marion, Pontiac, Michigan.

Preventing Frost on Show Windows

Procure an ordinary window squeegee, drive out the wood block and rubber and substitute a wick made of a No. 1 burner lamp wick. The wick is rolled lengthwise and inserted in the holder in a position the reverse of that occupied by the rubber. Drill a hole in the top part and center of the squeegee, fit the spout of a small oilcan in it and solder the joint tightly. Fill the can with alcohol and apply the wick to the inside of the window. The squeegee can be used in the hand, or on

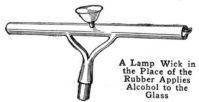

A Lamp Wick in the Place of the Rubber Applies Alcohol to the Glass

a pole for large windows. This application will prevent frost from forming on show windows.—Contributed by C. L. Herbert, Chicago, Ill.

To Remedy the Grip of an Automobile Clutch

The leather clutch on an automobile often grabs very suddenly, sometimes to the extent of doing damage to the transmission and differential. I

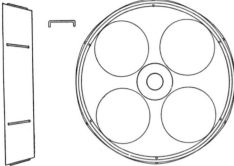

Wires Forming Humps on the Surface of the Clutch to Make It Take Hold Gradually

remedied this trouble on my automobile by dividing the clutch frame into six parts—the number of parts, however, is optional—and $\frac{1}{2}$ in. from each side of the clutch, on the dividing lines, I drilled $\frac{3}{16}$-in. holes, then I cut six pieces of $\frac{3}{16}$-in. wire, long enough for the face of the clutch and to pass through the holes. These wires were riveted on the reverse side of the clutch face. After putting the six wires into position I replaced the leather. This caused a hump where each wire was located, so that when the clutch was let in, it would take hold gradually without jerking. This device has been in use on my automobile for a year with entire satisfaction.—Contributed by K. G. Rummelhoff, North Yakima, Washington.

Substitute for Brass Castings

Purchase $\frac{1}{2}$ pt. of muriatic acid and make a saturated solution of zinc chloride. The manner of preparing this solution is to drop particles of zinc into the acid from time to time until no more zinc will be taken up in the solution. Do not inhale the fumes from the acid while it is working. Procure a quantity of brass filings—not spelter—and cleanse them thoroughly in the solution. Melt 8 parts of lead and 2 parts of solder together and, while molten, stir the brass filings in until the mass appears to be all brass; the more brass filings the better. The proportions should be about 8 parts filings to 1 part of the lead and solder.

This metal is especially adapted to work of inventors and can be used in making name plates, brackets, and kindred articles. For molds, either use sand or plaster of paris. If plenty of filings are added to the melted lead it will be hard to detect the finished casting from brass.—Contributed by J. B. Murphy, Plainfield, N. J.

A Reamer Holder

Having occasion to ream 40 taper holes daily for several months on a special job, a great number of reamers were broken in the common tap wrench. To reduce the breakage I made a holder, as shown, from two pieces of cold-rolled steel and two file handles. After cutting the pieces to the right length they were rounded on the ends, as shown, and the body B drilled, to take the reamer C and the crossbar A. The crossbar was then driven into the hole and the reamer shank soldered in place. The file handles were drilled and driven on the crossbar ends. One reamer would finish from 100 to 800 holes, and in all cases

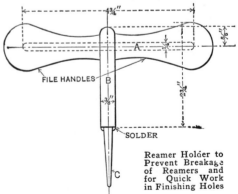

Reamer Holder to Prevent Breakage of Reamers and for Quick Work in Finishing Holes

would have to be removed, on account of being worn out, and replaced with a new one.—Contributed by Andrew Smith, Cleveland, Ohio.

A Simple Resistance Thermometer

It is a well-known fact that the majority of metals undergo a change in the resistance they offer to the passage of a current of electricity through them when their temperature is changed. This change in resistance is almost directly proportional to the change in temperature; that is, if the resistance of a certain coil of wire increases 1 ohm due to a rise in its temperature of, say, 1 deg., its resistance will increases 5 ohms due to a rise in temperature of 5 deg., and so on. Hence a coil of wire and some device for noting the change in the resistance of the coil, due to a change in its temperature, are all that is required in constructing a resistance thermometer. The best practical method of measuring the change in resistance of the coil is some form of the Wheatstone bridge. This bridge, to give reliable results, should be constructed of materials that do not change in resistance with a change in temperature, or proper correcting factors should be used. The thermometer coil itself may be made of a material having such initial resistance that a change in temperature of 1 deg. will result in a change in resistance of 1 ohm. That is, if a coil be made from copper, which has a temperature coefficient of approximately .0042, and it measures 238.1 ohms at zero centigrade, the resistance will increase 1 ohm for each degree rise in temperature. If the bridge indicates the resistance of the coil to be 275.1 ohms, then its temperature is 37 deg. centigrade.

Often it is desired to locate the thermometer coil at some point quite a distance from the bridge, or it may be located in some inaccessible place, such as a grain elevator, or the like, and in such cases the resistance of the leads connecting the coil with the bridge must be taken into account. A simple method of eliminating any errors due to the above cause is depicted in Fig. 1, which shows a simple Wheatstone bridge connected for measuring the resistance of the ther-

mometer coil. The two resistances, A and B, are the ratio arms of the bridge, and the resistance C is the rheostat, or adjustable resistance. The resistance of the leads to the thermome-

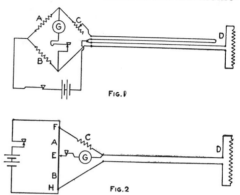

Simple Diagrams Showing the Wheatstone Bridge and the Slide-Wire Bridge, the Principle Used on the Thermometer

ter coil D is offset by introducing two leads, of exactly the same material and placed adjacent to those to the thermometer coil, in series with the rheostat of the bridge. The changes in the resistance of these two sets of leads due to any changes in temperature they may experience will always neutralize each other, and the only resistance indicated by the bridge is that of the coil D. The value of the resistance in the rheostat is equal to the resistance of D when a balance is obtained and the ratio coils A and B are equal in resistance.

If a resistance thermometer be constructed along the lines indicated above, its satisfactory operation will depend in a great measure upon a good Wheatstone bridge, the cost of which will be rather high if purchased ready-made, and if constructed, it will involve numerous difficulties, especially its calibration and adjustment. The following description of a simple resistance thermometer eliminates the necessity of a commercial bridge, a form of slide wire being used, as its construction is comparatively simple and the results obtained with its use are quite accurate. The electrical scheme of the bridge is shown in Fig. 2. The thermometer coil is represented by D; the rheostat of the bridge, by C, and the ratio arms, by A and B, respectively, just as in Fig. 1.

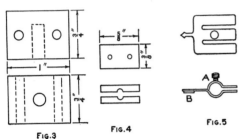

Fig.3   Fig.4   Fig.5

Supports for the Guide Rod, Clamp for the Slide Wire and the Sliding-Contact Piece

In operating the bridge shown in Fig. 2, the value of the resistance of the rheostat is maintained constant, and a balance is obtained by varying the relation between the two ratio arms, which is accomplished by moving a sliding contact, E, along the wire. The ratio arms themselves are composed of a piece of resistance wire of uniform cross section, stretched between the points F and H, as shown in Fig. 2. The connections of the galvanometer G and battery, in Fig. 2, with respect to the arms of the bridge, are just the reverse of their connections in Fig. 1, but the results are independent of these connections; that is, the galvanometer and battery can be interchanged without disturbing the operation of the bridge. In order to increase the sensitiveness of the bridge a long slide wire will be required, but it will only be necessary to use a small portion of it, about 3 ft. near the center, in measuring temperatures ranging from 20 deg. below to 100 deg. above zero centigrade. The portion of the slide wire that is not in use may be formed into two neat coils and the length of the mounting board required will be greatly decreased.

In using the slide-wire type of bridge, the change in the resistance of the leads to the thermometer coil due to a change in temperature cannot be compensated for by introducing similar leads in series with the rheostat of the bridge. The error caused hereby can be overcome, or rather reduced to a minimum, by making the leads from wire having a very low or negligible temperature coefficient.

To construct the slide-wire bridge to use with the thermometer coil, proceed as follows: Obtain a piece of $\frac{7}{8}$-in. hardwood board, preferably maple, 4 in. wide and 4 ft. long. Smooth this board down, round off the corners and the edges on one side and give it several coats of shellac. Cut from some well-seasoned maple two pieces having the dimensions shown in Fig. 3. Drill two $\frac{1}{8}$-in. holes in each of these pieces, and a $\frac{1}{4}$-in. hole a little over halfway through, as indicated in the sketch. Obtain a piece of $\frac{1}{4}$-in. steel rod, $3\frac{1}{4}$ ft. long, and mount it upon the base with these pieces, as shown in Fig. 6.

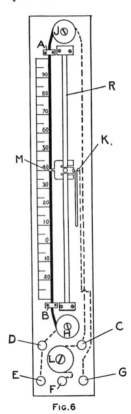

Fig.6

The upper end of the rod should be about $2\frac{1}{2}$ in. from the upper end of the board upon which it is mounted, and about $\frac{3}{4}$ in. to the right of the center of the board. Make two clamps, to be used in mounting the slide wire, from some thin sheet brass, similar to that shown in Fig. 4. These clamps should be mounted on the base alongside the supports for the rod. Cut out a piece similar to that shown in the upper part of Fig. 5, from some thin sheet brass, and bend it into the form shown in the lower part of the same sketch. Solder a small metal handle, A, to this piece and also a contact piece, B, as indicated. The lower edge of the contact piece should be fairly sharp so that it will make contact with a definite point on the slide wire.

Procure 30 ft. of No. 22 gauge cotton-insulated "Advance" resistance wire. Fasten this wire in the two clamps, A and B, Fig. 6, so that its center is about 8 in. above the lower clamp. Carefully remove the insulation from the wire between the clamps and mount directly under it a piece of heavy cardboard upon which the scale is to be marked. Mount five small back-connected binding posts on the lower end of the base, as indicated in Fig. 6, by C, D, E, F, and G. Wind the lower portion of the slide wire on a small wood spool, H, and solder the end to the binding post D. The upper portion of the slide wire should be wound on the spool J, and its end connected to the binding post C. Connect binding posts D and E, as indicated. A connection should be made from binding post G to the sliding contact, the portion shown by the full line being a flexible conductor, passed through the hole K. All connections shown by dotted lines should be made in grooves cut in the under side of the board forming the base. Provide a third wooden spool, L, upon which to wind the wire forming the rheostat of the bridge.

The thermometer coil should be made by winding about 250 ft. of No. 40 gauge cotton-insulated copper wire very loosely upon an open wooden core or rectangle of thin mica. The coil should be well protected from mechanical injury, but the protection should not interfere with the free circulation of air about the winding. The leads to this coil should be made from "Advance," or some other wire having a low temperature coefficient. Solder the coil and leads together and fasten the free ends of the leads under the binding posts E and F. Connect a battery of several cells through a contact key to the binding posts C and D, and a galvanometer, or telephone receiver, to the binding posts F and G. Now wind on the spool L a sufficient

amount of No. 30 gauge cotton-insulated "Advance" resistance wire so that the bridge balances with the contact M about 8 in. from the lower clamp when the temperature of the thermometer coil is zero centigrade. After this adjustment has been made the remainder of the scale may be marked by noting the positions of the contact M for various temperatures of the thermometer coil, which can be determined by means of a good mercury thermometer. Give the thermometer coil ample time to reach a constant temperature before marking the scale, as the accuracy of the instrument will depend in a great measure upon this calibration.

Snowplow for Clearing Sidewalks

The illustration shows a V-shaped plow made of boards and attached to the shank of an ordinary garden plow after removing the shovel. Each board is 10 in. wide and 2 ft. long. The rear ends are 2 ft. apart, braced with a crosspiece, fastened securely as shown.

The Shovel is Attached to the Shank of a Garden Plow and Used as When Plowing Soil

This plow surpasses a snow shovel many times for ease and speed.—Contributed by Dr. J. S. Burnett, Plymouth, Ohio.

¶Soya-bean oil, used as a paint oil, stands about midway between linseed and corn oil. It is fairly durable, but does not dry in very well.

Shield for Cleaning Buttons on Garments

Firemen, policemen, porters, or other persons wearing uniforms must remove the buttons from time to time and clean them. To save time and

The Two Parts Closed over the Shank of the Button Effectively Shield the Cloth of the Garment

trouble, one fireman made a shield to protect the cloth and hold the button while cleaning it, without removing it from the garment. The shield consists of two pieces of sheet metal, tin, aluminum, brass, or copper, cut in half-circular disks and hinged on one side, as shown, with a slot cut in each piece in different directions so that, when the shield is slipped over the button and closed, the latter is held firmly for polishing.—Contributed by Charles A. Kauffman, Pittsburgh, Pa.

An Oxyacetylene-Welding Torch

A very simple torch for use with an oxyacetylene-welding outfit can be made as follows: Procure a brass tee, A, about ¾ in. in size, and bush one of the openings and the side outlet down to ⅛ in. The upper pipe B is ⅛-in. brass, 16 in. long, after making

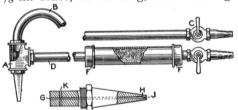

The Torch is Made of Brass Pipe and Fittings, Only the Nozzle Requiring Special Work

the gooseneck bend in it, as shown. The bent end is turned into the bushing of the tee and a gas cock, C, is attached to the opposite end.

Another piece of ⅛-in. brass pipe, D, 10 in. long, is turned into the side-outlet bushing. The end of this pipe is supplied with a filtering drum, which is made of ¾-in. brass pipe, about 4 in. long, with caps, FF, on the ends, the caps being drilled and tapped to receive the ⅛-in. pipe. The drum is filled with mineral wool, and a gas cock is fitted to the end as in the upper pipe.

The tip, or nozzle, is made of brass or copper with a $\frac{1}{16}$-in. hole drilled from G to H, as shown, and a very fine needle hole from H to J. Two $\frac{1}{16}$-in. holes are drilled through the nozzle, at K, at right angles and crossing the hole GH, thus making four inlets to the center hole. Thread the outside to fit the ¾-in. tee. The end, having the crossed holes, should be just long enough to seat against the upper bushing and of sufficient diameter to permit this seating and yet provide a space between it and the body of the tee A. The assembled parts appear as shown.

The oxygen is admitted through the pipe B, and this gas, having the higher pressure, helps to draw in the acetylene which is admitted through the pipe D at a lower pressure. The two are mixed in the tip and are forced out through the nozzle, where they are burned at a high temperature.

If care is taken to have the nozzle seat against the upper bushing tightly, so that no oxygen can escape except through the needle hole J, the torch will work as well as any made. The oxygen pressure should be from two to three times the acetylene pressure. The oxygen at 25 lb. and the acetylene at 10 makes a good, average working pressure.

To light the torch, turn on the acetylene, light it and keep turning the gas on until it burns steadily, then gradually turn on the oxygen until the flame becomes a clear white and cone-shaped, in the center of a blue flame. At this point it is ready for use.—Contributed by A. H. Waychoff, Lyons, Colo.

◖Use a solution of chloride of lime to remove fruit or grass stains from cloth.

Water-Heating Attachment for a Hot-Air Furnace

By J. A. McCRACKEN

As a means of utilizing the waste heat in a hot-air furnace I installed a pair of coils which supplied sufficient heat for three radiators with a radiating surface of 150 sq. ft. All three radiators were on the first floor, in the dining room, parlor, and reception hall. The expansion tank, which holds about 10 gal., was placed on the topmost shelf of the pantry. Two ¾-in. holes were drilled in the furnace jacket, after removing the outer casing, directly in the rear, and two ¾-in. holes in the frame of the fire door, just high enough from the bottom to let the fitted coil rest on the radiator shelf

pipe, one 1 in. in diameter, for one radiator, and the other, 1½ in. in diameter. The latter branches into two 1-in. pipes to the two other radiators.

The return pipes, carrying the cold water, are 1 in. in diameter until they meet, above and in front of the furnace, where the main is 1½ in. in diameter. This main branches just above the fire door, and a ¾-in. pipe is run across and down on the right to enter the door frame through the right-hand hole for the coil on that side. The expansion tank is connected by a 1-in. pipe to one of the hot-water pipes.

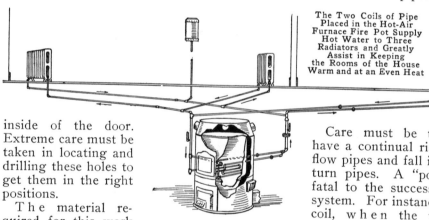

The Two Coils of Pipe Placed in the Hot-Air Furnace Fire Pot Supply Hot Water to Three Radiators and Greatly Assist in Keeping the Rooms of the House Warm and at an Even Heat

inside of the door. Extreme care must be taken in locating and drilling these holes to get them in the right positions.

The material required for this work is a coil of ¾-in. iron pipe—galvanized preferred—consisting of five turns, each a little shorter than the other, as it is built up toward the top and arranged so that the coil may be crowded on its side into a small space. In the instance referred to the fire pot of the furnace was 20 in. in diameter, and the length of the turns averaged 15 in. The last turn, which was uppermost, extends through the hole, on its side, in the back of the furnace. At this point unions were put in and, by means of a reducing tee, the hot-water leads run into a 2-in. main having a flange union which carries it to the level of the top of the furnace. Here it branches into two 12-in. lengths of

Care must be taken to have a continual rise in the flow pipes and fall in the return pipes. A "pocket" is fatal to the success of this system. For instance, in the coil, when the work of crowding the coil into a smaller space is being done, it is easy to let one length run down a trifle, then up. This would make a pocket. All threads, especially for the coil, must be well coated with white lead before turning them together. The bends, where the pipes turn from the almost horizontal to the vertical for connection with the radiators, cannot be exact, as some lateral extensions may be made, in some cases more than in others. The diagram is not intended to illustrate this point. To make such a connection where one pipe rises slightly and the other is vertical, use a street elbow and a common elbow. Wherever possible, a 45-deg. turn should be given to save loss of movement by friction. Thermometers are placed on the hot-water main and on the cold-water main. If the water is heated above 200 deg. it is liable to back up in the returns.

When the pipes are installed in the furnace, the space between the pipe and the wall of the drilled hole should be carefully plastered full with asbestos dough. The open space in the casing wall should be sealed with a metal sheet, asbestos cloth, and dough.

The coils will not disturb the working of the hot-air furnace and a great increase in the amount of heat will be supplied by means of the hot water.

Removing Tight Bushings

Quite frequently a worn bushing, A, or roller-bearing lining, must be taken out of a housing on the frame into which it has been pressed. In many cases it is impossible to get at the back end of the bushing to drive it out. For this special work a tool can be made as follows:

A piece of steel, B, is threaded on one end for several inches, and a nut supplied that will turn freely on the thread. Into the side of the piece near the other end is driven a ⅜-in. pin, C, which is filed down so as to be not over ¼ in. long. Where no oil hole is available, it is necessary to drill one through the housing and bushing. The puller is inserted with the pin entering the drilled hole. Naturally it is smaller than the hole in the bushing, so it must be blocked or wedged, as at D, on the opposite side, to hold the pin in place. A piece of pipe, or other piece of metal of similar shape, is procured and set over the end of the housing and a large washer placed on top, whereupon the nut is screwed on the threads. When turned with a wrench, the nut will usually remove any bushing, no matter how tight it is. The weak point is the small pin and, if it fails, a larger one may be tried, though, in average work, the cases are few and far between where a ⅜-in. pin will be sheared off.

Escape from a Locked Safe Trick

The mystifying trick of locking the performer in a steel safe and then having him come out of it without aid is very simple, although but few, even the safe owners, know how it is accomplished. All that is necessary for the performer is to provide himself with a small electric flash lamp, a good screwdriver, a bicycle wrench, and a small can of oil for emergencies. There is a small plate on the inside of the door which covers the lock and is held with screws. This is removed and the tumblers turned so that the bolt can be withdrawn. When out of the safe it is an easy matter to replace the plate quickly. Of course a covering of cloth is lowered over the safe during the time of unlocking the safe and coming out of it.

Recessing the Bottom of a Drilled Hole

An ordinary boring tool used to recess the bottom of a drilled hole will spring when the feed is applied. The tool as illustrated was devised to prevent the spring as the cut is taken. It is made of a piece of steel the size of the hole to be recessed. A small hole is drilled through the piece lengthwise and a little out of center. The distance the hole is to be drilled out of center will depend on the size of the tool. The cutter is made of a piece of tool steel that will fit the hole, the end being

The Revolving Cutter will Easily Make the Recess without Springing Away from the Work

turned and a cutting edge ground on it.

The projection A butts against the bottom of the drilled hole and prevents the tool from touching the end of the hole. The cutting tool may be turned by hand or in a drill press, and when the recess is cut the tool is turned in and the holder removed.—Contributed by A. Whittle, Quebec, Canada.

Exercising Poultry in Winter

An ingenious farmer installed a windmill on his poultry house as a means of giving the fowls exercise during cold weather when they could not get out. The windmill is connected to a large wheel with a shaft, the wheel being hung about 3 ft. from the floor. Cabbage and other vegetables are hung on the wheel. The windmill turns the wheel and the poultry chase around after the food.—Contributed by Herbert S. Spencer, Whitney Point, N. Y.

Stropping Handle for Safety-Razor Blades

Insert a safety-razor blade in an ordinary pair of scissors and use them as a handle in stropping in the same

The Blades of the Scissors will Hold the Wafer Razor Blade Securely for Stropping

manner as the ordinary razor. If the points of the scissor blades are too open to grip the wafer blade and hold it securely, insert a thick piece of paper with the blade.—Contributed by H. C. Hunt, Potterville, Mich.

A Hinged Watering Trough

As the usual method of draining a watering trough for horses by means of a plug or valve was unsatisfactory on account of the freezing up of the parts, I set out to devise some other means and the result was the hinged construction shown in the sketch. For this purpose the trough was mounted on crosspieces in the usual manner and hinges were placed at one side so that

the trough could be tipped upon its side to drain. A small handle may be

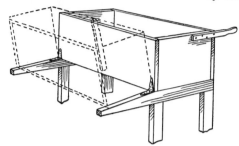

The Entire Contents of the Trough can be Dumped at Once and Left to Drain

nailed at the end of the trough to make the tipping easier.—Contributed by Thos. L. Parker, Wibaux, Mont.

Drying Rack for Seed Corn

Procure a barrel or a short log and drive nails into it, allowing their ends to project and spacing them about 3 in. apart. Push the large end of the cob on a nail. Several hundred ears may be kept on one barrel.—Contributed by R. H. Workman, Loudenville, O.

Stabilizing the Strap Hanger

One day as I was clinging to a street-car strap on my way to work I was struck with the idea of an easy way to keep my balance when the car started and stopped. Nobody used the strap next to the one I was holding, so I grasped the two in one hand as

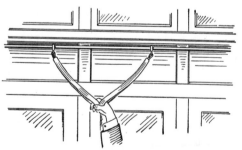

Grasping the Two Straps in One Hand Prevents the Holder from being Jerked in Either Direction

shown, and this made a stable support whether the car stopped or started.—Contributed by F. F. Ravlin, Chicago.

Forging Notch in an Anvil

A V-shaped notch filed or ground in an anvil, as shown, makes a depression or die to form braces while forging

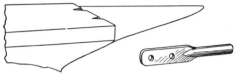

A Die is Formed in the Anvil Face for Forging a Brace on Flattened Rod Ends

flattened ends on rods. This not only makes a neat end, but strengthens the part where it is usually weakest.

The notch can be readily cut or filed on many anvils, but those having hard faces will require grinding.—Contributed by D. C. Goff, Knoxville, Tennessee.

Concrete Form to Make Round Inside Corners

To avoid sharp angles where a concrete floor joins a wall, it is best to make a slightly round corner. A bottle

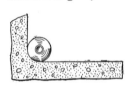

of the desired radius makes a good form for this work, as the cement will not stick to the glass and the surface of the concrete will be left smooth.—Contributed by N. M. Baldwin, New London, Conn.

Repairing a Broken Valve Stem

On the road and far from a repair or supply shop, a valve stem in my motor broke and I fixed it on the spot, so that it is still working as well as a new one, in the following man-

The Threaded End of a Bolt Fitted to the Broken Valve Stem will Lengthen It

ner: The stem having broken at the point A, I procured a ⅜-in. bolt, sawed the threaded end B off at the right

length and then filed it on one end to fit the slot in the stem. Three standard nuts were then run on to hold the parts solidly. The slot was shortened somewhat, and it was necessary to make a new key of soft steel, as the original one was casehardened and could not be filed down.—Contributed by A. B. Conkwright, New York.

Oil Feed for Milling Cutters

A milling machine having but one spout for feeding oil to cutters does not fulfill the requirements where two

or more cutters are used at the same time. The illustration shows one of the most satisfactory methods of flowing oil to one or more cutters. Two pieces of soft wire—wire solder will do—about ⅛ in. in diameter, are twisted together as shown, and the twist inserted into the oilcan spout. The oil will follow the wires and drop on the cutters.—Contributed by Joseph J. Kolar, Maywood, Ill.

Upsetting Tool for Punches

The body of the tool is forged of tool steel as shown in the sketch. The hardened piece A is secured in a dovetailed groove. The tool is used in the manner shown without danger of burring the edge by a misplaced blow of the hammer.

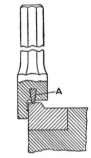

❡The greater the difference in temperature between two bodies, the more rapid will be the transfer of heat, so the hotter the fire the more quickly is steam generated in the boiler.

Increasing the Diameter of a Worn Crankpin

A crankpin was found to be considerably out of true, and to turn it up would necessitate the making of a new connecting rod and brass, so it was decided to build the piece up to fit the brasses in the old connecting rod. This was accomplished as follows: The crankpin was centered, as accurately as possible, in a lathe and a rounded-end threading tool used to cut a groove spirally on the surface of the pin. The groove was not cut deep and the feed was set for a large thread so that about $\frac{1}{32}$ in. was left between turns.

One end of a piece of steel wire was then brazed to the pin and tightly wound around it in the spiral groove. The wire was of such size that it filled the groove and fitted snugly against the preceding turn. When the whole pin had been wound, the wire was brazed and the pin was then turned in a lathe to the proper diameter. When completed the surface of the pin was perfectly smooth and it was almost impossible to detect that it had been wound with wire.—Contributed by John Downes, New Bedford, Mass.

A Toolmaker's Angle Plate

The angle plate shown in the sketch was designed as an adjunct to the toolmaker's bench plate. It also may be used on many kinds of small work that must be machined or ground. Just a little study of the construction will convince any toolmaker that it can be used for a large range of general work, such as laying out, testing angles, etc., surface grinding, boring holes and jigs and dies at an angle. It is provided with slot blocks for use on the milling machine or shaper.

The two V-notches, milled, crossing the face of the swinging plate, still further increase its scope of usefulness. The hardened and ground strip A can be used to good advantage when it is necessary to mill or grind a number of pieces alike. A few $\frac{3}{16}$-in. holes can be tapped in the plate and some clamps made with which to fasten the work. The edge of the base B should be ground off square to the proper dimension so that, when the screws are put

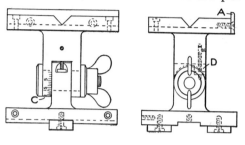

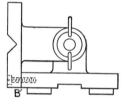

An Angle Plate for General Work Which may be Set at Any Degree of Angle

in as shown, it can be used as an ordinary angle plate. The surface C is hardened, ground, and graduated. The screw D is only to be used when the plate is in a parallel position.

The time required to make the angle plate will be repaid many times over by its use, and if four or five toolmakers are working at a bench one angle plate will be in almost constant use.—Contributed by A. Van Wagner, Newark, N. J.

Taper Gauge

If one wishes to turn a center or taper plug of any kind and there is no hole to fit it in, take the original taper piece and place it on a surface plate,

The Straightedges Form a Tapered Gauge in Which the Turned Piece is Tested

and clamp straightedges on the sides as shown in the sketch. This method will give as good results as if there were a hole to fit the plug in.

Loading a Balky Horse in a Freight Car

While loading horses in a car we were troubled by one large animal balking, and although we tried every expedient we could think of, the beast

Manner of Inducing a Balky Horse to Enter a Freight Car for Shipment

could not be induced to enter the car. After half an hour of useless work one of the cowboys suggested that we tie a rope around the animal's rump and pull on that as well as on the halter rope. This we did and it worked to perfection, proving a great help in future work of this kind.—Contributed by Harlow D. Burnside, Ekalaka, Montana.

Drilling Slanting Holes in Metal

A quantity of castings, shaped as shown in the sketch, required a hole in each corner to slant at an angle of about 15 deg. to the sides. It is readily seen that a different setting is required for drilling each hole. The tops of the holes slanted inward and imaginary continued center lines would meet at a

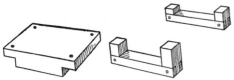

Supports for Holding a Casting at the Proper Angle for Drilling Slanting Holes at Each Corner

point about 8 ft. above the piece. To save the setting for each hole to be drilled, two supports were made as shown with end pieces attached, each one of a different length, which gave the proper slant to the piece for drilling the hole. By shifting the casting all

the holes could be drilled at the same slant without any special setting.— Contributed by Donald A. Hampson, Middletown, N. Y.

A Lathe Boring and Threading Tool

A boring and threading tool, suitable for both large and small work, is shown in the sketch. It is the invention of a correspondent of American Machinist, and consists of three main parts, the tool holder, A, the base, B, and the tool, C. The holder and base are attached together with a dovetail slide, which is on an angle with the center line of the tool, making it possible to change the height and at the same time always keep the tool parallel with the hole being bored or threaded.

In the rear end of the base an oblong hole is provided in which the threaded end of the tool holder can slide, and two knurled nuts are fitted

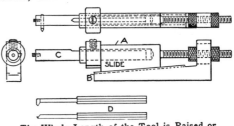

The Whole Length of the Tool is Raised or Lowered on a Parallel with the Hole

on the threads for the adjustment of the height. If used for large holes, the tool can be made as shown, where the smaller tools are inserted in the end of C and kept in place by the setscrew. If the work is to be threaded to the bottom of the hole, or the hole is too small for the tool, the part C may be changed for a forged tool, D, fitted in the hole in A and held to the desired length by the setscrew.

⫐Railroad painters use a mixture of one part of muriatic acid to six or seven parts of water, varying the proportions to suit the work in hand, to clean varnished surfaces that have become soiled with grime. Acid such as acetic, or strong vinegar, is also a good cleanser of varnished surfaces.

Setting a Kitchen Sink with Concrete

In removing an old galvanized-iron sink to replace it with a new white-enameled one it was found that the boards covering the rim had rotted so that they could not be used. A more sanitary plan than replacing the decayed boards with new ones was desired, and as concrete was suggested, we proceeded to carry out the idea with gratifying results. The hot and cold-water pipes were first firmly anchored to the wall behind by means of a board notched out to fit them. Where necessary other light boards were fastened for a form to hold the concrete. The new sink was then set in place over the bare framework and the concrete poured in. The concrete consisted of a rich mixture using about equal quantities of cement and as fine sand as was possible to obtain. This mixture would smooth up nicely and when worked with the back of a spoon, to

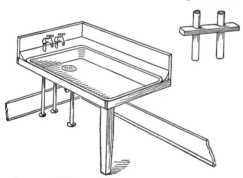

Concrete Filling and Support for a Kitchen Sink That is Sanitary and Bug-Proof

form the gentle curve between the splashboard and the inner edge of the sink, and painted, it proved a highly satisfactory job.—Contributed by Mrs. Paul S. Winter, Greenville, Pa.

An Adjustable Folding Ladder

While trying to paint the roof of my bungalow I found that the pitch was too great to walk upon comfortably,

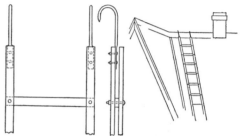

An Adjustable and Folding Ladder to Fit Any Slope or Angle of a Roof

and this caused me to devise the ladder shown in the illustration. A ladder of any length can be made on the same principle. The materials necessary are 2 hooks, 2 bolts for each rung, and sufficient lumber, 1 in. thick and 2 in. wide, to make the length of ladder desired.

The uprights consist of two pieces, separated to admit the rung material. The rungs are placed at the proper intervals between the sidepieces, and a bolt is run through them and the end of the rung. The nuts of all bolts, including those in the hooks, should be on the same side. If this ladder is properly made, it can be adjusted to any angle of the roof and also folded for carrying or for storage.—Contributed by R. R. Williams, Colchester, Illinois.

⟨Grease stains may be removed from cloth with benzine, ether, chloroform, or carbon tetrachloride. The latter is noninflammable and is, therefore, the safest to use.

Two Pulleys Driven by One Belt without Idler

The illustration shows a way of driving two smaller pulleys from one wheel by means of one belt without an

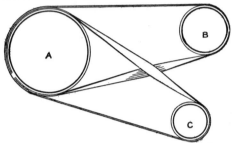

One Belt on One Driver Runs Two Small Pulleys without an Idler between Them

idler for the purpose of securing the required arc of contact on the small pulleys. The belt is placed on the driver A, then twisted as a crossed belt between the pulleys B and C, and passed over them in the manner shown. This will produce the effect of running two belts on A, one over the other.—Contributed by James E. McCormack, Haliburton, Ont.

Adjustable Template for Making Taper Keys

The making and fitting of taper keys is usually guesswork, as there is no means of accurately ascertaining the taper of the slot, for instance, in a piston rod. The sketch is descriptive of a simple jig that will be found quite efficient for this work. I made one of discarded hacksaw blades, 6 in.

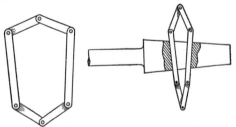

Template Made of Discarded Hacksaw Blades for Obtaining the Shape of a Taper Hole

long. When the jig is placed in the slot and spread to the inside faces of the ends it affords a perfect template to lay off the key for machining. The length of the key can be marked lightly with chalk on the template, allowing no chance for a mistake nor for waste of material.—Contributed by F. W. Bently, Milwaukee, Wis.

Cleaning Iron of Burned and Caked Grease

In cleaning molds or iron ladles that have grease burned and caked on them the following solution works well. A few ounces of potassium dichromate is dissolved in water. The article to be cleansed is placed under the surface of this solution, and then 1 oz. of commercial sulphuric acid is slowly added. Never pour the solution into the acid, but always pour the acid slowly into the water after the article to be cleansed is in position. This gives off a gas that attacks the burned grease and removes it. It is also good for cleaning kitchen pans that are caked with grease or black carbon. The solution should be placed in a glass jar for future use. It is harmless, but must be kept from the hands or clothing, as it burns and discolors the skin and removes the color from cloth and causes holes. The articles are left in the solution a short time and then washed and dried.

Painting Figures on the Dial of a Gauge

The paint or enamel figures on a steam-gauge dial will in time become almost invisible, because of the effect of the heat from the boiler which dries the paint, causing it to crack and drop off. The figures on these dials are first stamped in with steel dies and the sunken portion filled with enamel or paint.

A good way to recolor them is to daub the paint well down into the sunken figures, paying no attention to the paint that is apt to get on the dial face. After painting, take a piece of heavy cardboard and press its edge to the surface of the dial to wipe off the surplus paint. The cardboard edge cannot touch the paint in the sunken portions, and the figures will show up in full color, while the face of the dial will be clean and bright.

Pointing Rod Ends

Where it was necessary to bevel-point the ends of several thousand pieces of cold-rolled steel rods, each 6 in. long, true and concentric with the stock, a special tool for doing the work had to be constructed. This tool was made of two pieces of metal, ¼ in. thick and ½ in. in width, secured together as shown and having the ends centered and a $\frac{5}{16}$-in. shank turned on one end. Then a slot, $\frac{3}{32}$ in. deep and ⅜ in. wide, was cut in one member, to admit the cutter A, which was held in place by the fit and two screws. The hole B was made the size of the

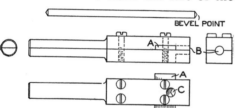

An Inexpensive Tool Used in a Drill Press the Same as a Drill for Pointing Rod Ends

rods and the hole C was drilled for clearance of the chips. The beveling edge of the cutter is plainly seen in this hole. The tool was held in a drill-press chuck and fed on the ends of the rods in the manner of drilling holes. The tool can be taken apart for sharpening. It was inexpensive and did its work quickly and satisfactorily.—Contributed by Donald A. Hampson, Middletown, N. Y.

Wagon Wheel Used for Grate over Sewer Opening

In a small village the problem of constructing an inexpensive sewer drop was solved by the mayor in the manner shown in the sketch. The spokes of a discarded wagon wheel were sawed off about 10 in. from the hub and the hub part set into the flange of a ver-

tically placed sewer tile. This is a very efficient grate as it stops all driftwood, twigs, leaves, and other solid ob-

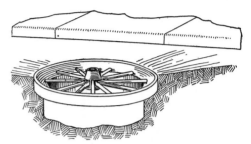

The Hub and Spokes of a Wagon Wheel Forming a Grate Covering for a Sewer Opening

jects, but allows the waste water to run into the sewer. When necessary to clean or repair the drain the wheel is removed.—Contributed by C. M. Mc-Clave, Pittsburgh, Pa.

Gold Varnish

Equal parts, by weight, of shellac and concentrated alcohol make a good gold varnish. A .5-per-cent solution of boric acid in alcohol is added to the solution to give the varnish proper consistency. This varnish is colorless, but if a golden shade is wanted, picric acid is added until the desired color is reached.

Long Envelope Made of Two Small Ones

Occasionally a person has use for a long envelope and if none is at hand, two smaller envelopes will answer the purpose as well. Cut the right end from one and the left end from the other and place one inside of the other so that the open ends will lap, and paste them at the edge. In this way an

A Long Envelope is Quickly Made by Joining the Cut-Off Ends of Two Small Ones

envelope of the desired length may be made.—Contributed by W. M. Braly, Blackwell, Okla.

Laying Off Parallel Keyways

The following is a simple method of laying off keyways of any width and length, any distance apart, and all parallel with one another, on round stock.

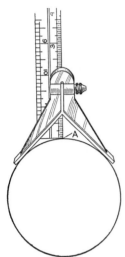

Arrange the square head and center head as shown. After the square head is set level, scratch a line at A. This line will be the center of the keyway. Any number of keyways may be scribed by repeating this operation without moving the shaft.—Contributed by James Connor, Alton, Ill.

Solder Connections for Copper or Iron Wire

To prevent corrosion it is not considered good practice to make an unsoldered joint where the copper wire is connected to iron wire. Such connections must be made in telephone work where an insulated copper wire is attached to the iron drop wire. The following device may be of help to those who have not become skilled in the methods generally used.

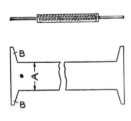

A piece of tin, the size of which depends on the length of the joint and size of the wires, is cut as shown in the sketch. For a joint where No. 19 gauge copper wire is wrapped around a No. 12 gauge iron wire the width, A, should be ½ in. Bend the body A over the joint and crimp the projections B at both ends over, to hold it in place. The space in the tin is filled with melted solder. This will make a well soldered joint that will not corrode.—Contributed by Earl Daniel, Kewanna, Ind.

Gasoline-Tank Gauge

After making a search along the side of the road and in the tool chest to find something for measuring the amount of gasoline in the tank of my automobile it occurred to me to make a device for the purpose, which resulted in the construction of the one shown in the accompanying illustration.

A wire is bent as shown, and a cork float slipped in between the branches so that it will rise and fall easily, except when the ends are pinched together, in which case it will be held for measurement. The wire is run through the opening in the tank, and down to its bottom, and the cork allowed to float on the gasoline, then the ends are pinched together and the whole withdrawn. The cork will then be in the exact position where it floated on the gasoline and the amount of fluid in the tank thus easily gauged. Notches can be filed into one of the upright branches of the wire denoting inch marks, and will save bothering with a rule.—Contributed by Richard Russell, East Lynn, Mass.

Protecting Bolt Threads While Passing Through Cored Holes

Machines not requiring accurate work usually have cored bolt holes. If more than two pieces are to be fastened with bolts it is difficult to enter a bolt without injury to the threads. Where there is a ½-in. clearance this can be readily remedied by making a point for the bolt, as shown in the sketch. The one illustrated was for a 2½-in. bolt entering a hole 3 in. in diameter through two stands and a machine base. In this instance it was difficult to get the three pieces so that the holes would line up accurately. The point protected the threads, also made it easy to drive the bolts into place.—Contributed by Fred W. Fravel, W. Homestead, Pa.

Emery-Wheel Arbor for Lathes

The owner of a small lathe who has no emery-wheel stand can make an arbor for use in a lathe that will do all the grinding necessary for a small workshop. The shaft A is made of ⅜-in. steel rod of any length suitable for the lathe, both ends being threaded to receive two nuts, two washers, and the wheels to be used. A length of gas pipe, B, is fitted with a brass bearing in

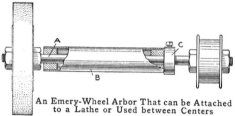

An Emery-Wheel Arbor That can be Attached to a Lathe or Used between Centers

each end to receive the shaft. The collar C is used to keep the shaft from slipping endways where it is necessary to have the pipe B shorter than the shaft.

The arbor can be used on the lathe centers or clamped to the lathe where it can be driven with a belt from a countershaft or from the main drive wheel.—Contributed by Arthur Jennings, London, Eng.

Ventilating Front Apartment of Automobiles

By the way of solving the somewhat troublesome problem of properly ventilating the front apartment of closed automobiles, one ingenious car owner hit upon the scheme shown in the sketch. The fan is arranged to be run by gearing from the engine. Its direction of rotation is such that a contin-

uous draft of air is forced out. As its rate of rotation is very rapid, it does not obstruct the view of the driver,

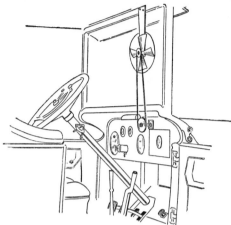

The Revolving Fan does Not Obstruct the View but Prevents Rain or Snow from Entering

and the current of air is sufficient to prevent the ingress of rain or snow.—Contributed by S. P. McMinn, Brooklyn, N. Y.

Keeping a Boat on an Even Keel Out of Water

To keep a boat on an even keel when the tide goes out and leaves it high and dry upon a mud shore, construct a frame of four strong planks and slip it over the bow while the boat is afloat. This frame should fit tightly

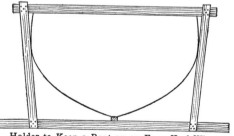

Holder to Keep a Boat on an Even Keel When the Tide Goes Out

around the boat amidships, as shown in the sketch.—Contributed by Forrest Clark, Coronado, Cal.

❧Banana oil or turpentine is excellent for pasting tin foil on transmitting condensers.

Substitute for a Snow Shovel

Having no snow shovel at hand I made a good substitute by fastening a board to a dung fork, as shown. Wire

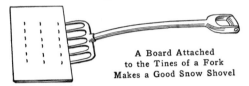

A Board Attached to the Tines of a Fork Makes a Good Snow Shovel

nails were used, clinched on both sides of the tines.—Contributed by J. Morton, Cochituate, Mass.

Homemade Toggle Bolts

The necessary toggle or twin bolt for use in metal was not at hand when I wanted to fasten a robe rail to the metal back on the front seat of my automobile. I made substitutes by threading the ends of two spring cotters, cutting the heads off and bending them as shown. They served the purpose as well as the regular toggle bolt.—Contributed by Chas. H. Sanders, Glendale, Cal.

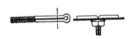

Repairing a Scarf Pin

When soldering the pin tongue in place on a scarf pin, use a piece of card-

The Cardboard Holds the Pin in a Horizontal Position While It is being Soldered

board as shown, and it will be kept level.—Contributed by W. A. Jones, Raleigh, N. C.

Trousers Guards an Aid to Drawing on Overalls

When a person's work demands the use of overalls, I find it very handy to keep a pair of bicycle trousers guards in the pockets, and have them ready to place on the regular trousers before the overalls are drawn on. This will keep the legs of the former from being drawn halfway to the knees, as is often the case. After the overalls are on, the guards can be removed and placed in the pocket.—Contributed by R. B. Strong, Homer, Mich.

Blower for Removing Dust in a Watch

Never blow the breath into a watch movement to remove dust, as the moisture from the breath will in all probability rust the hairspring. Use a

A Dentist's Blower is a Good Device to Use in Removing Dust in a Watch

blower, such as dentists have for blowing out cavities in teeth, as illustrated.

A Revolving Lathe Center

The revolving center has the advantage of keeping the work true that is run at a high speed, such as soft cast iron, brass and wood. The center is

A Revolving Lathe Center That will Prevent Wear on Work Running at High Speed

made of carbon steel and is bored a snug fit to receive the revolving center, which is grooved on the shank to run freely on the pin that holds it in place. An oil hole must be provided to lubricate the shank.—Contributed by G. Barrett, Hamilton, Ont.

Polishing Glass

Calcined magnesia, rubbed down with pure benzine, makes an excellent preparation for cleaning and polishing the surfaces of fine glass, such as costly mirrors, etc. The mass formed must be sufficiently soft to allow drops of the liquid to be squeezed out of it. The mixture should be kept in closely stoppered bottles, and, in use, a little of it is placed on a bit of cotton or a soft rag with which the glass is rubbed.

A Torsional Wire Galvanometer

The work at hand required a sensitive galvanometer and as the cost of such an instrument was beyond my means, I constructed a very good one from parts of a two-bar telephone magneto ringer. The sketch gives an idea of its appearance. The brass bearing heads of the magneto were drilled out and brass tubes, A and B, soldered into them. The top of the tube A was fitted with a brass cap, a long adjustment rod, and a small brass rod with a setscrew for holding the coil-suspension wire. The tube B was fitted with a black fiber cap, brass bushing and thumbscrew, to which was fastened the other terminal from the coil.

The instrument is mounted on a well varnished base, C, with three brass bushings and leveling screws, D, with fiber thumb wheels. It was fastened in place by a bolt through the base C to a fiber bar, E, supporting the binding posts F. One binding post is grounded to the instrument and the other is connected by a wire to the terminal on the end of B. A core, G, for the coil, was made from ¾-in. water pipe, turned up smoothly and held centrally in place by a short stud from a brass plate, H, fastened across the pole faces.

The suspended system was next in order. A coil mount was made of thin strip brass, bent to a rectangular shape, the ends being butted and soldered. A small brass-wire hook was soldered in the center of one end for suspension. A coil of No. 40 gauge enameled wire was wound upon the mount, leaving the ends long enough to suspend the coil from the top of the tube A and for a "pig tail" terminal connection at the bottom of the tube B. The coil was wound to a resistance of about 2,000 ohms. A small piece of mirror, J, was cemented to the hook. The coil was given a coat of shellac.

This type of an instrument must be used with a scale on the wall and a source of light, the light being reflected onto the scale by the mirror. If extra resistance is added and calibrated with a standard instrument, it can be used as a voltmeter. This instrument was inexpensive to construct

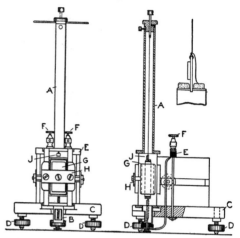

Galvanometer Constructed of Parts Taken from a Two-Bar Telephone Magneto Ringer

and it served its purpose admirably.— Contributed by P. K. McGall, W. Orange, N. J.

Counterbalance for a Cellar Door

The raising of a cellar door can be made quite easy if there is a counterbalance of almost the same weight as the door. One farmer attached this balance in the manner shown, with a rope running over a pulley in the upper end of the post on which the door rests

The Weight is Swung from the Rope in the Tiles Where It is Out of the Way

when open. To make room for the weight, two tiles are sunk into the ground at the right place.

Temporary Repair on an Automobile Spring

While making an extended tour in an automobile I had the misfortune to break a front spring through the cen-

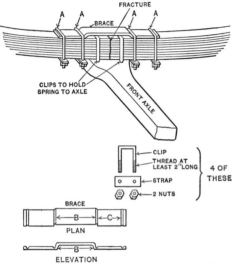

The Brace Clamped to the Broken Parts will Hold the Spring Temporarily Until It can be Repaired

ter. As there was no garage near, I had a blacksmith make a brace, and clips, AAAA, to go over the broken parts, as shown. The width of the brace should be equal to the width of the spring and the part B long enough to lay over the clips holding the spring to the axle. The ends C should be about 3 in. long. Such a brace will effectually repair either a front or rear spring.—Contributed by L. L. Llewellyn, Hayward, Cal.

A Homemade Valve Tool

A cheap and very serviceable tool, for compressing and holding the spring while removing or inserting the valve

A Tool for Holding Springs While Valves are Being Removed for Repairs

stem on an automobile or other gasoline engine, is easily and quickly made where one may have access to a forge. The tool is forged from an ordinary worn-out, flat 10-in. file. Carefully draw the temper, then flatten it out and shape the end as shown, making the slot ½ in. wide and ¾ in. deep for ordinary use, or any other dimensions to suit special cases. A notch is made in the side, $\frac{3}{16}$ in. wide and ½ in. deep, with a projecting prong.

The second member of the tool is a simple hook made of ⅜-in. stock of equal strength, having an opening of about 4 in. and a length of 6 in. A piece of dog chain, or any chain having flat links, about 18 in. long, the closed end of which is slipped into the notch on the side of the tool, is attached to the hook.

To use the tool, attach the hook to the exhaust manifold, or other part, of the engine, allowing the chain to hang in front of the spring to be raised. Insert the notch at the end between the coils of the spring near the lower part so that the valve stem will be between the prongs. Hook a link of the chain in the notch at the right height, and by bearing down on the handle the spring is easily compressed.—Contributed by C. F. Heizer, Falfurrias, Tex.

A Twist-Drill Driver

When a hole must be drilled in a deep groove, recess, or place, and an ordinary drill is not long enough, it is quite common practice to forge a

An Extension Twist-Drill Driver for Drilling Holes in Places That a Short Drill will Not Reach

former or flat drill on a length of tool steel, leaving a shank long enough to reach the required distance or more. But a flat drill cuts slowly and takes more power than a twist drill and it is apt not to drill the proper size.

If a twist drill is at hand, a strong and simple driver can be made for it by using a piece of machine or cold-rolled steel, and at a cost no greater than the forging of a flat drill. First make a saw cut through the center of the metal on the shank end and then cut out the piece so formed, about ½ in. long as shown. This leaves a positive driving-shank end on the drill. Drill a hole in the bar of steel, about 1 in. deep and having the same diameter as the drill to be used. Above this drilled hole cut a notch through one-half of the steel bar, making the notch fully as long as that on the drill-shank end and so that it will meet the end of the drilled hole. Slip the shank of the twist drill into the hole, passing its extending end up over the notch in the bar, and a combination tool will be had that is very good.

Temporary Leather Bearing Replaces Babbitt in Automobile Engine

While cross-country motoring, the crank case of the motor ran out of oil which resulted in the babbitt of the

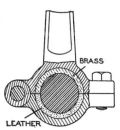

lower half on the connecting rod melting out, and we were left in the middle of a river with a badly disabled engine. I unscrewed the connecting bolt, cut off a short piece of my belt and clamped it in the place of the babbitt. The crank case was filled with the right amount of oil and we proceeded to our destination, 6 miles, then back 14 miles without any trouble, the motor running very quietly all the time. When arriving home the leather was removed and found to be in good shape, sufficient for another run. The sketch shows where the leather was used.—Contributed by Fred B. Stoner, Masontown, Pa.

Handy Arrangement of Bench Drawers

A good method of arranging drawers to hang under a bench, and one which permits any one working at the bench to sit down, is shown in the sketch and, as may be seen, consists of a small drawer, in which can be kept

the small and most-used tools, and a large drawer, to hold work under construction, or other things which would

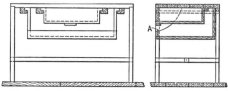

To Place One Drawer within Another under a Bench Top is Handy and Saves Space

otherwise have to be kept on the bench.

Another purpose for which the edge A of the large drawer can often be used is to rest work on while sitting down and filing, holding the work with one hand and filing with the other. This drawer is both handy and space-saving.

Cutting Spline Grooves by Hand

Having occasion to cut some grooves in segments for a pattern at a time when the power was temporarily removed, I found the following method very effective:

A fine-toothed ripsaw, A, and a board of the proper thickness were clamped to a flat surface so that the edge of the saw projected beyond the edge of the board a distance equal to the depth of the groove. The ends of the segments B were

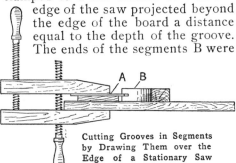

Cutting Grooves in Segments by Drawing Them over the Edge of a Stationary Saw

drawn across the saw teeth which readily cut the grooves.—Contributed by Alden T. Stubbs, Malden, Mass.

⁋When the notches in a glass cutter become worn or the glass happens to be a trifle too thick for them, use a monkey wrench. The wrench is better to use where a narrow strip is to be cut and chipped away.

An Emergency Burglar Circuit

Often a burglary might be prevented if it were possible for the watchman to turn on all the lights in a building at the same time from some more or less

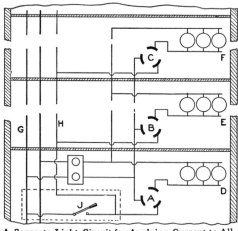

A Separate Light Circuit for Applying Current to All Lights of a Building from a Secluded Switch

protected and out-of-the-way place. The same arrangement will prove quite useful in cases of fire, as the firemen may easily turn on all the lights in the building by simply closing a single switch. The circuit shown diagrammatically in the accompanying sketch accomplishes the desired results, and, at the same time, it is impossible to turn any one of the individual groups of lights off so long as the master switch is closed. Referring to the diagram it will be noticed that each of the switches, A, B, C, etc., controlling the individual groups of lights D, E, F, etc., are of the two-way type, with one point connected to the main lead G; another to one side of the group of lamps the switch controls, while the third point of the switch is connected to the main H, which in turn connects with the main G through the switch J. The switches A, B, C, etc., are so constructed that the lead from the lamps into the switches will always be connected to either the main G or H. It is thus obvious that so long as the switch J is open the lamps will not light when the switches A, B, C, etc., are in one position, but will light

for the other position. If the switch J is closed, all the lamps will light, and it will be impossible to turn any of them out by operating the switches A, B, C, etc. Such a circuit can be installed so as to meet the underwriters' requirements and may pay for itself in a few minutes at some unexpected time.

Taper Attachment for Lathes

To turn a taper on a lathe not equipped with a compound rest necessitates shifting the tailstock, which, however, is not the best method for doing the work. The proper way is to have an attachment for controlling the feed of the tool, and this device can be easily made and attached to any lathe. Two bracket castings, A A, are bolted to the rear part of the lathe bed after they have been machined, so that the surfaces can be lined and leveled up true with the ways. One end of a bar, B, is pivoted to one bracket, and the other end is provided with a bolt that swings in a slot cut in the other bracket for adjustment. The block C slides on the bar B and carries with it the rod D which is inserted in a hole in a piece of metal, E, fastened to the cross slide of the carriage. The rod is adjusted to the work in hand by slipping it through the block E, and when set, it is clamped with two setscrews.

In turning tapers, the attachment is

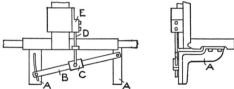

The Slide on the Bar Controls the Cross Feed So That a Taper Cut is Taken

applied and the cross-feed screw or nut is disconnected. The travel of the carriage lengthwise in taking a cut causes the tapering slide to control the cross feed in accordance with the taper for which it was set.

⊄Rough castings should never be slid on machine beds.

Dispelling the Odors from Cooking

To do away with the odors from cooking and the impure air in restaurants, just before serving the meals fill a bowl with steaming hot water, place it in the center of the room and pour in a few drops of oil of lavender. The oil is easily handled, is nonpoisonous and can be purchased at any drug store. It is inexpensive, as a few drops in each bowl is sufficient to deodorize a large room. The bowl may be removed after all the oil is evaporated. The process works equally well in private kitchens and dining rooms.—Contributed by Loren Ward, Des Moines, Iowa.

Substitute for Carpenter's Clamps

A very good substitute for clamps can be made as shown in the illustration. It consists of two side boards

The Clamp is Actuated by Wedges and Pins for the Adjustment to the Width

fastened together with one fixed jaw and a piece between their ends. The other jaw is loose so that it can be set as desired and clamped on the work with the pins and wedges. The size of the pieces will depend on the size of the clamp.—Contributed by A. S. Thomas, Amherstburg, Ont.

Cutting Thick Metal with Hand Shears

If it is necessary to cut a thick piece of metal with a pair of hand tinner's shears construct a shear holder of wood, as shown, and the cutting will be made quite easy. Place the holder on the bench, or floor, with the lower handle of the shears in it. Pressure is applied only to the upper handle, and a clean cut can be made. The

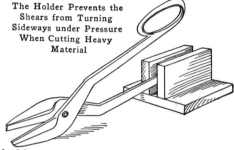

The Holder Prevents the Shears from Turning Sideways under Pressure When Cutting Heavy Material

holder consists of three blocks of wood nailed or screwed together, the upright pieces being placed just far enough apart to receive the handle snugly.—Contributed by U. B. Gilroy, Marysville, Cal.

How to Make a Felt Buffing Wheel

In making a felt buffing wheel of about 3-in. diameter, construct a center disk, A, of wood, about 1½ in. in diameter, and mount it on a straight wood hub, B, of sufficient length for the width of the wheel face. Two washers, each 1 in. in diameter, are fitted to the ends of the hub and three holes drilled through their outer edge for rivets. Holes are punched through the felt disks to coincide with the holes in the washers. An even number of felt disks are placed on each side of the wooden center disk and all are fastened together with the three rivets through the washers. The felt disks extending beyond the edge of the center disk are sewed together by making two seams, one near the edge and one close to the

The Felt Disks are Fastened over the Center Wood Disk to Hold Them Firmly

edge of the wood disk. Other sizes can be made by relatively changing the proportions.—Contributed by W. A. Henry, Galesburg, Ill.

A Wagon Feed Box for Horses

A teamster who is obliged to feed his horses during the noon hour at the wagon has devised a feed box to take

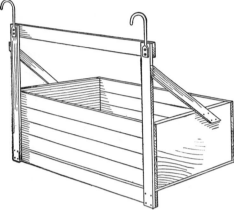

The Feed Box is Easily Attached to the Wagon Box When It is Time to Feed

the place of a nose bag. When the box is hooked over the top edge of the wagon box the height is just right for the horses. The box prevents waste of grain and provides a better way to feed the horses than in the wagon box.— Contributed by Vinton V. Detwiler, Manhattan, Kan.

End Gauges

A very useful set of end gauges that have proven satisfactory and flexible for the manufacturer of machine tools was made of tool steel, 1⅛ in. in diameter, as described by a correspondent of American Machinist. A piece of the steel was centered in a lathe and knurled the entire length; then pieces were cut off, faced, drilled and tapped,

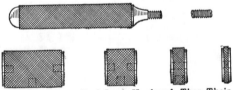

Gauges Cut from Tool Steel, Hardened, Then Their Faces Ground True to Size

and the ends turned down, as shown, so that they would have a flat surface for gauging. The tapped holes allowed

them to be turned on a stub arbor so that, after hardening, the surfaces could be ground to size. The use of headless screws permitted any number of gauges to be connected together so that almost any length could be obtained.

Removable Head on a T-Square

Having occasion to carry a T-square with me on daily journeys, I usually found it knocked out of true as it, being an unwieldy package, was always striking some obstacle. I overcame the difficulty by devising a demountable T-square, as shown. The square was taken apart and then screwed together again, using round-head brass screws. In the center of the head and blade a hole was bored to admit a bolt having a knurled nut. The heads of the screws were then filed off to make them into studs. The head of the T-square is thus easily taken off and replaced, and it always

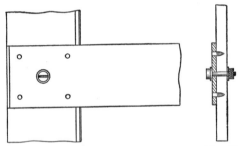

The Head can be Removed and Replaced and It will Always be Square with the Blade

adjusts itself to the original position. —Contributed by Edwin E. Hahn, Philadelphia, Pa.

An Emergency Nut

In doing some repair work I found that I had two bolts and only one nut. The nut happened to be of a good thickness and in order to make a temporary job of it, the nut was split with a hacksaw to make two nuts of one.—Contributed by Wm. A. Murray, Cold Spring, N. Y.

¶A lathe bed having a scale is handy for some classes of work.

Bonding and Grounding Aerial Cables
By GEORGE LITTEL

While electrolysis proper does not attack aerial cables, it is equally important that these cables are bonded and grounded in the same manner as for underground work. The large number of high-potential circuits which run parallel with, and across the telephone, telegraph, light and power cables makes the bonding and grounding necessary. The high-potential wires often drop upon the cables below, and the current jumps through the underground fuses, runs down into the underground cable and makes its way through to the heat coils on the main distributing frame in the central station. Also, in damp weather, where the high-potential circuits and the telephone cables are on the same poles, the induction will often seriously interfere with the proper working of the latter. Lightning also is liable to damage aerial cables and for these three reasons the aerial cables must be properly protected, as an accident may come to them at any time. The following instances of troubles caused and diverted by improper and proper insulation of cables show that too much care cannot be taken to reduce the maintenance expense.

In one instance the cable was struck by lightning, which jumped through the underground box, followed down the cable, and finally, about ½ mile from the underground box, jumped through the sheath to ground. The interesting part of this case was that the lightning had confined itself to one pair of wires all the way in the cable until it went to ground, where it fused off about 75 pairs of wires and burned a hole in the sheath about the size of a lead pencil. The second case occurred in a cable that ran parallel with an interurban trolley feed and on the same pole with it. In this instance the aerial was properly bonded and the damage was limited to that part of the aerial between the start of the trouble and the ground connection. The feeder dropped across the aerial

and melted the armor completely for over 300 ft., but there was not one single station, out of over 50 party lines, that was put out of commission.

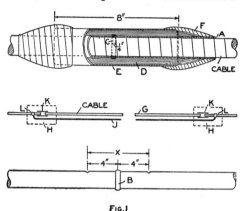

FIG. 1

Method of Insulating the Cable Sheath and Manner of Connecting the Bond Wire in the Manholes

It can be readily understood that the lack of bonds and ground in the first case caused a large repair expense, and that the proper bonding and grounding, in the latter, saved twice as much as otherwise would have been destroyed.

When cables are run across iron bridges the best plan is to insulate them at both ends. This can be easily accomplished, even though the cable is run in an iron pipe, with the aid of insulating joints, as shown in Fig. 1, in which A represents the cable sheath. This insulating joint is not made at a splice in the cable but a piece of sheath, B, about ¼ or ½ in. in width, is removed all the way around the cable. This cut is not made, however, until the cable is soaked with paraffin at that point. This is done by cutting small holes, about 4 in. each side of the place where the cut is to be made, as shown at X, and into which melted paraffin is poured until the cable is thoroughly saturated with it. The cut proper is then thoroughly boiled out with paraffin and the opening completely filled by winding candle wicking, C, around the cable until the slot is more than full. The wicking is then boiled out with more paraffin and the holes X closed with solder.

The entire cable is then tightly wrapped, for 4 in. each side of the cut,

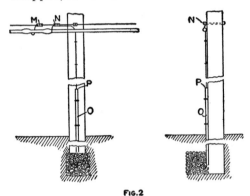

An Aerial-Cable Bond to the Messenger and a Ground Connection at a Pole

with alternate layers of common friction tape and okonite tape, using four layers of each and painting each layer with a good asphaltum paint, as shown at D. A lead sleeve, E, is then slipped over the cable and the ends dressed in to fit the tape tightly, so as to aid in excluding moisture in case the splice is exposed to dampness. The joints of the sleeve are then built up with tape, as shown at F, and given two coats of asphaltum paint. The part of the cable touching the bridge is shown at G, while HH are the manholes at each end in which the joint is made. The bonding wire, the size of which depends on the amount of current flowing into the cable, is shown at J. The position of the insulating joints in the manholes are shown at KK, and the point of connecting the bond wire with the cable sheaths, at LL. The ends of the bond wire should be securely soldered to the sheath. The object of these joints is to break the connection of the cable sheath and at the same time maintain a continuous circuit for the prevention of electrolytic action.

The proper method of bonding an aerial cable is shown in Fig. 2. This bond should be made every 1,000 ft., and a ground connection every 5,000 ft. The method of attaching the messenger to the cable is shown at M, where three bolt clamps are fastened to the messenger and also to a piece of messenger wire, about 3 ft. long. The far end of this short piece of messenger wire is then fanned out, placed around the cable and fastened with a small piece of copper wire. A solder joint is wiped over both the cable and the fanned-out wire, and a neat appearing as well as a mechanically perfect job is the result. When the ground wire is run, the bond and ground connection are made as shown at N, and the wire must be continued from the clamp, down the pole, and into a ½-in. galvanized-iron pipe, O, which extends about 3 ft. above the ground. The wire should be a 6M guy wire and is fastened to the pole with galvanized staples, about 2 ft. apart, and the pipe is held to the pole with clamps. Where the wires enter and leave the pipe, at P, the openings in the pipe must be closed with solder to exclude all dampness. A hole, about 18 in. square, is then dug at the base of the pole and 4 ft. below the surface of the earth. The hole is filled with coke or charcoal and a 15-ft. coil of ground wire placed in it.

Taper Gauge for Boring Mills

The fact that the boring mill is one of the most difficult machines to set for a true taper, brought about the making of the gauge shown in the sketch for this work. It consists of two pieces of steel, $\frac{1}{32}$ in. thick, 1 in. wide, and 15 in. long, jointed like a blacksmith's rule. A true center is left in the jointing screw and from this point a center line is drawn on each blade. The upper blade is cut along this line to within about 2 in. of the joint, and the edge is trimmed and beveled so that it coincides with the line on the other blade. An arc of a circle is marked on both blades 12 in. from the center of the joint, and the space between is graduated as fine as desired, but for ordinary purposes a fine center-punch mark at a corresponding point on each 12-in. arc of the two blades will be sufficient, if accurately measured.

To use the tool for any machine, set the dividers to 60 deg. of the graduated arc and lay out that distance on both blades. When the points at 12 in. are the required distance apart, the distance through which the zero mark on the machine must be moved is found at the arc which represents the circle of the machine, and it is only necessary to transfer this distance with the dividers. The distance A is equal to one-half the required taper per foot, and the distance B is the distance to move the zero mark to cut the required taper. It must be remembered that the boring

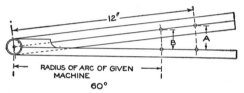

Gauge for Setting Boring Mills or Other Machines to Do Accurate Taper Work

head is set just one-half of the total taper per foot, and it is most important that the cutting point of the tool is set on the center line parallel to the cross rail.—Contributed by Thomas M. McKnight, Willoughby, Ohio.

Lathe-Tool Guard

A guard placed on a lathe tool, as shown in the sketch, is a great aid in preventing injury to the workman's eyes, especially where the work must be closely watched. The guard consists of a piece of celluloid, about 2 in. square, cut as shown and slipped over the tool with the tongue folded in between the tool top and the end of the setscrew. The guard being transparent, the work can be seen through it.—Contributed by Jos. J. Kolar, Maywood, Ill.

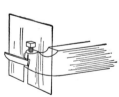

Tongs for Holding Flat and Round Stock

These tongs differ from the ordinary kind in the jaws only, having side projections with curved inside surfaces to

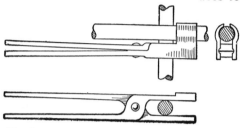

The Jaws' Shape is Such That Either Flat or Round Stock may be Held in Them

hold the round stock. They will be found especially useful in welding short pieces of iron with a jump weld, as the stock can be held either sideways or endways, as shown.—Contributed by Edward Miller, Northampton, Massachusetts.

Measuring Tubing with an Ordinary Micrometer

A little inexpensive attachment for any ordinary micrometer can be made for accurately measuring the walls of tubing. The attachment is made as follows: A piece of $\frac{5}{16}$-in. cold-rolled steel is drilled to make a push fit for a $\frac{1}{4}$-in. hardened steel ball. The steel is fitted snugly on the anvil of the micrometer. The steel ball is adjusted in the bushing so that it will protrude $\frac{1}{16}$ in. The bushing is then placed on the anvil of the micrometer so that the ball touches it. In measuring the wall of a tubing all that is necessary is to subtract $\frac{1}{4}$ in., or .25 in., the exact size of the steel ball, from the amount designated on the scale.—Contributed by Walter Butz, Pearl River, New York.

❡Heat the drill when drilling frozen earth for blasting purposes and the drill can be easily withdrawn.

Shifter for Overhead Belts

Overhead belts at a considerable distance from the floor are hard to throw from the pulley, when necessity requires it, without stopping the entire machinery in the shop.

The sketch shows a device consisting mainly of a pointed or t a p e r e d p r o n g and a circular plate behind it, to engage the belt. Attached to a long wood handle, the arrangement is very handy and convenient as a safe means for throwing overhead belts. The prong and plate engage the belt at the same time, in throwing a belt, no matter which way the pulleys may be turning.

Coloring Copper

Copper and brass lend themselves readily to a coloring process and may be worked to all shades imaginable, excepting the lighter shades, which are lost on a copper surface, as that metal cannot be given a tint lighter than its natural color, says a correspondent of Sheet Metal Shop. Zinc colors fairly well sometimes, through a narrow range, while tin is a hard metal to handle as regards oxide colors.

Copper can be carried through the entire range of shades, from a very light copper color to the darkest brown, or even black, by merely oxidizing the surface of the metal. Make a paste of iron oxide and graphite, with wood alcohol or with plain water, and apply this to the article, which is then heated in an oven or over a gas flame. It is better to use alcohol, as it dries out much quicker. The color obtained will depend on the amount of iron oxide mixed with the graphite, and the length of time the heat was maintained. The more oxide in the coating, the darker the shade given to the copper.

The remains of the coating should be removed with a brush or cloth moistened in alcohol, and when the surface has become quite clean, the color should be protected by applying varnish, lacquer, or pure wax, which may be laid on with a brush while the copper is heated. Some brown colors are obtained by using a mixture of verdigris, sal ammoniac and vinegar, using two or three times as much verdigris and sal ammoniac as vinegar. The heat treatment is the same as in the previously related process and the color obtained can be made much darker by adding some blue vitriol to the solution.

A red brown may be given by using a vinegar paste containing equal parts of verdigris and cinnabar, together with two and one-half times as much each of sal ammoniac and alum. The heat treatment is the same as for the other coatings.

A wide range of colors, comprising shades from blue-black to blue-gray, may be given to copper by dipping it in a hot "liver of sulphur" solution and then washing thoroughly, redipping or scratch-brushing and again dipping and washing according to the tint desired. This can only be learned by experience.

Holding Thin Brass Tubing for Turning

In cutting off, turning, or filing thin brass or copper tubing much trouble will be experienced from its buckling or crushing under the pressure of chuck jaws or vise jaws. To prevent this trouble use a plug of wood driven lightly into the hole. Where a number of pieces of the same size are to be handled, a metal plug or arbor can be made; and if a still greater number are to be worked, it will pay to have an expanding arbor which may be made by splitting the metal plug, making a taper hole in it and fitting a plug in the hole.

❡The part of a metal post that is set in the ground may be kept from rusting by painting it over with a coat of cement.

Grinding Piston Rings

The base of the casting from which the piston rings are cut is left on the faceplate of the lathe and bored out to snugly receive the piston. On new work the piston should be turned to $\frac{1}{64}$ in. oversize. 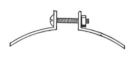 The bored-out base is used as a gauge in cutting the rings, after the edges have been ground to fit the ring grooves in the piston. After cutting them, they are placed in the piston in the usual manner.

Provide as many sheet-metal strips as there are rings, each about ¼ in. wider than the ring and not over $\frac{1}{64}$ in. in thickness. Bend these around the piston and turn the ends out at right angles so that there will be a gap of about ½ in. Drill or punch holes in the projecting ends for a small stove, or other, bolt. The clamp end with bolt is shown in the sketch.

Procure some engraver's wax, which is made of resin, beeswax and a little shellac. Heat the pistons in an oven until hot enough to melt the wax. Melt the wax in a ladle and pour it in the cut in the ring until the space is well filled, then slip on a clamp with the bolt over the cut in the ring and well centered. Draw up the clamp, squeezing out the surplus wax until the ends of the ring are close together. The clamps, being of thin metal, allow the rings to take their own shape and also center them in the piston groove. All rings are treated in the same manner, then the piston is set aside to cool.

When the wax is set, remove the clamps, then wipe off the surplus wax with a rag soaked in gasoline. Center the piston in a lathe and grind both piston and rings to snugly fit the bore of the cylinder, which should also be ground to size. Place the piston in a pan, return it to the oven and heat sufficiently to remove the wax, then set it in gasoline for 48 hours to clean it thoroughly of the wax. If it is desired to remove all clinging wax quickly, boil it in soda water. In this manner the rings can be fitted accurately, so that their entire surface will be in contact with the cylinder walls.—Contributed by S. A. Asquith, Waterloo, Ia.

An Auxiliary Chuck Jaw

The illustration shows an auxiliary jaw which sometimes is very handy for use in a lathe chuck. The jaws should be made of soft brass or copper so that they will not mar the piece gripped in them. Make them about three - quarters the length of the regular chuck jaws. If the regular chuck jaw is 1 in. wide, make the 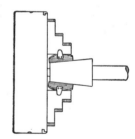 auxiliary jaws .005 in. smaller. Fasten a small spring, or clip, on each side of the jaws. These serve to hold the auxiliary on the chuck jaw while placing the work in the chuck. As will be seen, the back of the jaws are convex or rounding. This allows the auxiliary jaws to conform to odd-shaped pieces or tapers. The illustration shows the jaws gripping a taper shank.—Contributed by Chas. Homewood, Waterloo, Iowa.

Bell and Door-Lock Circuit for an Apartment House

The accompanying diagram shows the method of wiring the front and back-door bells and the electric lock

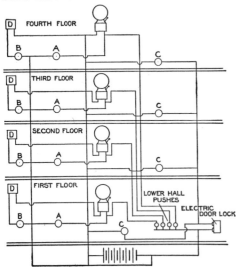

Complete Electrical Circuit for the Front and Back-Door Bells and the Electric Lock

on the front door. Four separate push buttons are located in the lower hallway and connected so as to ring the bells in the different apartments. These buttons are usually mounted on the mail boxes and near the mouthpieces of the speaking tubes, which are also, as a rule, mounted on the mail boxes. Another button is often added to operate a bell in the janitor's quarters. The push buttons marked A are mounted on the side of the doors entering the flats from the front hallway. These push buttons, of course, operate the same bells as the push buttons in the lower hallway. Buzzers or bells, D, of different tones than those in the front of the apartments are wired to be operated by push buttons, B, located at the back doors. Push buttons, C, are located near the mouthpiece of the speaking tubes leading to the vestibule or entrance which control the electric door lock. These circuits can be elaborated to meet almost any requirements. The wires used should be well insulated and in-

stalled in such a manner that there is little likelihood of shorts or grounds occurring on any of the circuits. A small bell-ringing transformer may be used in place of the battery, thus doing away with the trouble due to exhausted batteries and the cost of renewing same. It is always best, if possible, to make all splices and branch connections at a push button or bell, as this often reduces complications in testing out the circuits and locating causes of trouble.

Starting a Forge Fire

If a forge fire is used only occasionally, the starting of a fire requires considerable time, but where gas is available the fire may be hastened by equipping the blower with a gas-supply pipe, as shown.

The pipe leading from the blower to the tuyère is drilled and tapped for a ⅜-in. pipe at any convenient location, as at A, and connected to a gas line. A valve, B, is located in the gas line where it will be handy for the operator.

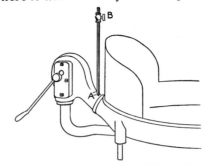

The Burning Gas Starts the Coal Fire and Leaves No Harmful Residue in the Forge

All that is required to start the fire is to lay a lighted match on top of the coal in the forge, turn on the gas lightly and turn the blower, slowly at first, and then gauge the gas and air to the proper mixture. The coal will be ignited and burning at a welding heat in a short time.—Contributed by Earl Pagett, Coffeyville, Kans.

⚓A piece of paper placed between finished metal surfaces keeps them from sliding.

Thumb Rest for a Hacksaw Frame

In using a hacksaw for a considerable length of time, I found that the pressure applied with the thumb of the

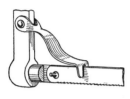

left hand resulted in a blister or the breaking of the skin. To overcome this difficulty I made and attached the thumb rest shown in the sketch. The rest consists of sheet metal thick enough not to bend under the pressure, and is cut and hinged to the front end of the hacksaw frame so that, in use, it lies on the back of the blade. This makes a thumb rest and also stiffens the saw blade —Contributed by Chas. Walte.

Threading Studs in a Lathe with a Solid Die

Having occasion to hurriedly thread quite a number of small studs when no bolt cutter was at hand, and the usual stock and die being an unwieldy affair for this kind of work, I accomplished the threading quickly in the following manner. There was a small lathe in the shop and the die was centered in

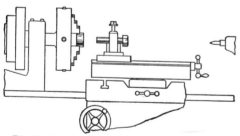

The Studs were Clamped in the Tool Post and Threaded in a Die Held in the Chuck

the jaws of the chuck. The studs were of a size that easily passed through the tool slot in the post, and were tightened down by the holding screw. A few shims were laid in the slot to line the studs with the center of the die, and it was a quick piece of work to thread them by simply starting the lathe to cut the threads.—Contributed by F. W. Bently, Jr.

Obtaining the Relative Intensity of Two Sources of Light

The following simple device may be used in determining the relative intensity of two sources of light, or measuring what is called the candlepower of one lamp in terms of the candlepower of another lamp which is known. The operation of the device depends entirely upon what is known as the law of inverse squares, which may be illustrated as follows:

Take a point source of light, such as A, Fig. 1, and consider the illumination on surfaces located different distances from this source. It is quite obvious that the illumination on a given area decreases as the distance between the area and source of light increases, and

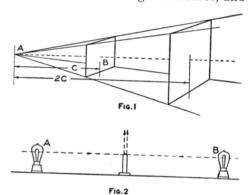

FIG.1

FIG.2

Illustrating the Law of Inverse Squares, and a Simple Photometer

it can be shown that there is a definite relation between the illumination on a given area and the distance between the area and the source of light. If an area, B, be located a distance, C, from the source of light A, and lines be drawn from the source of light through the four corners of the area B, a pyramid will be formed. A certain quantity of light will be contained in this pyramid and it will be distributed over the area B. If a second area be taken at twice the distance—2C—from the source of light, it will be four times that of B, but the same quantity of light will be distributed over this new area that was distributed over the area B. A third area may be considered at a distance of 3C from the source of light, and it will have an area nine times that of B, and the same quantity of light will be distributed over it as was distributed over the first and second areas. Other areas may be taken at less, intermediate, or greater distances than those just given, but they will be related to each other as the square of their respective distances from the source of light. Now, since the same quantity of light falls on each of these areas, the quantity per unit area must decrease as the areas increase, or the light per unit area varies inversely as the square of the distance the area is from the source of light. If, then, two sources of light be placed a given distance apart, as shown in Fig. 2, there will be some point between them where the illumination from each source is the same. This point may be located with a fair degree of accuracy as follows:

A block of wood, about 1 in. square and several inches long, is cut V-shaped at one end so that the surfaces thus formed will be at right angles to each other. Cover these two surfaces with pieces of pure-white drawing paper. The edges of the pieces of paper should be beveled where they join. Now, by moving this block so that the surfaces move on a line joining the two sources of light, and at the same time observing the relative illumination on the two surfaces, a point may be located where the two surfaces will be equally illuminated. If the total distance between the two light sources A and B is 100 in. and the source of light A is 40 in. from the wedge and the source of light B, 60 in. from it, when a balance is obtained, the light obtained from A on one of the white surfaces will be equal to $\frac{A}{40^2}$, and that from B, on the other, equal to $\frac{B}{60^2}$. These two values being equal, it is easily found that, in this case, the intensity of the light source A is four-ninths that of B, so that when the candlepower of one of these sources is known, the candlepower of the other source is easily computed.

Better results can be obtained by using a screen of some kind to cut out all the light from the observer's vision except that coming from the two paper surfaces. The surfaces of the wood block as well as the base on which it slides, should be given a coat of dull black paint. A number of balances should be obtained by moving the wedge in the opposite directions, and the average taken as a final value.

Repairing a Leak in a Heating Boiler

A heating boiler sprung a leak at a time when it was most needed. The boiler was of the sectional type, 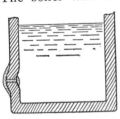 the sections arching over the fire box and carrying the water. To remove one section would have made it necessary to take the whole boiler apart to repair it. This would have required a week or more, during which business would have been suspended unless the weather moderated. The leak was seemingly caused by corrosion in the pocket where the core had been supported by a wire when cast. The corrosion made the casting at what is usually a weak spot very thin, and finally a small pinhole was blown through. When over 2 or 3 lb. of steam was carried the increased heat caused greater expansion, and the hole was so enlarged as to let a good stream of water through on the fire. The location was too confined to permit drilling or plugging by any ordinary methods. It was then suggested to try a plug of softer material. The hole was enlarged, by pricking it, and filled with asbestos, but this would not hold when under pressure. Fireclay was then mixed and enough forced in to fill two holes of like diameter, and the outside well smeared over. This repair was entirely successful.— Contributed by Donald A. Hampson, Middletown, N. Y.

Filler for Patterns

Cracks, holes, corners and irregularities in wood patterns must be filled up before the patterns are in shape for the foundry. Beeswax, plaster of Paris, paraffin, etc., are used for this purpose, but a better substance is metal filler that is sold in paste form for smoothing castings. The color of the paste is the same as that given to most patterns. The paste is applied after putting on a coat of shellac. It is rubbed in with the fingers after dipping them into water. When all the holes have been filled and the filler has partly dried apply another coat of shellac, and a good surface will be the result. This is not a substitute for a filler in corners of patterns requiring a definite radius; it is only a filler for holes and depressions.

Auxiliary Drill Chucks for a Jeweler's Lathe

The chuck on my dentist's lathe would not hold smaller drills than the size of the hole in the chuck satisfactorily, and I proceeded to make auxiliary jaws for the drill sizes, each having an outside diameter of $\frac{5}{32}$ in., the size of the hole in the lathe chuck. These were made of wire nails, $\frac{5}{32}$ in. in diameter. The heads and points were cut off and the squared ends, thus made, were centered accurately. A hole, A, was drilled through the center, to admit the drill used in drill-

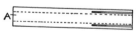

Each Small Drill was Supplied with a Chuck to Fit the Lathe Chuck

ing the hole. One end of the piece was then cross-slotted, as shown at B, with a small saw, thus making a small holder to fit the lathe chuck.

After using the auxiliary chuck a few times it would cling tightly to the drill and, in a manner, make a drill shank of the size for the lathe chuck. It would also prevent very small drills from being lost. Each of the small drills was supplied with a chuck of its own.—Contributed by L. L. Llewellyn.

Sawhorse for Heavy Timbers

When it is necessary to saw a heavy board lengthwise and no bench is at hand, the job can be easily done by the

A Horse for Holding a Heavy Timber While Ripping It with a Handsaw

aid of the simple device shown herewith, the construction of which is self-evident. The board is clamped in the upper angle of the A-shaped horse by means of the movable crossbar which is held in position by pins, as shown. By allowing the larger end of the board to drop to the ground, it is held very rigidly for sawing. When sawed through about halfway, the split end is pushed out and the other end sawed.

Counterbore Attachment for a Twist Drill

The attachment can be used on a twist drill for countersinking the hole when it is drilled through the metal, or be set to make the countersink when the drill reaches a certain depth. The attachment is made of a piece of cold-rolled steel, drilled through its center larger than the drill upon which it is to be applied. Two pieces of tool steel are ground to fit the flutes on the drill and of sufficient thickness to form cutters for the size of the countersink. The cold-rolled steel can be shaped as desired, but it is always best to have a piece large enough so that a flush screw can be used for safety. The attachment can be set on the drill at any point desired and used as a stop.— Contributed by Chas. G. England, Washington, Pa.

Making Holes in Glass Bottles

A firm of chemists preparing a certain lotion for bruises and sprains decided that its sale and field of usefulness would be increased if t h e preparation were put up in a bottle having a hole through the bottom. The purpose of the hole is not important, but the manner of making it may aid some

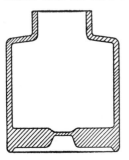

other workman, having similar work to do. The hole, of course, was to be corked after filling the bottle. The size of the hole was not essential, but it was found impossible for the bottle makers to blow the hole in the bottom.

The bottom of the bottle was ⅜ in. thick and, in submitting an estimate on drilling the holes, I placed the cost at 5 cents for each bottle. As the bottle only cost 2 cents, this method was too expensive, and I suggested a plan which the chemists adopted.

The molds for the bottles were altered slightly by the addition of parts that would form a recess in the bottom, as shown in the sketch. This left a thin web of glass at the bottom of the recess, or depression, and added nothing to the cost of the bottle. A boy was put to work with a punch and hammer to knock the web out of the bottom. Only a few bottles were broken, so that the added cost was very small. The break was irregular, but this was of no consequence. The surrounding wall was so heavy in comparison with the web that the glass gave away without any trouble.—Contributed by Donald A. Hampson, Middletown, N. Y.

⊄The most convenient way of hanging plans, bills of material, or other papers, in the shop is to make a small hole in one of the upper ends of an ordinary spring clothespin and hang it on a brad.

A Hydrant Cup and Basin Holder

The yards about a shop, factory, or boarding house usually have an ordinary hydrant where water is obtained

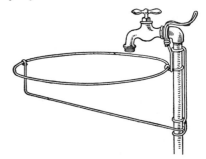

A Basin and Cup Holder Made of Wire and Attached to a Yard Hydrant Pipe

for drinking and washing purposes. As a rule, the basin is filled and carried to a resting place on some box or barrel. The attachment shown holds both basin and cup. The basin can be filled and then turned to the rear or side, as desired, while others obtain water. Two pieces of heavy wire, preferably copper, is all the material necessary, and the sketch clearly shows how it is applied.

Prick Punch with Hammer

The prick punch made as shown does not require the use of a hammer. The punch is turned from tool steel and a steel ball is drilled centrally to fit on the handle part. The upper end of the handle is threaded to receive a cap to hold the ball in place. The point of the punch is properly hardened. To

The Ball on the Handle is Used for Driving the Point of the Punch into the Metal

use, place the point on the spot and raise the ball to the upper end of the handle; then it is brought down quickly to strike the flange at the lower part, which forces the point into the metal. —Contributed by Abner B. Shaw, No. Dartmouth, Mass.

To Lengthen a Short Cap Screw

Finding the cap screw in a socket just a little too short to clamp the spindle and not having a longer one of the same size, I filed away a portion of the bottom of the head, removing a part of the body below the threads as

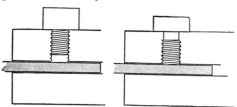

The Extra Length for the Screw was Made by Cutting Away Part of the Head

shown. This made enough extra length to clamp the spindle tightly.— Contributed by James M. Kane, Doylestown, Pa.

Shop Ladder Made of Pipe

A small ladder is a handy article about a shop, but the uses to which shop ladders are sometimes subjected are too severe on most wood ladders.

The sketch shows a light, durable and strong ladder made of pipe. At each point where a rung is to be located, the pipe is flattened to allow a long ⅝-in., or ¾-in., stud to pass through and be secured at each end by two nuts. The lower ends of the ladder are drawn to a point to prevent its slipping. The upper ends are improved in appearance by the application of two pipe caps.

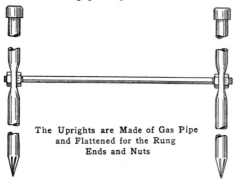

The Uprights are Made of Gas Pipe and Flattened for the Rung Ends and Nuts

A ladder of this type is both valuable and durable and its uses are almost innumerable.

Automatic Feed for an Oil Cup

Hand-adjusted oil cups very often become clogged with particles of dirt, which results in a hot bearing or a damaged shaft, if not watched closely. The cup illustrated is hand-adjusted when starting the machine, but later the feed is operated automatically by a thermostat spring, if the bearing begins to heat up a trifle.

The cup is similar to the ordinary sight-feed kind with the needle valve operated by a thermostat spring. The spring consists of two pieces, one brass, 16 gauge, and one steel, 20 gauge, bent as shown, then drilled for rivets and the holes countersunk. The brass piece is placed on the inside of the bend and both pieces are riveted together solidly. If any substance clogs the opening at the point of the needle, the bearing will begin to warm up, which will cause the spring to raise the valve and let the oil rush through. It works automatically without attention when set.—Contributed by Louis Stankewitz, New York City.

A Flat Water Paint

To make a good flat water paint, take 50 lb. of gilders' bolted whiting, place it in a tub and pour water over it until the mass is covered. Allow this to stand several hours, say, over night, then pour off the excess water and add 2 gal. of hard oil finish—gloss or resin oil will do—and any desired color, then beat up the mass until it is perfectly smooth. Use water color or dry color, not oil color. Thin the mass down to a brushing consistency with turpentine, benzol or benzine, and it is ready for use. This will make a very nice, flat, lusterless finish as good as the much advertised water paints of the same character.

Swinging Telephone Shelf for Two Rooms

Quite often two persons occupying adjoining offices wish to make use of the same telephone. If the partition

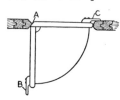

dividing the two offices be a thin wooden one this can be accomplished very easily by making use of a swinging shelf similar to that shown in the accompanying illustration.

A small opening, of sufficient size to accommodate the telephone, is cut in the partition so as to place the telephone as near the desks on opposite sides of the partition as possible. The edges of this opening should be shaped as shown in the sketch. The shelf proper is in the form of a quadrant of a circle whose radius is a little less than the breadth of the opening in the partition. Two sides are attached to the shelf as shown, and are of such size and shape that they will just fit into the opening when their common edge is beveled off at a 45-deg. angle. The shelf may be supported by double hinges, A, attached to the beveled edge. Two stops, B and C, should be provided to prevent the shelf from swinging too far through the opening or past its proper position. These stops may be so shaped that they will serve as handles in moving the shelf. The edges of the opening may be covered with heavy felt, which will serve to close any crack that might otherwise exist. A small piece of quarter-round is shown fastened in the corner between the two sides to give a good anchorage for the screws holding the hinges. The cord leading to the telephone should pass through a hole in the back corner of the shelf.

⊄A painter's brush having reasonably stiff bristles is much better for dusting heavily carved furniture than the ordinary feather duster.

Spacing Letters on a Sign

Frequently it is a more difficult task to space letters properly than to write them on a sign. I often find it con-

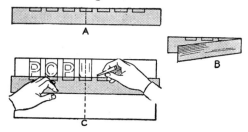

The Letters are First Spaced on Paper Which is Creased to Show the Center Line

venient to first lay out the letter spaces on a strip of paper, A, double it as shown at B, and then lay the crease on the center line of the design. The spaces are then easily and correctly laid out on the sign C, without spotting the surface with trial marks.—Contributed by James M. Kane, Doylestown, Pa.

Enlarging the Capacity of Calipers

It is not an uncommon occurrence in the routine of general lathe work, to come across some work with a diameter too great to be measured with the largest pair of calipers in the tool kit. The sketch shows how to fasten two pairs of calipers together with a hand vise to increase their reach for measuring large diameters. The hinges on both pairs of calipers can be brought into use while on the work, and when

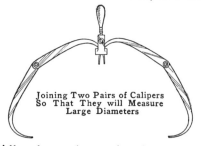

Joining Two Pairs of Calipers So That They will Measure Large Diameters

rigidly clamped together by means of a small hand vise, the arrangement is as practical as a large, heavy pair of calipers. The adjustment is made with the two extending arms.

An Emergency Indicator

The regrinding of an air-cooled cylinder made it necessary to chuck it accurately, and as I had no indicator, a temporary tool was made of wood.

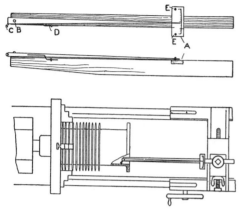

This Homemade Tool will Indicate Any Slight Setting Out of True

The main beam, or pointer support, was made of white pine, 5/8 in. thick, 1 1/2 in. wide, and 1 ft. long. One end was tapered, as shown, for the sake of appearance. The pointer was made of another piece of white pine, 3/16 in. thick, 5/16 in. wide at one end, and tapered to a point at the other, the length being 9 in. A groove was cut in the upper edge, at A, and a piece of wood inserted for a graduated scale. The pointer was pivoted 1/4 in. from the end, at B, to the beam, and a small pin inserted, at C, on an angle, as shown. The pointer should swing freely. A small spring was made of spring wire and fastened with staples, at D, to apply pressure on the pointer. Two small pins, EE, were placed in the scale, to keep the pointer from swinging too far either way.

The indicator in use is shown in the sketch. The shank of the beam is placed in the tool post of the lathe, and the pin at the end of the pointer is run against the bore of the cylinder. Any small deviation out of center will show by a slight movement of the pointer on the scale.—Contributed by Joe V. Romig, Allentown, Pa.

Oiling System for Main-Shaft Bearings of an Automobile

The main-shaft bearings on my automobile were not oiled sufficiently by the wick oilers, and I supplied an oiling system as shown in the sketch. An ordinary sight-feed oiler was attached to the dash with a bracket, made of No. 16 gauge sheet brass. The oiler was clamped in place on the bracket by turning a pipe coupling on the threads after they were run through the hole in the bracket. The valve controlling the flow of oil was screwed into the coupling and the pipe lines were made of 1/8-in. brass tubing.

As I did not have a three-way cock at hand, I made one out of an ordinary shut-off cock. A 1/16-in. hole was drilled through the body of the cock, at A, and into the cross hole of the valve, as shown at B. The position of the valve for running oil to the front bearing is

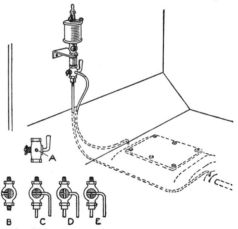

An Oiling System to Take the Place of Wick-Oiling the Bearings on an Automobile

shown at C, and to the rear bearing, at D, while E represents its position when the oil is entirely shut off from both bearings.—Contributed by L. L. Llewellyn, Hayward, Cal.

Filler for Metal Surfaces

In finishing a piece of machinery, use a filler as follows: Dry filler, 6 parts; whiting, 3 parts; lead in oil, 3 parts, and pulverized silica, 6 parts.

Make this into a paste with a liquid composed of 3 parts of rubbing varnish, 2 parts of coach japan, and 1 part of turpentine, all by weight. Mix to a stiff paste and run through a paint mill, or work up on a slab. Fill the surface of the metal with the paste, and when it has become dry and hard, rub smooth with fine sandpaper. If it is desired to have a darker color add some lampblack. Thinned, the filler can be used as a paint for iron.

Centering Gauge for Lathe Tools

The gauge shown is a recent addition, and one of the handiest in my kit. The usual way for turning tapers, no

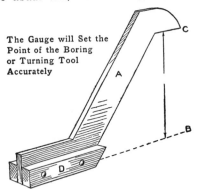

The Gauge will Set the Point of the Boring or Turning Tool Accurately

matter whether the lathe has a taper attachment or not, is to cut in with a parting tool to the size at both ends of the taper, then setting the lathe until a small scale has the correct "feel" between the parting tool and the taper sizes. When a heavy piece of work is between centers it is difficult to set the tool exactly at the center of the stock, which is absolutely necessary for accurate work either in setting or turning, without removing the work and setting the tool to the lathe center. This gauge will overcome these difficulties and can be used also for boring, which is the hardest job of the two for tool setting.

The body, A, of the gauge consists of a piece of ⅛-in. soft steel and the distance from the base line B to the point C is the same as from the top of the tool rest to the lathe center. The base may be reinforced with ⅛ by ⅜-

in. strips, as shown at D, to rest firmly on top of the tool rest. In setting a tool for cutting or turning tapers, the top or cutting edge is placed under the point C. For boring, the gauge is set on the tool rest and up against the work and marked with a scriber, then the boring tool is set to the line before starting the lathe head.—Contributed by G. O. Reed, Stratford, Can.

Covering Capacity of Paint

To ascertain the amount of white-lead paint required to cover a given surface of wood, divide the number of square feet by 200, which will give the number of gallons of mixed paint required for a two-coat job. It is usually estimated that a gallon will cover 500 sq. ft. of average wood or smooth metal surface one coat.

The number of pounds of keg white lead required to cover a certain area is found by dividing the area in square feet by 18, which will give the number of pounds of lead required for a three-coat job.

Exclusive of glass, the paint materials required to do an average dwelling will be from 20 to 30 per cent of the total cost of the painting. The labor will be the largest portion.

Blue Ground for a Level Bubble

The bubbles in level glasses, set directly into the plaster-of-Paris bed, are difficult to see in some of the many positions the level is necessarily held while in use. The sketch shows an excellent way to set

BLUE PAPER

a glass so that the bubble will show up clear and plain in any position the body of the level may be held. Just before the glass is pressed into the plaster a thin strip of dark blue paper is wrapped halfway around the glass on the under side and pressed into place with the glass.—Contributed by F. W. Bently, Jr., Milwaukee, Wis.

Hand Tool for Facing Small Bosses

For machining small bosses where power is not available, or cannot be used owing to the location of the boss

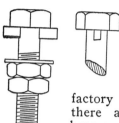

on the machine, a tool similar to that shown in the sketch will be found to accomplish the work in a very satisfactory manner. Where there are a number of bosses with holes of varying sizes it is best to have bolts turned to fit the holes, but the same facing cutter may be used for bolts of different sizes, and by the use of bushings, one bolt may be used on several different-sized holes.

The tool shown was made to face a boss, $1\frac{5}{16}$ in. in diameter, with a $\frac{5}{8}$-in. hole through it. It consists of a $\frac{5}{8}$-in. hexagon-head turned bolt with a slot under the head to take a $\frac{3}{16}$ by $\frac{3}{8}$-in. tool-steel cutter, backed off on opposite sides, at the ends, for clearance. A washer and two hexagon nuts with rounded corners complete the arrangement. The nut directly beneath the washer is the feed, while the function of the locknut is to prevent the bolt from turning in the feed nut, and from jamming when the wrench is applied to the bolt head.—Contributed by J A. Shelley, Brooklyn, N. Y.

Black Varnish for Leather

A varnish for use in making a mixture to coat leather black, so that it will not break by rough handling, is as follows: Equal quantities of turpentine, turpentine oil, and resin are mixed together, 30 parts each. Then 6 parts of sandarac gum and 120 parts of shellac are added, whereupon the whole mixture is dissolved in 900 parts of 90-per-cent alcohol. The liquid thus prepared is filtered and then 15 parts of fine lampblack, previously dissolved in a little alcohol, is thoroughly mixed in it. Apply with a soft rag.

Grinding Machine-Cutter Knives without Special Machinery

The knives used on paper cutters, wood planes, in leather work, etc., require a special machine for grinding. They must have a keen, straight edge, preferably a little hollow ground. The grinding machines are expensive, and as their field of usefulness is limited, they are seldom found except where much of this work is being done. However, with the rig described, such knives can be well ground on any emery wheel, or grindstone, having its bearings well fitted and being of a grade adapted to some form of tool grinding. Theoretically, the only proper wheel is the one of the grit and grade for knives, but, with care in not overheating, any wheel can be made to do the work.

Take two pieces of flat iron, A, say $\frac{1}{2}$ by 1 in., bend a hook on one end of each and clamp them with C-clamps, B, one on each side of the wheel, to the frame of the machine. Procure a piece of angle iron, C, of any size, and lay across the two bent ends. Place the knife as shown, and grasping its back with a hand at each end, feed it back and forth across the wheel's face. If the pieces A are set about right, the weight of the blade will furnish sufficient pressure to grind without bearing

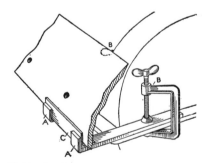

Holder for Grinding Machine-Cutter Knives on an Ordinary Stone or Emery Wheel

down on it and the hands simply move the knife across the stone. If a straight edge is required check it with a straightedge, unless this can be determined with the eye.

To Plane Aluminum Segments

In a certain machine an aluminum band was required. This band being 3⅛ in. wide, 34½ in. inside diameter and 36 in. out-side diameter, was cast in four segments. The only finishing required was to

cut the width from 3⅛ in. down to 3 in., to smooth the edges and make each segment the same width.

To hold them so that they would not be bent out of shape was not an easy thing, as the light metal was readily sprung. All four pieces were put to-gether on edge on the planer and placed against two angle plates to which they were lightly held with two clamps. Blocks of wood were wedged down in the spaces between the seg-ments in their centers and then the clamps could be tightened sufficiently to hold the cut taken without bending the segments out of shape. After tak-ing a cut on one side a clamp was put on the center to keep the pieces in po-sition while turning them over and un-til the end clamps were again applied.

For roughing off aluminum use a keen, round-pointed and slightly V-shaped tool. For finishing, say, remov-ing $\frac{1}{100}$ in., use a broad, flat tool, and a highly polished surface will be the result.—Contributed by Donald A. Hampson, Middletown, N. Y.

How to Plug a Boiler Tube

A leaky tube in a fire-tube boiler may be fixed at reasonable cost by means of plugs and a rod, as illus-

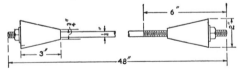

Tapered Cast-Iron Plugs and a Rod Used to Stop Up a Leaky Boiler Tube

trated. The dimensions given are suit-able for a tube length of 40 to 44 in. and a diameter of about 2½ in. Two pieces of cast iron are drilled with a ½-in. drill and then turned tapering on the outside. A ½-in. rod, with a short thread on one end and a longer thread on the other, is provided. One plug is driven into each end of the leaky tube, the rod is put in and the nuts are tightened. A little asbestos packing is of advantage. Other sizes may be made in proportion. A tube plugged in this manner will last for years, but it should, nevertheless, be taken out and replaced at the first opportunity, for the plugs are only intended as a temporary repair.

Lengthening the Stroke Limit of a Shaper Head

A small shop with limited equipment but doing a great variety of general work is the birthplace of a great many ingenious methods for getting the work out in spite of innumerable obstacles. One small shop possessing a shaper with a limited stroke had a job of machining the bottom faces of a large crossyoke. The side toward the head of the shaper could be reached readily, but the head could not be thrown for-

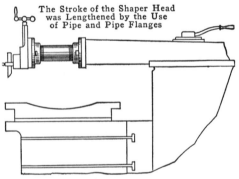

The Stroke of the Shaper Head was Lengthened by the Use of Pipe and Pipe Flanges

ward far enough to finish a cut on the opposite side of the yoke. It was im-practical to shift the work in the chuck, as it was necessary to have the faces of the cuts true. The method used to overcome the difficulty was a last re-sort to prevent the job from going to another shop, and was very practical.

After the inner side of the yoke had been machined, the head of the shaper was removed and again applied after two pipe flanges and a short nipple had been inserted, thus throwing the head of the shaper ahead of the limit allowed by its construction. The cuts taken were necessarily a trifle lighter to prevent chattering of the improvised head extension, but aside from that the results were very satisfactory. The sketch will readily show how the head was extended by means of the large pipe fittings.

Oil Feed for Machine-Cutting Tools

A simple but good oil feed can be made of an old oilcan, as shown. The

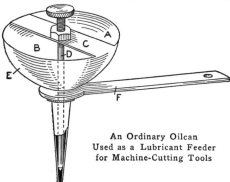

An Ordinary Oilcan
Used as a Lubricant Feeder
for Machine-Cutting Tools

sections A and B are cut from the bottom of the can, leaving the strip C, which is the width of a small-sized nut. The nut is soldered to the center of the strip, and a pin, D, threaded part way, is screwed through the nut, the unthreaded part being filed to a size a trifle smaller in diameter than the threaded part. A piece of sheet iron is shaped as shown at F, and slipped over the neck of the can, where it is held by the spout when the latter is in place. The can may then be attached to any part of the machine for use. Oil or lubricant is poured into the can and the flow regulated by the pin D.—Contributed by Jos. J. Kolar, Maywood, Ill.

Glass Gauge Used as a Ruler

A heavy glass gauge makes an excellent ruler for ink work. In addition to its being transparent, it safeguards against accidental blotting, as any ink adhering to its surface is clearly seen.

Holder for a Center-Clearance Drill

A very simple and handy tool for machinists, especially for those not supplied with combination centering

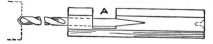

Holder for a Center-Clearance Drill
to be Used in a Lathe

drills, is shown in the sketch. The tool consists of a piece of hexagon brass with a notch cut out, as shown at A, a V-shaped opening cut in the center with a hacksaw, and a hole drilled to receive the shank of a drill and a center hole drilled in the opposite end. The hexagon shape affords a ready grip for the hand. The dotted lines show the work when the holder is in position for use after being centered. The straight shank of the drill is ground tapering, like a chisel edge, to fit into the V-shaped notch cut in the holder. —Contributed by John Harger, Honolulu, H. I.

Plunger Repair in an Automobile Gear Box

The plunger which prevents the gears in the gear box of an automobile from any movement broke, as indicated in the sketch, at A. As a new one would cost more than I cared to pay I decided to repair it at home. The repair was made as shown. A piece of hardened drill rod was inserted to replace the broken upper portion and a steel ball was placed between the two pieces. By forcing the two together a firm and secure joint was made, the metal of the upper portion B being forced between the ball and the lower piece. This joint is much better than a threaded joint. —Contributed by Adolph Klein, New York City.

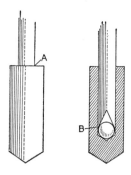

Cutting Special Threads without a Lathe

To make a screw on a rod or shaft of any diameter using only a standard thread cutter, proceed as shown in the

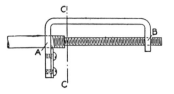

SECTION C-C

The Standard-Size Threads Make a Feed for the Tool Which Cuts the Threads on the Large Part

sketch. A piece of flat iron is bent and drilled, at A, to receive the shaft, and tapped, at B, with a standard thread of the required pitch. A thread-cutting tool is made of flat tool steel, ground to a 60-deg. cutting point and clamped to the flat iron with two screws, as shown.

The shaft on which the screw is to be made is turned down at the end and a standard thread cut on the end. The shaft is then inserted in the large hole in the flat iron and turned into the threaded hole, which causes a thread to be cut on the large part. A better thread can be made by taking several light cuts. The end with the standard threads is cut off, leaving only the special thread on the shaft.—Contributed by Phillip K. McGall, W. Orange, N. J.

A Hinge to Make a Door Self-Closing

When fastening strap hinges on a barn door it is a good plan to bend the wings of the lower hinge at right angles as shown.

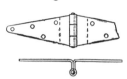

This is easily done by gripping the hinge in a vise ⅜ in. or more below the joint, the amount depending on the size of the hinge. A door arranged with a lower hinge of this kind will have a tendency to swing shut at all times.—Contributed by J. V. Loeffler, Evansville, Ind.

Supplying Drinking Water to Shop Hands

A manufacturing concern found that their men lost about 15 minutes by stopping their machines, laying down their tools and walking to the cooler, located in the center of the shop, for a drink. Sometimes they had to wait their turn, or they would swap a story, walk back and start their work. The cooler was taken out and at regular intervals during the day a boy passed water to the workmen in individual glasses carried in wire trays. They also offered it to everyone in the offices, and it was rarely refused. This practice saved a large amount of time in a year and in addition improved the drinking habits and consequently the general habits of the men.—Contributed by T. F. Webster, Pittsburgh, Pa.

Measuring the Thrust of an Aeroplane Motor

Sometime ago I had occasion to measure the thrust of my aeroplane motor, and as I had no scale large enough, I rigged up the arrangement

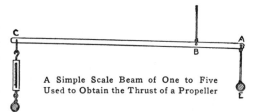

A Simple Scale Beam of One to Five Used to Obtain the Thrust of a Propeller

shown in the drawing, making the distance AB 1 ft., and AC, 5 ft. At A, the lever was fastened to the stake E by means of a wire; at B, the wire from the machine was fastened, and a 50-lb. spring balance was attached at C. The reading of the spring balance should be multiplied by 5.

If a larger balance were used it could be moved nearer B with more accurate results, the reading always being multiplied by the number of times AB is contained in AC.—Contributed by Geo. F. Hess, Corvallis, Ore.

Draw Collets for Milling Tools

The milling machine I was using had a draw collet for $\frac{1}{2}$-in. cutter shanks, and as some work required the use of a $\frac{3}{16}$-in. end mill, I had no way of holding them. I therefore made a collet for these mills as follows:

A piece of cold-rolled steel, 2 in. long, was drilled centrally with a $\frac{3}{16}$-in. hole

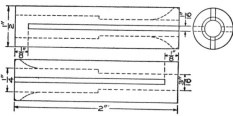

A Draw Collet Having Different Diameter in Each End for Small Mills

through its entire length, and then a $\frac{1}{4}$-in. hole halfway. A slot was cut through the diameter, beginning at one end and extending to within $\frac{1}{8}$ in. of the other; then another slot was cut at right angles to the first slot and finishing $\frac{1}{8}$ in. from the end in the same manner, only beginning and finishing at opposite ends from the first slot. This formed a double-end socket for $\frac{3}{16}$ and $\frac{1}{4}$-in. end mills.

A draw collet can be made in this manner very cheaply, and it has two sizes. The smaller mills have the shank the same size as the cutter, which must have a holder, or else the tool will not run true.—Contributed by Walter Butz, Pearl River, N. Y.

A Substitute Packing Screw

After breaking the last packing screw I had, in an effort to remove some old packing from the gland of a main feed pump, I used the next best thing that happened to be at hand, which was a $\frac{3}{8}$-in. lag screw, 6 in. long. This proved to be a better device to remove the packing, as the large thread took a good hold in the soft packing and did not pull out.—Contributed by Edwin M. Davis, Philadelphia, Pa.

To Repair a Flush-Tank Float Valve

The outlet valve in my closet flush tank leaked badly and when I examined it, the rubber on the under side of the ball was found to be roughened by contact with the outlet seat and let the water through. The repair was made, after turning the water off, by removing the valve and cleaning the roughened surface well with

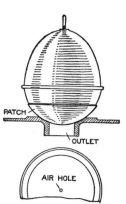

gasoline, then applying rubber cement and a rubber patch larger than the valve seat. This fitted the valve seat smoothly enough to hold the water.— Contributed by W. E. Crane, Cleveland, Ohio.

To Handle Large Blueprints

Experience in handling large blueprints on the drawing board has proved the simplicity of the following method in saving much wear and tear on the prints and greatly facilitating the reference to any part. Fold the print into at least six parts, the folds running from the top to the bottom of the print. The folds can be turned over like the pages of a book, and the whole print occupies so much less space and is so much more easily handled that it can be kept on the drawing board without

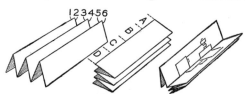

Folding and Indexing Blueprints for Ready Reference in Using on a Drawing Board

in the least interfering with the work.

To still further facilitate reference where there is much confusing detail, divide each print vertically into 6-in. spaces, giving each space a letter, beginning at the top with A. Number the folds 1, 2, 3, etc., as if they were pages in a book. By means of simple notes, as A-3, B-6, etc., like the marginal key to a map, this system provides a ready means of finding any desired part easily.—Contributed by J. Harmer Knight, Philadelphia, Pa.

Claw Hammer Used for Detaching a Rim

An automobilist recently asked me to help him remove what he termed a quick-detachable rim from one of the wheels on his car. After watching him try to pry it loose with a screwdriver, I procured an ordinary claw hammer

The Claw on a Carpenter's Hammer Inserted under a Rim will Quickly Remove It

and, inserting the claw in the space he had opened with the screwdriver, easily removed the rim. No doubt it would be a good plan to include a claw hammer in the auto tool box.—Contributed by James M. Kane, Doylestown, Pa.

Removing Oil from Marble

In shops it is sometimes desirable to remove grease and oil from marble floors, or marble used in machine construction. An easy and effective way is to apply strong lye and quicklime. Any-strength solution can be made as needed and no matter how strong it may be, it will not injure the marble. The best method of application is to simply throw on the lye, powder with the quicklime and use some water with a scrub brush. The solution can be kept ready for use and marble slabs can be cleaned daily.—Contributed by Loren Ward, Des Moines, Ia.

Temporary Repair on a Valve-Gear Link

One of my men informed me that one of the larger boiler-feed pumps was disabled, says a correspondent of

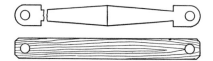

The Broken Link was Removed and One Cut from a Piece of Wood Substituted

Southern Engineer, and it was found that one of the links in the valve gear had been broken. As we had no spare pump at that time, something had to be done, and done in a hurry. Seeing a piece of 2 by 4-in. scantling in the boiler room, I grabbed a saw and soon had a wood link made, as shown in the sketch. In 35 minutes I had the pump running, and this served the purpose until there was time to have a new link made.

A Double Lock for a Door

When a lock is of simple construction and a more secure one is desired an additional safety device can be

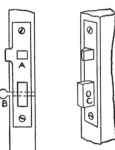

easily attached to it. The door is closed and the lock bolt turned, then a hole, about 1/8 in., is drilled through the frame of the door, just back of the plate A, passing through the bolt, as shown at C. By this arrangement the door can be secured from the inside with a pin, B, pushed into the hole and through the bolt C. A skeleton key, or other lock-picking devices, cannot withdraw the bolt. The hole in the bolt should be a trifle larger than the pin and countersunk slightly on both sides to allow for any slight movement out of line.—Contributed by Joseph J. Kolar, Maywood, Ill.

Tool for Cutting Square Holes in Metals

A special tool for cutting square holes in iron, or other metals, is shown in the sketch. It is made of the best grade of tool steel with the body square and tapering and teeth cut, as shown, the top one being the size of the required hole. As accuracy in graduating the thickness and pitch of the teeth is of great value, it is advisable to cut them in a machine, although it can be done by hand with a file. In tempering the tool, be careful to secure an even hardness throughout.

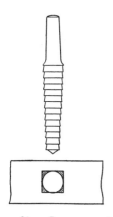

To cut the square hole, first drill a hole of the same diameter as the sides of the square hole desired. Hold the iron over the open jaws of a solid box vise, an anvil hole or a dressing plate, and insert the cutter, then, with a few blows of a hammer, start the cutter, which takes the corners out gradually as the tool penetrates the hole, the material removed dropping from the hole until finally the cutter passes through, giving it the desired dimensions.

In order to prevent the cutter from heating and to insure a smooth cut, it is advisable to dip the cutter in oil before using it. To protect it from striking the hardened surfaces of the vise jaws, pieces of hardwood should be used on the jaws.

With a properly made tool, round holes in iron, ½ in. thick, can be made perfectly square quickly. Holes of other shapes, oval, triangular, penta-hedral, hexagonal, etc., can be cut successfully by using a tool made on this principle.—Contributed by Pierre Wagner, Indianapolis, Ind.

Drill Press Used to Cut Spiral in a Shaft

Having a long spiral to cut in a shaft that was too long for the lathe or milling machine, I did the job very successfully in a drill press. After it was finished, mechanics who had varied experiences would not believe that such a good job could be done on a drill press.

As the lead had to be four turns per foot, a piece of ¼ by 1-in. bar iron of suitable length was cut and placed within a 1-in. pipe, 12 in. long. One end of the flat iron was gripped in a vise, while the other end was turned with a strong wrench to make four complete turns. The spiral thus formed served as a lead screw for the work. The spiral and stock were

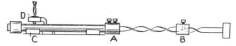

The Spiral Thrust Gave the Proper Turns to the Shaft under the Drill Point

fastened together with a coupling, at A, and a guide block, B, was clamped to the table, while the work was resting on V-blocks, C. The drill was guided with a jig, D, which was fastened to the platen of the machine.—Contributed by Albin P. Swaidmark, Orlando, Florida.

A Basement Hotbed

What might be termed a greenhouse in miniature may be easily constructed in one side of the basement of the if the hotbed is built at the side of a room containing a furnace, sufficient heat will be provided by the furnace to enable one to raise tender crops even though the glass is only one thickness.

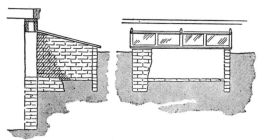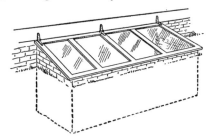

The Hotbed is Merely an Extension of the House Wall and is Covered with Double-Glazed Sash, the Entrance Being from the Basement of the House, so That the Bed is Kept Warm by the Furnace and the Sun's Rays

average house at very small expense. If the hotbed is to be built in a new house it will be an easy matter for the workmen to build up the walls, as shown in the sketch, leaving the side open into the basement. As there is practically no weight to support, the walls need not be any thicker than 4 in. or the width of one course of brick.

The bottom of the bed should be at such a height that it may be easily reached while standing on the basement floor, yet not so deep that the outside walls will interfere with the rays of the sun striking the bed.

The walls are built up a trifle higher than the surface of the ground on the outside and the ends slope up to the house until they are 1 ft. higher than the front. Make the surface of the sloping ends smooth with mortar so that a close joint will be made when the sash is laid on it.

Timbers, 2 by 8 in., are placed over the opening in the wall between the hotbed and the basement, so that their upper edges are level with the top of the wall for the house. The sash that cover the hotbed are hinged to the outside timber. If they do not fit on the walls snugly, pieces of felt may be cut in narrow strips and glued to the underside of the sash where they strike the upper surface of the walls.

The sash should be double-glazed, that is, have two pieces of glass with an air space between them. However,

The bed is filled in with rich soil and fertilizer to a depth of 10 or 12 in. Such a hotbed will produce all the early lettuce, radishes, etc., required for the average table before the ground in the garden has thawed sufficiently to work it. It also provides an excellent place to force tender plants in the spring and to have them started and vigorous by the time they can be safely set out in the garden.—Contributed by O. J. Thompson, Petersburg, Ill.

Starting a Tap in a Pulley Hub

It is not an easy matter to start a short tap in a hole drilled in the hub of a small pulley. Having a number of these to tap for setscrews, I devised the tap starter shown. It consists of an ordinary bolt, of a size to pass through the drilled hole in the pulley face, and with its nut placed on the inner surface. If the bolt does not have a square or octagon head, it can be turned at right angles, as shown, to make a handle. The tap can be easily started straight with the bolt.—Contributed by J. W. Madison, Oshkosh, Wis.

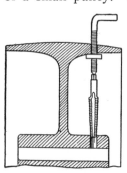

Locking a Cork in a Bottle

The sketch shows a bottle cork which will not slip out and spill the contents of the bottle while carried in the pocket, suitcase or grip, if bounced or jolted. I have found this a very efficient method and by using glass-headed steel pins a neat appearance is presented.

The pins are run through the cork so that their lower ends, or points, extend under the shoulders of the bottle neck. —Contributed by M. C. Erwin, Gallup, New Mexico.

Inserting Rod in a Lace Curtain

To put a rod through a sash or window lace curtain usually is a rather trying matter, as the rod often catches in the material, which is easily torn. To avoid this, place a thimble or a glove finger tip on the end of the rod before pushing it through the hem of the curtain. The result will be found satisfactory and the job done with little difficulty.—Contributed by Freda Nehls, New York City.

Plummet-Cord Adjuster on a Transit

In using a transit, I have tried many different methods of adjusting the length of the cord supporting the plummet without perfect satisfaction, but I have now adopted a device of my own that I like best of all and which is as follows: A loop, about 3 in. long, is made on one end of a small silk or linen cord, having a length of about 10 in. This I suspended, loop down, from the leveling head. On the cord which suspends the plummet I tie single overhand knots, about 1 in. apart, for almost its entire length. By passing the end of the cord through the loop, I can use whatever length is needed, and a knot will prevent it from slipping when suspended.—Contributed by J. L. Bayley, Ione, Wash.

Pipe-Thread Lubricant

A lubricant for the threads on large pipe fittings is a mixture of ½ pt. black machine oil, 2 oz. white lead, 8 oz. graphite, and about half a teaspoonful of flour of emery. The emery will smooth the threads, and the oil and lead will make a fine lubricant of enough body to stop any leak.

Location Board for Employes

The whereabouts of any employe, regardless of the number of floors and departments, may be easily kept track of on a board similar to that shown in the illustration. The board and spaces can be of any size. A check is used for each employe with his or her name as well as the department lettered on it.

The board is placed at the doorway of each floor, or at the desk of the foreman in charge. If an employe works most of the time on the fourth floor, the check is kept as designated in the lower row, but on leaving to go to the second floor in the department employed, he hangs his check on the second-floor row of that department column.

PLACE CHECK IN RIGHT SPACE BEFORE LEAVING							
OUT	DEPT 1	DEPT 2	DEPT 3	SMITH	DEPT 5	DEPT 6	DEPT 7	DEPT 8
1ST Floor								
2d Floor							JONES	
3d Floor								
4th Floor		BROWN						

A Board on Which to Hang Checks to Designate the Place Where an Employe is at Work

Then, if the foreman should have a call over the telephone for anyone, he would only have to look at the board to know where to find that person. When anyone leaves the building his check would be placed on the space designating the department in which he is employed.—Contributed by Milton Pilhashy, San Francisco, Cal.

Entrance Signal for a Garage

One ingenious garage owner rigged up an electric bell to ring when an automobile was entering the runway

Trip Bar in an Entrance Runway to Make Connections for an Inside Electric Bell

on the outside, so that the assistant could be called to open the doors. This is an especially handy device for winter, or when the doors of the garage are kept closed. The device consists of the ordinary electric-bell connections with the wires running underground to the curbing on the runway, where they are connected to the switch. The runway has a trip bar, set in the paving with the end extending into the curb, where it works the switch when pressure is applied by the automobile wheels. A coil spring is placed under the curb end of the bar to keep it in its upper position and the electric contact broken. The runway end of the bar is hinged.

The electric switch, which is well protected from the weather by being boxed over, is a simple arrangement of two springs pressed together by a projection on the end of the bar.—Contributed by F. H. Tillotson, Chicago.

Removing a Stuck Shank from a Drill Spindle

The usual method of removing drills or drill chucks from the end of a drill-press spindle is to use a tapered drift.

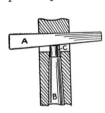

Occasionally, however, some one drives a drill in that has a short stem or shank, which does not reach up to the drift slot so that it can be driven out. The illustration shows such a condition. The drift A cannot touch the end of the drill shank B. Instead of pounding and twisting to get the drill out, procure a short piece of round rod, C, slightly smaller than the drill shank and of such length that, when dropped in on the end of the drill, the drift may be entered in its slot. A little oil on the edges of the drift will be of assistance in either case.—Contributed by Donald A. Hampson, Middletown, N. Y.

A Garden Cultivator

The cultivator can be constructed of ordinary materials found about any farm, but the stock can be purchased

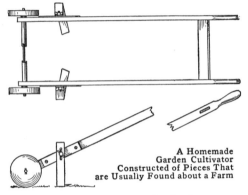

A Homemade Garden Cultivator Constructed of Pieces That are Usually Found about a Farm

and the amount required does not make the cost very great. The width of the cultivator will depend on the width of the planted rows of seeds.

The wheels and handles are wood, the axle is a 3/8-in. steel rod with 1/8-in. holes drilled near each end for cotters. Two washers are used on each side of a wheel. A piece of 1/2-in. pipe is placed on the axle to keep the handles apart at the lower end, and a tenoned crossbar, mortised in the upper part of the handles, separates them in a like manner.

The blades are made of suitable steel, bent as shown and sharpened on the edge where they touch the ground. The upper ends of the blades are slotted and fastened to the handles with a bolt having a thumb nut.—Contributed by W. E. Crane, Cleveland.

¶Heat together 10 parts lime, 12 parts resin and 1 part linseed oil, and when thoroughly dissolved and hot, apply to a wood surface. This will make a coating almost as hard as stone.

A Homemade Solar Heater

People living in sections having a goodly proportion of sun every day realize the value of a solar heater both in convenience and the saving of fuel. A heater equal in all respects to any factory-made can be built at less than one-fifth their cost by using an ordinary cylindrical range boiler or hot-water tank for the heater part. Select one of suitable size for all requirements, either new or second-hand. Make a box, into which the tank will fit, with about 1 in. space between the sides of the tank and box, leaving one side open for the glass. Nail narrow molding of door-size stop around the inside of the box and about ⅜ in. from the open edge, to form a rest for the glass, which must be set in with putty.

Bore holes in the box for the pipe connections, and any extra holes in the tank should be plugged. Paint both tank and the inside of the box with two coats of lampblack.

After placing the tank in the box and connecting the service pipes, stop all holes and joints with putty, fasten the glass on the face, just as a window pane, and the heater is ready for service. If pressure water is used, it can be placed near the ground and it will give as good service as if placed on the roof. The box should be placed in a horizontal position, the length running due east and west, with the face at such an angle as will expose it to the direct rays of the sun.—Contributed by E. C. Knopf, San Ysidro, Cal.

Flexible Sandpaper Block

Plane a number of strips, 1 in. wide, and taper them from $\frac{3}{16}$ in. at one

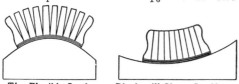

The Flexible Sandpaper Block will Shape Itself to Fit and Smooth an Uneven Surface

edge down to ⅛ in. at the other. If desired, the outside strips can be made thicker, to permit a groove to be cut

for the finger tips. After giving them a coat of shellac, assemble the strips to make the size of block wanted. A convenient-size block is one made 8 in. long by 2 in. wide. Obtain a piece of single-ply belting, the older the better, and stick it to the broad surface of the block with thick shellac.

When it is dry, drive some brads through the leather into the strips to securely fasten it in place. The sandpaper is glued to the leather, or held on with the ends extending under the grip of the fingers. This block is very handy, as it can be used on both flat, and convex or concave surfaces.—Contributed by C. White, Brooklyn, N. Y.

A Bag Holder

The bag holder shown in the sketch is designed to hang on a barrel, bin, truck, or any other convenient place. The parts are made of strap iron and shaped as shown, requiring no exact lengths. The yoke should be the size of the bag top. The U-shaped pieces at the sides permit the top of the sack to be turned over the yoke. Two clips are riveted to the moving part,

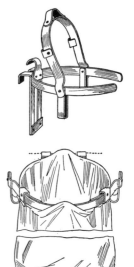

projecting over and catching on the yoke sides to prevent it from dropping too far down. The hooks and vertically extending parts are used to hold it on a box or barrel.

To fill the bag, place its upper edge over the hook at the back and between the yoke, so that the edge overhangs. The clamping band is drawn down over the bag top where it holds the cloth securely without injury.—Contributed by J. F. Reed, Johnstown, Pa.

Line-Shaft Polisher

Nothing makes a better impression in a well-appointed and tidy shop than to see the line shafts free from rust and oil, and at the same time polished. A little attention each day with the polisher illustrated will keep a shaft in such a condition. The polisher is made of a piece of soft wood, about 4 in. thick, 5 in. wide, and 12 in. long, to which a hardwood handle, 8 ft. long, is attached. A semicircular groove is cut on each side, as shown, a little larger than the diameter of the largest shaft in the shop. One groove is lined with several thicknesses of heavy cotton cloth, and the other, with a sheet of coarse emery cloth, both tacked securely in place.

Apply the emery side first, then use the cloth side, moving the polisher along slowly back and forth on the shaft while it is turning. This will produce the desired result. A hook is provided so that on long stretches of shaft a weight of 10 or 15 lb. may be hung on it, thereby making the operation easier.—Contributed by A. Dane, Pottstown, Pa.

Calculating Pipe Size to Take Flow from Two Pipes

To ascertain the proper diameter of a pipe to take the flow of water from two pipes of any given diameter, lay out a right-angled triangle with the base equal to the diameter of one pipe and the height equal to the other. The length of the hypothenuse will be the desired diameter. A carpenter's steel square is handy for this problem within its limits.—Contributed by J. A. Shelley, Brooklyn, N. Y.

Cleaning Marble Floors

A good way to clean marble or mosaic floors when the dirt clings in the crevices is as follows: Apply powdered table soda over the floor or the dirty spots. Then apply a 5-per-cent solution of acetic acid. This solution may be purchased at any drug store. There will be considerable foaming for a few seconds. As soon as this stops, the solution should be removed at once and the floors washed with clean soapsuds. The articles mentioned are harmless to the hands. The acetic acid should not be left where small children might drink it.—Contributed by Loren Ward, Des Moines, Iowa.

A Feeding Trough

The feeding of hogs in a trough is always a troublesome task, as the hogs will get in the way of the food if it is in a liquid form, and prevent the trough from filling evenly. One farmer overcame this difficulty by setting the trough on the outside of the fence and hinging a panel of the fence so that the bottom would swing outward. A stop is placed at each end to hold the panel in place while the food is poured in the trough. The stops are also used to prevent the panel from being pushed farther than the outside of the trough. The food is placed in the trough evenly and then the stops

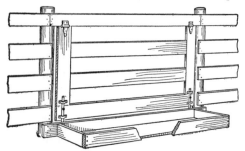

A Feed Trough on the Outside of a Fence to Prevent Swine from Getting in the Food

are raised and lowered to catch on the outside edge of the trough. The trough should be secured to the fence post at each end.

Reinforced Babbitt Bearings

The sketch illustrates a valuable and easily applied improvement for pillow-block and all forms of bearings that are babbitted. The coiled soft-brass or copper wire prolongs the life of the bearing, makes a better fit, and will be found specially valuable in the upkeep of high-speed and heavy machinery.

The application is as follows: Before pouring the babbitt take a piece of soft, not hard, brass or copper wire

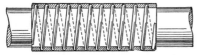

A Babbitt Reinforcement of Coiled Brass Wire to Make a Harder-Wearing Surface for Bearings

of such gauge that it will just fill the space allotted for the babbitt and make surface contact with the shaft, and prepare the coil by winding the wire around a piece of shaft or wood having the same diameter as the machine shaft, the coils to be ¼ in. apart for the entire length of the bearing. Remove the arbor and place the coiled wire in the bore to be babbitted and pour the babbitt around the wire, then scrape to a fit.

Hard wire should not be used because of the extra care required in fitting, and, besides, the soft wire is better in many other ways. This is an easy and cheap way of producing bearings that will last, and also gives a chance to utilize the scrap wire about a shop or factory. Furthermore, it is a good method to use in constructing models or machines in the home workshop.

Packing between Storage Cells and the Case

A toy hollow rubber ball forced into the space between a storage battery and its case is an effective means of keeping it from jostling around and also absorbs all jolts and jars. These balls can be purchased cheaply in various sizes suitable for the space to be filled.

Drawing Brass Tubes by Hand

Small tubes of light brass or copper are easily drawn by hand with a pair of pliers through a hole drilled in a piece of ¼-in. iron or steel held in a vise. The flat strip of metal should be exactly as wide as the circumference of the hole through which it is to be drawn, and it should be pointed on one end sufficiently to start it through the hole. Then it is grasped in a pair of pliers and drawn through with a good steady pull. If the metal has been cut the proper width, the resulting tube will be tight enough to convey oil without soldering.

Ferrule for Straight-Shank Tools

The ordinary ferrule, as applied to file and chisel handles, is all right as long as the article to be held has a tapered shank, or tang, so that it can be tightened when becoming loose. When the shank is straight, it is not easy to tighten the tool in the handle. In order to cause a handle to grip a straight shank, I use a special ferrule as shown in the sketch.

This ferrule is made of brass or steel tubing and is tapered on the inside. The taper is formed with a taper reamer. The ferrule seat on the handle is given approximately the same

taper as the inside of the ferrule. After drilling the hole for the shank, the handle is sawed lengthwise, two cuts being taken at right angles to each other, as the sketch clearly shows. The saw cuts form the handle into a four-jawed chuck, so that when the shank is placed in the handle and the ferrule driven down on the seat, the jaws will grip the shank tightly. If the tool works loose, a few taps of a hammer on the ferrule will close the jaws and tighten it again.—Contributed by Clyde L. Adams, La Grange, Ill.

Anchors for Babbitt Bearings

Usually designers of machinery give the patternmaker a great deal of trouble in allowing for babbitt anchors

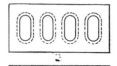 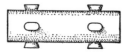

Box for Molding Cores to Make Holes in Machinery-Bearing Boxes for Babbitt Anchors

in bearings. With my method this is simplified. In making a bearing core box, only show some spots with red shellac and make a core box for the core maker, as shown to the left in the sketch. These cores can be kept as a standard by the foundry and used always for bearings. This will eventually save many dollars, as complicated core boxes are often needed. The manner of pasting and nailing sand anchors on the ordinary stock cores is shown at the right. If the bearings are cast in green-sand molds, the anchors will be placed on the green-sand mold.—Contributed by J. C. Hansen, Maywood, Ill.

Supports for Reinforcing Rods

A support for reinforcing rods, used in concrete-floor construction, is shown in the sketch. The supports are made

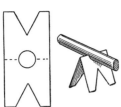

of heavy galvanized sheet metal, about 2 in. wide and 4 in. long. A hole is punched in the center for the size of the rods used, and notches are cut in the ends to facilitate the flow of concrete. The metal is then bent on the center line, leaving the ends 1 in., or more, apart, so that the support can stand alone. They are placed at proper intervals under the rods, to support the latter above the floor forms and allow the concrete to flow under them. Their cost is slight and they answer the purpose in every way.—Contributed by C. W. Thomas.

Under-Inflation of Automobile Tires

Many automobile owners do not realize the importance of properly inflating their tires. This is mainly due to ignorance of the real nature of the tires. Two things must be considered in the construction of a tire, the envelope and the air cushion. The casing cannot support the weight; that is the function of the air cushion. Then it is evident that the greater the weight, the larger the air cushion must be, and as the air cushion increases in size the more pressure is required, hence there must be a certain pressure for a certain size tire.

If the air pressure is insufficient the tire itself must support some of the weight. The result of this is a flattened tire at the point in contact with the ground, and when the wheel is turning, every part of the casing is forced into this unnatural shape, then resumes its original size, so that each side of the casing bends out and springs back again at every revolution of the tire.

The casing is made up of several layers of rubberized canvas, vulcanized together. With a sufficient air cushion these layers all work together as one unit, but in the case of a flattened tire the working of the sides causes them to pull apart. This, in time, will result in the separation of the layers and then the working will cause them to chafe and heat so that the fabric becomes too weak to sustain the weight and a "blow-out" occurs.

There are several kinds of tire abuse, but under-inflation is the worst of all. The statistics of the leading tire manufacturers show that 75 per cent of the tires go out of service prematurely on account of insufficient inflation. Under-inflation not only wears out the various layers, but it also loosens the tread. The flattened condition of the tires, when the pressure is low, causes a little roll of rubber right in front of the point of contact of the tire with the ground. This tends to loosen the tread. In case of the clincher tire, under-inflation usually causes the tire to rim-cut before the fabric gives way. The continual working in and out over the hook of the rim soon cuts the tire.

The standard rule for right pressure is 20 lb. to every 1 in. of width. The following table is adopted by the leading tire manufacturers for correct pressures as applied to tires:

2½-in. tire,	50 lb.	4½-in. tire,	90 lb.
3 -in. tire,	60 lb.	5 -in. tire,	100 lb.
3½-in. tire,	70 lb.	5½-in. tire,	110 lb.
4 -in. tire,	80 lb.	6 -in. tire,	120 lb.

To pump a tire up to the right pressure and then take for granted that it will stay at that pressure, will result in a flattened tire, sooner or later. No tire is absolutely air-tight; each one should be tested at least twice a week, and if possible, every day, and air added as required. It is surprising how quickly the pressure will be reduced although there is no visible leak.— Contributed by W. A. Yoakam, Granville, O.

Care of Eyeglasses

To prevent glasses from covering with a veil of steam when one enters a warm room, rub them with some moist soap of any kind—not a sand soap—and polish while the soap is moist. If an accident should happen to the lens and cause it to break, a temporary repair can be made by pasting the parts together with liquid shellac. The shellac dries quickly and the mended lens will give good service until a new one can be procured.—Contributed by H. Martine Warner, E. Orange, N. J.

Clarinet-Reed Trimmer

Clarinet players will find a very cheap and efficient substitute for a reed trimmer in the ordinary finger-nail clip. A perfectly new reed is sometimes useless on account of being too soft, but it can be used by clipping, or trimming, the end in the same manner as finger nails are clipped.—Contributed by Wm. H. Patten, Belleville, New Jersey.

To Fill an Engineer's Torch with Wicking

Pass the end of the lamp wick down through the sleeve in the usual way, then bring the end up and tie it, at A, so that in pulling on the wick, at B, it will increase in size until the hole is filled tightly. Cut the wick off at the top and assemble the torch parts. This will save the wicking, and the hole can be easily filled as tightly as desired.—Contributed by C. G. Green, Toronto, Canada.

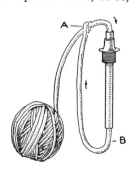

A Street-Gutter Cleaner

The superintendent of streets in a suburban city did not have a large number of street cleaners, and to quickly accomplish the work with a few hands, he devised the gutter cleaner shown in the sketch. The cleaner is made like a large hoe with shafts instead of a tongue or handle, and a horse is hitched to it. Two handles for the operator are attached to the rear part as on a plow. The scraping edge has a steel bar attached, and the scraper part can be set straight or at an angle as desired. The refuse

A Cleaner for Removing Dirt That Collects in the Gutters of a Street

falling into the gutter is thus easily and quickly scraped into piles and gathered into wagons.—Contributed by H. H. Sherer, Evanston, Ill.

Automobile Windshield for the Baby

It is almost impossible to keep a pair of goggles on a baby and dust out of its eyes while taking a ride in an open

A Windshield Made of Celluloid with a Metal Edge to Hold in Front of the Baby

automobile not having a windshield. The illustration shows a simple device made of sheet metal, preferably brass, and a piece of celluloid. The metal may be of double thickness riveted together over the edge of the celluloid to keep it in place. The shield is held in front of the baby in a very comfortable position.—Contributed by R. F. Pohle, E. Lynn, Mass.

Setting Difficult Work in a Chuck

In setting difficult work in a chuck to a finished surface that must not be marred by adjusting to the sound of a tool; where the part to be set true is out of reach to take a chalk mark; or where it cannot be seen, I find the appliance shown in the sketch to be indispensable.

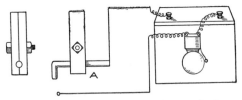

The Work must be Set True to Make a Perfect Electrical Contact during the Entire Revolution

The apparatus is made of a square box, just large enough to contain one dry cell of battery, and a bell attached on one side of the box, the connections being made as shown. This makes an outfit of convenient size for the tool kit.

In use, one terminal is connected to the lathe or boring bar, and the other, which is set in an insulated clamp, A, is used in the slot for the tool in the boring bar. Proceed to true up the piece in the same manner as if setting with a tool, and when the bell rings for the entire revolution of the piece, it is set absolutely true. On work in sight, this device in many cases produces quicker results than when setting to chalk marks.—Contributed by Ross Williams, St. Louis, Missouri.

Tying Horses to a Hitching Post

The illustration shows a way of tying horses to a hitching post so that the tie can be easily loosened. Double up the lines and insert the loop thus formed through the ring of the post. Then also double up the remaining end and pull this loop through the first one. This tie will hold the horses securely,

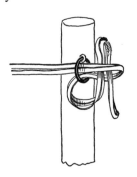

and is very quickly loosened by a quick pull on one end.—Contributed by C. H. Thomas, Norristown, Pa.

To Prevent Mucilage Accumulating on the Receptacle Edge

In our office a quantity of mucilage is kept in open pots. These pots soon gather an accumulation of hardened mucilage on their upper edges, and the brush handles become covered with it. This causes great inconvenience on account of the brushes sticking to the pot edges.

This trouble was avoided by applying a thin coat of paraffin on the edge of the pots and on the brushes above the bristles. The paraffin was melted in a tin can over a gas jet and was applied by "painting" it on with an old brush. This treatment is very effective, as the mucilage will not stick to the paraffin.—Contributed by Jas. A. Hart.

Hoisting with a Concrete Mixer

The problem of getting material out of an excavation for a reinforced-concrete job was solved in an unusual way by one contractor. The electrically driven concrete mixer was rigged up so it would do the lifting of the earth from the excavation. The mixer, which was of the cylindrical type, had a rope, leading out of the hole and fastened to the drum after passing over a set of sheaves. To hoist, the motor was run and the rope wound up on the drum of the mixer. For lowering, the weight of the empty bucket was usually sufficient and when it was not, or a braking action was required, the motor was reversed.—Contributed by Sidney K. Eastwood, Germantown, Pa.

Inserting a Fiber Gasket

A round gasket, cut from sheet packing, leaves some waste, and if a small portion of this waste is left attached, as shown, it can be used as a handle for inserting the gasket in place. Where flanges cannot be spread very far apart without removing a piece of the pipe, put one bolt through a hole in the gasket, and then it can be turned either way by the aid of the attached piece to locate the other holes. The piece can be cut off after the joint is tightened up.—Contributed by J. B. Bedore, Crivitz, Wis.

A Planer Clamp

There is a certain amount of work done on metal planers that cannot be bolted down directly to the bed or held in vises on it. Such work is held by what might be called compression; that is, a block, rib or plate is fastened to the planer bed, the work is placed against this fixed piece and by means of fingers, setscrew posts, etc., the work is pressed against the fixed piece hard enough to enable a cut to be taken on it. A holding or clamping

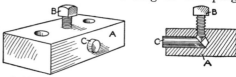

A Clamping Block Having a Laterally Sliding Pin Forced Out by a Vertical Screw

device for producing this lateral pressure is easily made as shown in the sketch. A block of steel, A, is drilled and tapped for a cone-pointed setscrew, B. At right angles to this hole, another hole is drilled in the block and a pin, C, fitted so that it will slide. The end of the pin on the inside is beveled to an angle of 45 deg., the same as the point of the setscrew. It is obvious that turning the screw downward drives the pin out of the side at the same rate. As many of the blocks as may be necessary or convenient may be grouped about a piece of work, or the device may be put in a long strip, in series. It is neat, simple and inexpensive, and should take the place of the various devices kept for the same kind of work.

Large Hand-Ladle Supports

Large and heavy hand ladles, filled with melted metal, are just a little more than a person can handle, especially when slow, steady pouring is required after carrying the metal quite a distance. If a support is placed on the handle, it holds the entire weight and the operator merely steadies and turns the handle. When walking and carrying the ladle, the support is held against the handle, and when ready to

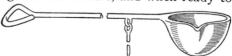

The Support Attached to a Hand-Ladle Handle Carries the Load for Steady Pouring

pour it is released. The pointed end prevents any slipping on wood or earthen surfaces.—Contributed by Bert Verne, San Diego, Cal.

Instruments for Taking Foreign Matter from the Eye

The sketch shows two very handy instruments for the shop "eye doctor." The loop, formed of ⅛-in. soft-iron wire, is pressed firmly over the outside

Instruments for the Use of the Shop Eye Doctor in Removing Foreign Substance from the Eye

of the eye. This loop holds the eye steady and the eyelid well down, thereby giving the operator a much better chance to remove the foreign substance.

The "pick" can be made of an old 6-in. round file, with the ends ground as shown. They should be stropped to a razor edge, and used only by one having a perfectly steady hand. These two articles have been in use for several years and have given complete satisfaction.—Contributed by A. Dane, Pottstown, Pa.

Cutting Keyways in a Lathe

Few of the small garages or the amateur workmen have other facilities for making keyways than chipping them in the pieces. This is slow work, requires considerable skill and is never satisfactory. The ever-present lathe, the king of tools, may be made to do the work very nicely.

If the keyway is to be cut in a shaft, place the shaft between the centers of a lathe, then put a tool of the proper size and shape in the tool post—preferably a tool of the gooseneck or spring type, but turned one-quarter way around from the normal position of the lathe tools. Block the gears of the lathe so that the spindle cannot revolve, run the tool up against the work and move it lengthwise of the lathe by turning the carriage wheel. This will make the first cut for the keyway. At each succeeding travel of the carriage, move the tool in a little deeper, and soon a very creditable keyway will be produced. This may seem to be hard

work, but it is a better way and easier to do than chipping out one with a chisel.

To cut an internal keyway, the principle is the same. Forge or grind a boring tool so that it will cut when moved lengthwise of the lathe. It is better to have the tool cut when it is being pulled out, as it is less apt to dig in when so operated. By this method a gear or pulley may be bored and keyseated at one setting.—Contributed by Donald A. Hampson.

How to Repair a Cylinder Lock for Worn Keys

Remove the cylinder from the lock, insert the key and turn it ¼ in.; loosen the screws in the cam on the back end of the cylinder and remove the cam, as shown at A. The plug is removed by placing the end of a ½-in. rod against the end of it, as shown at B. Push the plug out of the cylinder and follow it closely with the rod to hold the driving pins and springs in place.

When the plug is removed from the cylinder, as shown at C, the ends of the pins will be below the surface, due to the worn condition of the key. Smooth the plug down flush with the ends of the pins to overcome the catching of the pins in turning the cylinder. Replace the plug in the cylinder, in the same manner as it was taken out. Be

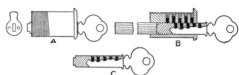

The Cylinder is Removed and the Surface Filed Down to the Level of the Pin Ends

sure to fasten the cam in place securely, and the cylinder will work as well as a new one.—Contributed by Wm. J. Tolson, Lyons, Iowa.

Substitute for a Demijohn

A handy demijohn for carrying drinking water in the fields, to laborers, on picnics, or to store liquids can be easily made of three large bottles of uniform size. The bottles are held together with several thicknesses of burlap drawn tightly around them and sewed in place. The contents can be kept cool by wetting the burlap.

To Make a Taper Hole with a Straight Reamer

If no taper reamer is at hand, a taper hole can be cut with a straight reamer by the method shown in the illustration, which is described by a correspondent of the American Machinist. A hole, the size of the small end of the taper hole wanted, is drilled into the work and a flat bottom cut, allowing a small portion of the drill-point depression to remain, which is drilled out slightly with a small drill to admit a steel ball halfway.

A Straight Reamer, the Shank of Which is Offset with the Tailstock, will Cut a Taper Hole

The center hole of the straight reamer is set on the ball as shown. The lathe tailstock is clamped to the ways solidly, and the holding-down bolt is loosened so that it can be crowded over with the adjusting screws to the taper required.

Coat Hanger in Coaches

The top or overcoat is a bothersome garment on a rail trip. There is no place provided for one to keep it from becoming wrinkled. One traveler suspends his extra coat by inserting the hanging strap through the bars of the package

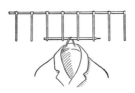

shelf, as shown, then putting a lead pencil through the loop. The pencil resting on the bars will hold the coat firmly in place, no matter how long or rough the journey may be.—Contributed by Wm. N. Robson, Pittsburgh, Pa.

Towing an Automobile with a Broken Rear Wheel

An accident left me several miles from a garage with a rear wheel brok-

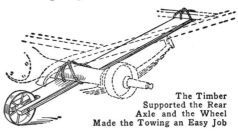

The Timber Supported the Rear Axle and the Wheel Made the Towing an Easy Job

en off from my automobile. A timber, 3 in. thick, 6 in. wide, and 12 ft. long, was lashed to one of the transverse angle irons under the front seat and extended under the rear axle, the end resting on the ground, but a team of horses could not start the machine. I finally hit upon the scheme of inserting a cultivator wheel in the end of the timber, as shown in the sketch. A slot was sawed in the timber end as wide as the wheel hub was long, and the wheel was held in place with a bolt inserted in a hole bored through the extending ends.—Contributed by L. L. Llewellyn, Hayward, Cal.

Oiling Piston Rings

It is necessary to use a sufficient amount of oil on piston rings, or they will score the cylinder bore. The neglect of this one thing often results in having to equip an engine with an entire new set of rings, and, in many cases, where the scoring is deep and reboring is necessary, new piston rings and piston also will be required to fit the new size.

Ground Colors for Paint

For vehicle painting it is found that while the very pale yellows, such as straw, light primrose, chamois, and canary appear best placed over a white groundwork, some of the deeper tones of yellow, such as primrose, sulphur, and deep chrome yellow, are at their best on an ivory-white ground.

Ink-Bottle and Print Holders on a Drawing Board

Sometimes it is required to incline the drawing board more than the

The Rod at the Upper Edge of the Drawing Board Has Holders for Ink Bottle and Prints

usual angle and it is then impossible to hold the ink bottle or the reference prints on its sloping surface. An attachment for this emergency, simple to make and also very effective, is shown in the sketch. A rod, ¼ in. in diameter, is held to the top of the board by means of supports at each side. U-shaped holders of sheet metal, with holes drilled through their ends, slide on the rod and provide means of attaching cords for holding a weight or the ink bottle.

The weight, which is made of 1½-in. cold-rolled stock, about 1 in. thick, is placed on the reference print to hold it in position. The ink bottle is held in a wood base and is connected to the rod with a cord. Thus they can be moved to any part of the board without trouble, and the device will prove helpful to those who do not possess other means to attain the same results.—Contributed by H. P. Reston, Rochester, N. Y.

How to Set a Lathe Steady Rest

There is quite a variety of lathe work that demands the steady rest to support one end of the work, while drilling, boring, centering and special turning are some of the jobs in which the tailstock is removed and the steady rest used. It is a well-known fact that a piece of work, held by the chuck and supported by the steady rest, will work out of the chuck if the steady-rest jaws are not set to bring the work in a true center line of the lathe.

Many mechanics can set the jaws of a chuck near enough central by eye, but there are some that cannot do this quickly. Of course, a piece of work can be put in true in the jaws and laboriously measured to center it, but a much quicker method is as follows: Place an arbor of the same diameter as the piece to be worked, between the centers of the lathe. Set the steady-rest jaws to the arbor with the fingers and tighten the binder screws. Put away the arbor and slide the tailstock out of the way. It is assumed that the steady rest is made with one or two V-shaped projections on the bottom and that, in setting it up, these projections are placed in position on the ways, or guides, of the lathe. The steady rest can be pushed along on the ways to the point where it is needed, and the work will be truly centered. The rest can be removed from the lathe and, if later on it is desired to do more of the same work, it will center as truly as before when replaced.

A Small Engine-Room Water Heater

In a boiler room, not having up-to-date conveniences, it is difficult to secure easily and quickly water of the right temperature to wash with at the termination of the shift or the day's work. The sketch is descriptive of a small water heater that can be constructed of old pipe fittings, and from which steam and water are very easily

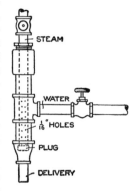

tapped so as to supply hot water whenever such is required. A little experimenting with the two valves will enable anyone to get a stream of water instantly of the exact temperature desired from the delivery.—Contributed by J. W. Bently, Jr., Milwaukee, Wis.

Oiler on a Diestock

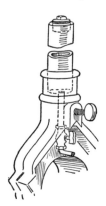

Plumbers always do most of their work on the job wherever it happens to be, and it is, therefore, difficult to keep an oilcan handy and filled with oil for lubricating the threads of the die. For this reason I provided an oil reservoir in one of the handles on my diestock, with 1/8-in. pipe connections at the end near the die and a petcock fitted in it for regulating the flow of oil. The illustration shows the connection. Only a few parts are required to have this oil supply always at hand, and one filling will last a long time.—Contributed by E. I. Beicher, Marion, Ohio.

Inserting Wires in Gas Pipes

Inserting electric wires in gas pipe is very difficult, especially if the pipe has any bends in it. A contractor having one of these pipes in a newel post that had three 90-deg. turns easily overcame the trouble by inserting a line for drawing in the wire with the use of a vacuum cleaner. A string was made into a ball almost as large as the inside diameter of the pipe and, fastening one end, the ball was started in the pipe at one end and the smallest nozzle of the cleaner placed over the other end. The ball was quickly sucked through the pipe, leaving a line that was used to draw in the wire.

Resilvering an Old Mirror

Clean the glass with powdered chalk, being careful not to scratch the glass. Dampen the chalk with a little alcohol and rub it dry with tissue paper. Make a liquid preparation by melting, in a porcelain vessel, 1 dr. of lead, 1 dr. of tin, and 1 dr. of bismuth. When these are melted together add 10 dr. of quick-silver before the mass cools. This will cool it sufficiently for use. Lay the glass flat, with the cleaned side up, and pour the liquid over it, completely covering the surface. Raise the glass to almost a perpendicular position and let the amalgam drain off quickly. When the coating has become perfectly hard and dry, coat it with drop black, ground in japan and then thinned with turpentine.

Fireproof Base for a Laundry Stove

To eliminate all danger of fire resulting from a laundry stove in the basement, I made a concrete base or shelf, as shown in the sketch. A form was made and set against the wall, the back being 6 in. lower than the front, with a border, 3 in. high, on the two outer sides. A hole was bored in the projecting corner large enough to admit a piece of 1-in. pipe, which was fitted with a floor flange on the bottom and set up in the hole, the top extending into the form about half as high as the edge. The wall and side of the chimney were cleaned and plastered with a rich mixture of cement to make it binding, then the form was filled to the top with cement. The form was removed after the setting of the cement, and it left a hard stone shelf firmly cemented to the wall with an iron leg in the outer corner fastened

A Fireproof Base Made of Cement for a Basement Laundry Stove

solidly in the cement. The shelf is 30 in. long by 24 in. deep, 3 in. thick in front, and 9 in. thick at the back.—Contributed by L. M. Johnson, Emsworth, Pa.

A Homemade Whip Socket

A whip socket can be made quickly from a length of pipe flattened on one end and bent at right angles, as shown. Two holes are drilled and countersunk in the flattened end for screws, to hold it in a convenient place. — Contributed by F. H. Tillotson, Chicago.

To Straighten a Miter Saw

In using a miter saw on wood with a spring to it, the saw is apt to stick so that a warp or uneven cutting edge is produced, which can be seen by sighting lengthwise of the teeth.

This warp can be removed by striking the top of the metal flange on the back of the saw, directly opposite the warp or kink, a sharp blow with a hammer. The necessary force can be determined by beginning with a light blow and increasing the force until the edge is straight.—Contributed by E. C. Knopf, San Ysidro, Cal.

Stiffening the Legs of a Bow Pencil

It is very common that a bow pencil has a tendency to run from its previous mark on account of its being weak, or having lost its rigidness. This can be easily remedied by placing a small piece of soft rubber, A—a piece cut from an old eraser will answer the purpose well—between the

A Piece of Soft Rubber Placed in the Crotch of the Bow Pencil Makes It More Rigid

springs. The stiffness can be varied by the thickness of the rubber.—Contributed by Ralph D. Curtis, South Bend, Ind.

A Wax-Fillet Machine

The construction of the machine shown in the illustration allows it to be fastened with screws to the bench, or it can be attached to a block and the block gripped in a vise. The machine consists of a cylinder, A, cap, B, and a plunger, C, all of brass; and the screw D, T-handle, E, and screws of steel.

The wax should not be mixed too hard. It should be of such consistency that it can be easily inserted through

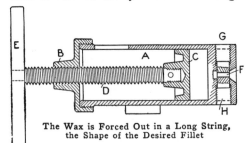

The Wax is Forced Out in a Long String, the Shape of the Desired Fillet

the hole in the side of the cylinder A, then the plunger C is screwed down to compress the wax and force it through the opening F, formed by the screws G and H. The opening in these screws can be made in any shape desired. The forming hole should be cut into the end of the screw G, the other screw H acting as a lock screw.—Contributed by E. W. Voss, Cincinnati, Ohio.

Boring Catcher on a Bit for Ceiling Work

Having some wiring to do in an office, several holes had to be bored in the ceiling. To accomplish this without covering the rosewood desks and tables with plaster dust seemed to be unavoidable, but a paper cone or funnel, about 8 in. deep and 5 in. in diameter at the top, was fastened firmly around the bit to catch the borings. After boring the holes not a particle of plaster could be found on the furniture; the funnel had caught it all.—Contributed by F. E. Searl.

Calking Tool for Elbow Fittings

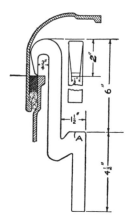

Finding it a hard job to properly calk the lead into soil-pipe connections where the fittings have a close bend, such as a short-sweep elbow or a Y-fitting, with ordinary tools, I designed one as shown in the illustration. The tool is made of ¾-in. octagon steel. The part, or anvil, A, is made as shown, to provide a striking surface. This tool will be found very useful to stop a leak in a fitting near a ceiling.—Contributed by O. F. Germaine, Mansfield, Ohio.

Cover for a Stair

A very convenient contrivance for moving heavy articles up and downstairs consists of a door of hard wood, so hinged that it will fit down snugly over the steps when in use. When not in use, it is turned up against the cellar wall and held there by means of a catch. Barrels, bags, machinery, etc., may be lowered into a basement or elevated to upper floors with comparative ease in this manner.—Contributed by J. G. Allshouse, Avonsmore, Pa.

Draining an Automobile Radiator

Never open the petcock at the bottom of an automobile radiator and then go away supposing that the cooling system will be drained. Scale, rust or any foreign matter may clog the mouth of the petcock, and a frozen and burst radiator will be the result. Always wait and dislodge any particles that may stop the flow, or, better still, dilute the water in the radiator with alcohol and glycerin, about half and half.—Contributed by D. C. Goff, Knoxville, Tenn.

Tying Strings on Tools

A wrench, dropped accidentally into the gear case of an automobile, caused the workman to spend about one hour's time trying to fish it out with a piece of wire. This could have been avoided, if one end of a length of string had been tied to the wrench and the other to his wrist. It is always best to tie a string to any tool and fasten it to the person, if the tool is to be used where dropping it would cause trouble.

A Homemade Block Signal

A homemade block signal, like the one shown in the illustration, has been in use for some time in a freight yard of an Ohio railroad. An upright pole holds in place a horizontal arm which is fastened in the center, and on each end of the arm is suspended a trainman's lantern of appropriate color. The device is operated by a rope, fastened to either end of the arm, by means of which the arm can be held at any angle desired, the rope being fastened like an ordinary awning rope. The crosspiece is called a target, and the device is stationed where one road crosses another. When the target is in

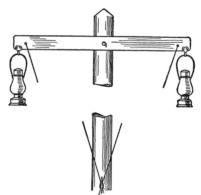

The Target with Two Lanterns Used for a Block Signal on Railroad Crossings

one position the track is clear for one road, and when in the other position the road is clear for the other line.—Contributed by Wm. N. Robson, Pittsburgh, Pa.

Displaying Hosiery on the Ends of Stock Boxes

The usual way of keeping hosiery in stock boxes on shelves is to allow a part of the top pair to extend out and

Showing How to Exhibit the Color and Kind of Hose Contained in a Stock Box

over the end as in the first illustration to show the kind and color contained within. In selling hosiery from the box the top pair is taken out or displaced in getting out a pair below. Instead of allowing a part of the top pair to extend out, place the bottom pair in the box as shown in the second illustration, so that a part of it will lie on the inside of the box against the end and a portion overhang on the outside. Then, in selling a pair from the box, the pair used for display need not be disturbed and the trouble of rearranging the contents is lessened.—Contributed by Miss J. Schwartzberg, Shreveport, Louisiana.

Guard for the Sliding Jaw of a Vise

There is no member of the bench vise more abused by the careless workman than the screw of the sliding-jaw part. It affords a ready but costly means of cutting wire and other small stuff with a hammer, to the destruction of this part of the vise and its roughing so that it will not pass freely through the slot in the guide-jaw head.

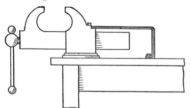

A Guard to Protect the Sliding-Jaw Part of a Bench Vise

The sketch shows a guard strip securely bolted to the bench over this portion of the vise, to afford a permanent and lasting protection for it. In a large shop, where laborers of all kinds are allowed access to vises, this safety device would reduce repair expenses to a great extent.—Contributed by F. W. Bently, Jr., Milwaukee, Wis.

Commutator Lubricating Stick

A very simple little device that can be made by anyone, and yet serves the purpose very well, is shown in the illustration. Select a cylindrical piece of wood, about 4 in. long and 1 in. in diameter. Bore a ½-in. hole through the center longitudinally, then saw one end off diagonally, to fit the surface of the commutator. A piece of fine muslin is tacked over the sloping end. The hole is kept filled with vaseline, which is a good commutator dressing.—Contributed by Stanley Radcliffe, Laurel, Maryland.

Refitting an Automobile-Engine Wrist Pin

In a great many automobile engines, the wrist pins are made a tight fit in the pistons and are held in place by a setscrew and lock nut, or a pin and cotter, on the inside of the piston. With such a construction the rod turns on the wrist pin. Generally the rod end is solid and is bronze-bushed. When the wear in the bushing and on the pin becomes great enough, a "knock" develops in the engine. As the thrust of the engine's work is all one way, the bushing will soon be worn out of round, the wear being on the side toward the cylinder head, and the pin will be flattened on the side next to the crankshaft. Where such damage has been done, the best kind of repair is, of course, to supply new bushings and pins.

Sometimes, however, for reasons of economy or because the automobile's condition will not warrant the new parts, the repair is made without them. One of the best ways of doing this is as follows: Mark the position of the bushing in the rod, remove the bushing and turn it 90 deg., then replace it. This will place the short diameter on the thrust. Remove the wrist pin, after marking the position, turn it also 90 deg. and replace it, then "spot" the pin for the setscrew in its new position, or drill it through for the cotter, as the case may be. With a little scraping, the fit of the rod and pin may be made as good as when new in the direction of the engine's thrust. The play sideways, of course, is as great as it was endways, but this will not cause any knocking of the engine. This will make a cheap but good and satisfactory repair.—Contributed by Donald A. Hampson, Middletown, N. Y.

A Nonspilling Soldering-Acid Can

Soldering fluid can be conveniently kept and carried in a small copper receptacle to which a cover has been soldered. A hole is cut in the center of the top and a ⅜-in. tube soldered to it, the tube being long enough to extend almost to the bottom. Should the holder tip, the acid will not be spilled. When carried in a tool bag where it is liable to be roughly handled, a cork can be put into the tube as an extra precaution.—Contributed by Gertrude M. Bender, Utica, N. Y.

Umbrella Hanger for Day Coaches

An umbrella is a friend in need, when it is raining, but usually a nuisance at other times, especially when

traveling by rail. There is no convenient place to put it, and if laid in the package shelf it is often forgotten. Then, too, the shelf is generally filled with parcels. Simply hook the handle through the bars of the package shelf and secure it with a rubber band, as shown, and the umbrella will remain where it cannot be broken or forgotten.—Contributed by Wm. N. Robson, Pittsburgh, Pa.

Automobile Guide Rail in a Narrow Passage

A narrow passage that requires careful driving, to keep from scratching the body of an automobile, can be fitted

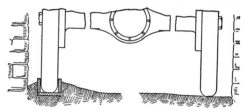

The Rail Guides the Automobile in the Passage so That Neither Side will Strike

with a guide rail that will make the driving easy. The rail consists of three pieces of lumber, one for the bottom of the rail, which is 1 in. thick and 6 in. wide, and two for the sides, each 1 in. thick and 5 in. wide. These are nailed or screwed securely together, as shown, in the form of a miter box. The rail should be somewhat longer than the passageway and if possible the sides should spread out a little to enable the driver to start the wheel into it without difficulty.

When ready to set the rail, drive the automobile into the passage, carefully centering it, and mark the location. Remove a sufficient amount of earth to permit the rail to be sunk to within 1 in. of the top and tamp the dirt in solidly on both sides.—Contributed by James W. York, Ottawa, Can.

Testing Rollers for Straightness

A mechanic was asked to straighten some long rollers of a printing press that had been bent, and having no lathe long enough to take in the rollers, he was momentarily at a loss how to test them after in part straightening them. However, he hit upon a plan that was as good as it was simple. It is illustrated in the sketch.

The workbench was supplied with two vises about 8 ft. apart. In each of these was placed a large center used on the planer. When they were tightly gripped by the vise jaws and approximately lined up they were as good as the lathe centers for the work. A block on the bench brought up close to the roll showed exactly the high

Testing Long Rollers for Straightness by Placing Them between Centers Clamped in Vises

spot when the roll was turned by hand. Repeated bendings at the high spots, followed by checking or testing between centers, produced a most satisfactory job.

A Deaf-Mute and a Blind Man Conversing

For a time I was employed in a private sanitarium and while there I noticed two men who were very fond of each other, but had no means of communication whatever, one being a deaf-mute, the other having become blind by accident some time after having made the mute's acquaintance. I was called on several times to transmit messages between them, which led to the following idea: I purchased two telegraph keys, a sounder and a small green electric bulb, and wired them in the same way as two sounders, the deaf-mute using the light and the blind man the sounder. Both being very intelligent men, they soon learned the Morse code and made very rapid progress; in fact they became nearly expert telegraphers and were both very much delighted with the result of the idea.—Contributed by Joseph C. Laackmann, Philadelphia, Pa.

A Holder for Loose Papers

One of the most convenient methods of holding loose papers, which are very apt to be thrown around and blown off a desk, consists of a piece of fiber board with clips at one end. All papers which are sent to the different departments in a large factory are always put on these boards with clips, and by means of them any additional sheets can be easily attached with red tags on the clips to designate rush work. Two sizes of this board are used, one 5½ by 8½ in., and the other 8½ by 11½ in., made of fiber, $\frac{1}{32}$ in. thick. These boards accommodate practically every size of paper ordinarily found in an office.—Contributed by Geo. L. Colburn, Norfolk Downs, Mass.

Reducing Gearing Noise

The space, on each side, between the rim and the boss of the hub is fitted with disks of sheet metal, and the spaces between the disks, with sawdust and small shot. This will eliminate vibrations. Wheels with a diameter greater than 1½ ft. should be fitted with wooden instead of sheet-metal disks. A packing should be used between the disks and the metal of the wheel so that the sawdust will not sift out when the wheels are in motion.

The disks with the sawdust-filled space will not only prevent much of the noise, but will also make it impossible for a workman to get his arm or tools caught in the wheel.

Soldering Irons for Rivet Heads

Where a large number of rivet heads are to be soldered to make them air or water-tight for tanks or blower pipes, a pair of coppers, shaped as shown at A and B, will do neat and quick work. The irons are shaped by heating them red hot, clamping each in a vise, C, and driving a rivet head into the end.

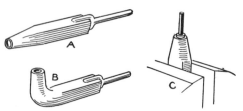

Soldering Coppers Having a Cup-Shaped End to Fit the Heads of Rivets

The edges are then filed to the right shape and tinned in the same manner as an ordinary soldering copper.—Contributed by Lorin A. Brown, Washington, D. C.

To Find the Cubic Contents of an Irregular Object

Desiring to measure the cubic inches in some rocks, I knew of no way to calculate it, but after some thought I decided to use the following method: A vessel large enough to admit the rocks was procured and filled with water to such a height that the rocks would be covered when they were placed in it. The water level was marked and after putting the rocks in, the level was again marked. I used a square vessel, and the cubic contents was easily obtained by measuring the height to which the water rose and multiplying this dimension with the inside area of the vessel, both expressed in inches.—Contributed by Ernest Range, Johnson City, Tenn.

A Simple Electric Pull-Socket Switch

A simple pull-socket switch may be made by tying a strong cord around the base of the electric globe, then screwing the globe into the socket just tight enough to secure a connection. The knot should be at the upper side with one end of the string hanging down on either side. By pulling one end of the string, the globe will be turned outward, thus breaking the connection, while a pull on the other end closes the connection.—Contributed by Paul W. Trier, Maywood, Ill.

Governor Attached to a Marine Gasoline Engine

Desiring to use a marine gasoline engine for stationary work, I found, after installing it, that I had a very

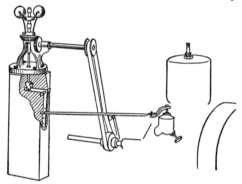

The Speed of the Gasoline Engine is Regulated by the Use of a Steam-Engine Governor

uneven power owing to the lack of a governor. To remedy this trouble, I attached an ordinary steam-engine governor, as shown in the illustration. I purchased the governor from a dealer in junk. As the governor did not have a sufficient stroke, I made a bell-crank lever with the vertical arm of sufficient length to secure the desired throw of the rod. The extending rod is connected to the throttle lever on the carburetor. The illustration clearly shows its application.—Contributed by James Hughs, Mexico, N. Y.

Universal Joint for a Drawing-Board Support

The device illustrated is fastened securely with screws to the center of the back on a drawing board. The construction of the universal joint permits the board to be revolved and tilted to any desired angle. The materials are easily obtained, and the making not difficult.

The joint and holder consists of four

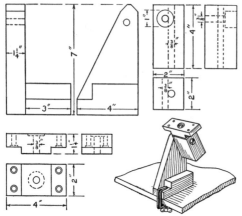

The Universal Joint Permits the Board to be Set at Any Angle Desired

blocks of wood, having the dimensions given in the drawings. When these are fastened to the board and joined with bolts, the device is ready to be clamped to the edge of a table or any other convenient place.—Contributed by Arthur C. Hetrick, Bucyrus, O.

Heating an Automobile

Working as a chauffeur for a private family and driving a car of the limousine type without front doors, but equipped with complete curtains, I suffered very much from the cold until I constructed a heating device that is very simple to make. The engine pan extended back under the body of the car to the front seat, and all that was necessary to do was to obstruct the heated air passing over the motor and force it up through holes in the footboard. A piece of wire-insert asbestos was procured and fastened to an old shade roller, which was cut the width of the body under the front seat, the curtain part being made long enough to touch the engine pan. A new floor board was made to prevent mutilating the one in the automobile, and 1-in. holes were bored in it, about 3 in. apart, and the heater was complete.

All the fresh air drawn through the radiator thus was forced to pass over the motor and through the holes entered the front of the automobile in a heated condition. With the side curtains up and the window open into the rear part, a temperature of about 45 deg. could be maintained in zero weather; and by closing the window a temperature of about 60 deg. was obtained in the front of the car.

A very fine mesh screen is attached under the floor board, to catch any dust that may be in the air. In moderate weather, the curtain can be rolled up and the automobile will not become too warm. As the exhaust opens up in the rear, there is no trouble with gas fumes.—Contributed by Walter Broeker, Chicago.

A Fire Extinguisher

A simple and effective fire extinguisher may be constructed as follows: A piece of brass tubing, 14 in. long by 2½ in. in diameter, is fitted with a screw cap at each end. One end is drilled and tapped for a petcock and the other for an automobile-tire valve. A cross section of the assembled parts is shown.

The pressure disk, or piston, consists of a cupped leather held in place by a flanged brass plate, A, on one side, and a brass disk, B, on the other, like that used in a bicycle pump but

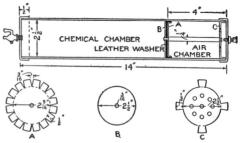

A Chemical-Filled Tube with Driving Disk and Air-Pressure Compartment for Extinguishing a Fire

larger, with a guide disk, C, fastened to it with a ¼-in. rod, about 3½ in. long.

Fill the chemical chamber with 1 qt.

of carbon tetrachloride and pump up a pressure of about 80 lb. with a tire pump. The extinguisher is now ready for "fire only" and, if well made, will retain pressure indefinitely to throw a 25-ft. stream.—Contributed by H. W. Loweree, New York City.

Gears for Model Work

If a pair of gears of any size with teeth of small pitch are at hand, it is an easy matter to make gears of various sizes for experimental or model work. Procure a strip of light tin of a width suitable for the face of the desired gear, and run it through the gears. This will give the shape of the teeth to the tin.

Bore a shallow hole in a block of wood with a carpenter's expansive bit to the size of the gear wanted, and carefully fit the tin in the circle so that all the teeth will touch the wood.

The Tin is Formed by Running It through Gears, and is Then Used in a Mold to Form the Gears

It will be necessary to make a perfect tooth where the ends of the tin meet. Coat the inside of the tin with soldering flux and pour it full of melted babbitt or babbitt and solder, half and half. If the size of the bore is known, a core of wood can be pointed and driven in the center made by the feeder of the expansive bit. The tin should be weighted to hold it in the mold when the melted metal is poured.—Contributed by Edwin M. Davis, Philadelphia, Pennsylvania.

A Universal-Chuck Plate

The plate shown in the sketch is for use in a universal chuck, to face work against or to prevent the work from pushing back into the chuck. When holding a shaft in the chuck while a cut is being taken, the shaft is apt to work back into the chuck and the cen-

ter drop from the tailstock. Its principal use is for chucking washers or small pieces having one true surface.

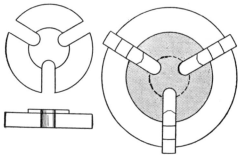

Plate to be Used in a Chuck for Holding Thin Stock to be Faced

The plate is made of a disk, perfectly true on both surfaces and slotted to fit the jaws of the chuck. The slots should be only long enough to allow the jaws to grip the smallest piece to be worked, so that the plate may not be made too weak. The thickness and outside diameter will depend on the kind of work for which it is to be used.—Contributed by L. F. Calhoun, Los Angeles, Cal.

Tack Puller on a Putty-Knife Handle

The putty knife is the only tool carried by painters outside of brushes and is often used for pulling tacks, nails, etc. The blade of a putty knife is too thin for this purpose and is usually damaged beyond repair. It is better to make a tack puller and attach it to the upper end of the knife handle. Such a puller can be easily made from a piece of sheet steel, $\frac{1}{16}$ in. thick, bent to

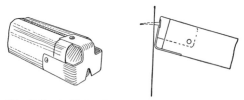

The Puller is Made of Sheet Metal and Attached to the End of the Putty-Knife Handle

shape and fastened on the handle end. The illustration clearly shows the manner of attaching it to the handle and of pulling a tack.—Contributed by J. V. Loeffler, Evansville, Ind.

Singling Out a Key on a Ring

The latchkey on a ring is usually the one most difficult to find, but if it is attached to the ring as shown in the sketch, it will come out, right side up, ready for use.

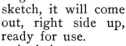

A chain saves one the annoying experience of reaching home to discover that the keys were left at the office, but for those who do not like a chain, an extra ring may be attached to the important key in place of the chain. It is then easy enough to find the ring among the keys, even in the dark, and on getting hold of it, a slight shake brings the desired key in position for use.

If the head of the key should be of the type shown at A, it will be necessary to drill two holes, C and B, to make the combination work.—Contributed by F. R. Cunningham, Denver, Col.

A Memorandum-Book Holder

The handiest place to carry a memorandum book is in the upper vest or outer coat pocket, but it is easily dropped out when stooping, and thus valuable data may be lost. The method shown in the sketch of insuring against this loss is simple and effective. Most vests have a button

sewed at the top of the pocket with a buttonhole in the outer part forming the pocket. Remove the button and sew it on a short length of ¾-in. elastic band, then sew the ends together, thus forming a loop of such diameter as to fit snugly around the book to be carried. After the elastic has been placed around the book, the whole is put in the pocket and buttoned. To release, simply unbutton and withdraw the book and elastic. A buttonhole can be easily made in the outside part of the pocket.—Contributed by Victor Labadie, Dallas, Texas.

To Prevent Wire Violin Strings from Cutting Bridge

In using a wire E-string on a violin, it soon cuts into the bridge and lowers its position so that the bow hairs will

wear on the side of the violin. The gut string causes a great deal of trouble and will not wear long, and the silk string does not produce the right sound. Where it is necessary to use a violin from 5 to 8 hours a day, a wire E-string is almost a necessity. To prevent this string from cutting into the bridge, I insert a piece of ivory into a slit cut with a jewelers' saw in the upper edge of the bridge, as shown by the dotted lines. Such a piece may be put in the entire edge for all four strings, but it is only necessary for the E and A-strings.—Contributed by Roy Douglas, Terre Haute, Ind.

Clearance Groove for Threading Tools

A groove turned in the rod, or shaft, at the termination of the thread will give the tool clearance at the end of the cut.

Threads can then be cut without close attention and the breaking of tool points. The groove should be cut no deeper than the depth of the finished thread.—Contributed by J. Harger, Honolulu.

How to Make a Portable Cottage

By FRANK L. RUSSELL

The summer camp that provides a shelter for the toiler during vacation days has become one of a more substantial nature, and the cottage has taken the place of the tent. But the short season a cottage can be used increases the expense of a vacation trip, even though the vacationist owns it, as taxes and interest on the investment amount to no small sum, in fact, equal to quite a large rental. Then, too, a cottage naturally is a permanent affair, and if one desires new scenes and surroundings, it cannot be readily moved. This calls forth a desire to have something better than a tent, more along the cottage line, yet something that can be taken up, stored and easily made ready in a new location, where it can be set on a bit of

The Cottage as It Appears with the Front Entrance on the Side, Which can be Changed at Will to Any Other Part of the House to Best Suit the Location

ground obtained for a few weeks at a nominal sum.

Many attempts have been made to construct what is called a portable house, originating from the making of portable garages, but when these were set up they were found to be more of a permanent nature than portable. When the time came for a removal many nails and screws had to be withdrawn, which left the parts in bad condition and sometimes so broken that new ones had to be procured. To avoid all these troubles and to make a really portable house in which the parts are almost entirely interchangeable, the building shown in the illustration was designed. A close examination of the drawings will reveal the fact that the sections, when taken apart, can be laid together flat and crated for shipment. Also, that the

door and window sections have the same width and the same joint, so that they can be set in at any place desired, and the building changed from year to year. The manner of construction makes it possible to build a house of two or more rooms, as desired, for as the sections are the same, it only requires a few more of them to add another room. The floor plan, Fig. 1, shows a good size for a three-room cottage.

The description of this portable house being more in detail of the construction of the sections, the stock list in general will be left to the builder. However, in making it of flooring boards, he should remember that these come in thicknesses and widths of 1 by 4 in., and 1 by 6 in., in white pine; and that when finished, they will measure only $\frac{13}{16}$ by $3\frac{1}{4}$ in., and $\frac{13}{16}$ by $5\frac{1}{4}$ in., respectively. Yellow pine can be had in various widths, but taking only the two mentioned sizes into consideration, the builder can estimate how much material he will require and get the price at which the different kinds of lumber are quoted from a local lumber dealer.

Take the first mentioned size, for instance, 1 in. thick and 4 in. wide. This is the basis on which the lumber dealer figures his selling price, so that while one pays for a certain gross amount of board feet, the space this amount will cover must be reduced in accordance with the finished dimensions of the lumber; in this instance to $\frac{13}{16}$ in. in thickness and $3\frac{1}{4}$ in. wide. It is best to figure how many boards will be required at the finished width, namely 3¼ in., then multiply by the gross width to find the amount of board feet for the cost.

4 and 5, are made in the same general manner as the wall section, Fig. 2. The window consists of an eight-light, 8 by 10-in. glass sash, commonly

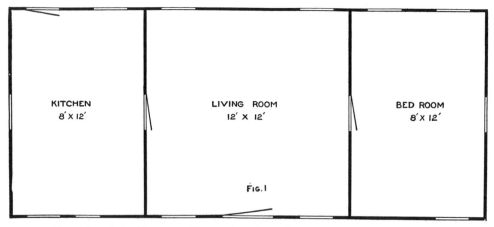

KITCHEN
8′ X 12′

LIVING ROOM
12′ X 12′

BED ROOM
8′ X 12′

FIG. I

Floor Plan of the Cottage as Illustrated, with the Large Living Room in the Center

The sections are designed to take lumber of standard lengths and the cost will not be excessive on this account. The side-wall section, shown in Fig. 2, illustrates the general construction of all the sections for the outside, including the gables, also any partitions. The boards are of matched lumber, preferably of good flooring, fastened to battens, one at the top and bottom, and one in the center, the edges being reinforced with upright battens, which project on one side and recede on the other, 1 in. in width. This forms a lapping joint where the parts are set together. The upper cross batten is fastened with its upper edge 4 in. from the top of the wall boards. This provides a place for a 2 by 4-in. piece—finished size, 1⅝ by 3⅝ in.—to be set on, and makes a depression for the batten on the roof section to be set against when it is hooked. This detail is shown in Fig. 3. The lower batten, Fig. 2, is fastened so that its lower edge will be 1¾ in. above the lower edge of the wall boards. The batten is set on the top of the floor and the ends of the wall boards extend down over the floor boards on the outside.

The window and door sections, Figs.

known as storm sash. A frame for the sash is made of ⅞-in. material, with a width equal to the thickness of the wall boards and the battens combined. The sash is hinged at one side and has a catch at the other. This construction permits these sections to be placed between two wall sections, and the glass is in a safe place where it will not be broken in shipment.

The door is set in a frame in the same manner as the sash, except that the bottom cannot be joined. This makes it necessary to crate the door sections with care, to prevent racking of the whole section. The part with the door will lie flat just as the other sections, but the lock will have to be removed.

The gable sections are made like the wall sections except that the battens are put on to fit the slope of the roof. The outline of the positions battens take is shown in Fig. 6. The dotted lines in the sketch show the positions the wall boards will occupy. The upper batten, on the center section, is set in such a position that it will form a support for the end of a 2 by 4-in. ridge piece. Dimensions for these sections are given in Fig. 7. The notches at the top should be accurately cut, after the sections are made, so that they will receive the battens that are fastened to the roof boards. Cross lines are shown on the upright battens, at the edges of the wall and gable sections and at the bottoms, with dimensions giving the location of holes for bolts that are used to fasten the sections together. The detail of this construction, with the bolt A, is shown in Fig. 8. These locations should be accurately laid out and ⅜-in. holes bored so that the sections can be used at any place around the building. The end sections are the same as the sides, and the gable boards overlap the walls, as shown by the lower dotted line in Fig. 6.

The roof sections are constructed in the same manner as the walls, the battens being located as shown in Fig. 9. This is the only place where it becomes necessary to depart from the same general width of the sections. All sections in the roof, save two, are 4 ft. wide. Two sections must be 2 ft. wide, so that an extra 1 ft. will be provided for the eave at the gable ends. The narrow widths should be placed in the roof at the center of the building, so that a wider section will

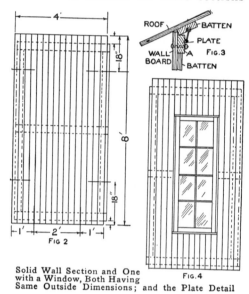

Solid Wall Section and One with a Window, Both Having Same Outside Dimensions; and the Plate Detail

same general construction except that all battens run crosswise, and that they are flush with the edges. The number of battens on these sections can be determined by the builder and depends on what is intended to be used as a foundation.

In building up the floor, which is the first thing to set up, it will be found

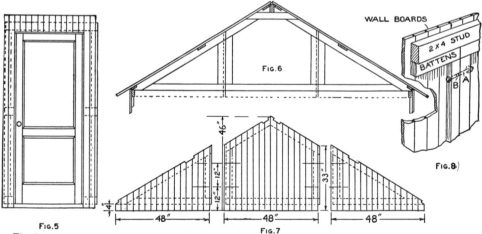

The Door Section Has the Same Outside Dimensions and Same Construction as the Wall Section, But Those of the Gable are Somewhat Different, the Battens being Cut to Fit the Slope of the Roof and the Boards Fitted to Them in the Same Section Widths

come at the end and three-quarters of it will lie on the plate and the ridge, to hold the projecting edge.

The floor sections, Fig. 10, take the

that in placing the corners of the wall boards, as shown in Fig. 11, there will be a space of about ⅞ in. at two side and two end corners. This can be taken care of by tacking a lath on the sides of the sections, also on the ends of both end floor sections.

A 3/8-in. hole is bored through the

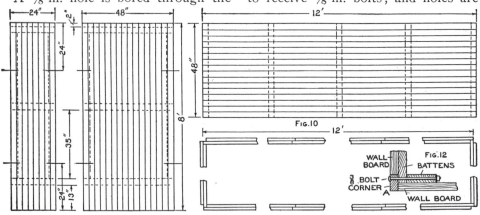

FIG.9   FIG.11
Two of the Roof Sections are Half-Width, to Provide Eaves at the Ends. On the Floor Sections, Which do Not Lap, the Battens are Flush with the Edges. How the Empty Spaces at the Corners are Filled, and Manner of Joining a Corner

upright battens, as shown at B, Fig. 8, so that if a section is placed with its projecting edge at the corner, a bolt can be used to hold the joint and the corner board A, Fig. 12.

At equal distances apart, on the upper ends of the wall boards, 3/8-in. holes are bored, and holes of the same size are also bored in the plate, or the 2 by 4-in. piece, A, Fig. 3, for bolts to draw them together. These plate pieces should be as long as possible; for instance, for a two-room house that is 20 ft. long, they should be 10 ft. long, two on a side. Those used across the ends should be the length of the width of the house. These plates must fit closely at the corners, one end butting against the side of the other piece running at right angles to it. Where they butt end to end in the center another piece should lap the joint, and longer bolts should be used through the wall boards and plate in the 3/8-in. holes.

Ordinary hooks and eyes are used, in the manner shown in Fig. 3, throughout the construction, and especially for the roof sections in holding them to the ridge and plate. To keep the eyes out of the way for shipment, they should be set in a groove, as shown, or, if possible, in the edge of

the batten. The battens across the lower ends of the wall boards are evenly spaced for bolt holes and bored to receive 3/8-in. bolts; and holes are also bored in the ends of the flooring boards to match them. Bolts placed in these holes will hold the wall sections to the floor.

If the cottage is to be set up in the woods, small, straight trees can be cut, dressed and laid on a level place, on which to lay the floor sections. As many poles, or joists, are used as there are battens on the sections, and they are located so that the battens will lie on their upper surfaces. If care is taken in placing the underpinning, the floor will be quite solid. Dressed timbers, 2 by 6 in., or 4-in. square, can be used for joists.

All side-wall boards, roofing and floor boards are fastened to the battens with well-clinched nails, but at a trifle higher cost and by expending a little more time, they can be fastened with screws, which will make a much better and more solid section. The roof sections are covered with prepared roofing of good quality, and after placing them in position, a strip of roofing is fastened over the joints, and a strip lapping over the ridge is also attached.

The partitions are made in the same manner as the wall and gable sections, the only difference being that the extending upright battens and the ends of the battens projecting on one section will have to be removed, as well as the 1¾-in. projection of the boards below the lower batten. They will then fit inside of the building at any place. A small notch is cut out of the central gable section to admit the ridge.

A porch can be attached by using sections for a roof held up by porch columns at the outer edge, and by a 2 by 4-in. piece bolted to the house at the end, or under the eave at the side, as the case may be. This can be determined when the location and manner of setting the window and door sections are laid out. Three roof sections and two floor sections will make a good porch. All sections should be well painted and the floor oiled.

Fireproof Stand for Portable Gas Stoves

To deflect the heat thrown down by a gas stove, I built a low stand, having a sheet of asbestos millboard sandwiched between the wood base and the sheet-metal top. This was secured in place with tacks, fastening the top and passing through the asbestos into the wood base. This device prevents excessive heat on the floor near the stove, and is a safeguard against a possible fire as well.—Contributed by James M. Kane, Doylestown, Pa.

Pill-Dispensing Box

After having considerable difficulty in dropping a certain number of pills from the box into my hand I hit upon  the idea of fixing the box as shown, to drop the pills one by one. A notch, the size of a pill, was cut in the edge of the box, then by raising the cover partly one pill at a time could be dropped out.—Contributed by Wm. H. Patten, Belleville, New Jersey.

An Emergency Pressure Gauge

In a case of emergency I used a pressure gauge made as follows: A tee-joint was inserted in the line, and

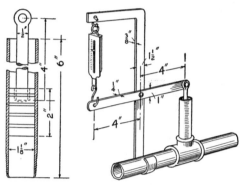

A Pressure Gauge Applied to a Pipe Line Where a Scale Registers the Pressure

in the side outlet of the tee, a piece of pipe, 1⅛ in. in diameter and 6 in. long, was fitted. This pipe was bored out smooth, and a piston, made of cold-rolled shafting, was fitted in the bore. The piston was about 2 in. long, and several grooves were cut in its surface for packing. The upper end was drilled to receive a ½-in. rod end loosely. The upper end of the rod was shaped into an eye which was attached to a lever, crossing a vertical standard fastened to the pipe. The opposite end of the lever was attached to a spring scale suspended from the right-angle projecting end of the vertical standard.

The inside area of the 1⅛-in. pipe will be so close to 1 sq. in., that the reading on the scale will be direct. To prevent the piston from dropping into the tee, the lower end of the pipe should be turned in a trifle. The dimensions given will make a correct-working gauge.—Contributed by Lee B. Green, Cleveland, O.

⟨In making window screens, put white netting on the outside of the frame and black on the inside; thus the vision of a person inside will not be obstructed while no one on the outside can see through the screens.

A Flywheel Pattern

There are several methods used in the construction of wheel patterns. They differ mainly in the way the

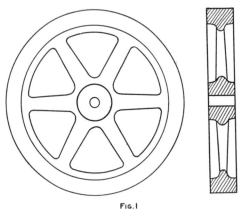

Design of a 48-In. Flywheel to be Made in a Pattern for the Foundry

arms are fastened together at the hub and in the manner in which they are secured to the rim. The pattern shown in Fig. 1 has stood the test of time and the hard usage of the foundry. A wheel about 48 in. in diameter is shown with arms of the usual elliptic section. The pattern is easily and quickly made in the following manner:

The first thing to be considered is the arms. The stock for these should be planed up to a parallel width and thickness and long enough to extend from the center to a point halfway through the rim. They are then fitted together at the center with the joints running at an angle of 30 deg. to the center line of each piece. These pieces should be fitted on a perfectly smooth surface, or faceplate, to which they are securely fastened with screws. The arms are then laid out and numbered 1, 2, 3, 4, 5, and 6. The arm No. 1 is first removed and cut out on a band saw to the layout lines, and then the taper is laid out and dressed off the flat way of the arm. A flat place, about 1 in. wide, is left on the bottom side of each arm, at the rim end. This is to keep the end from dropping down when the arm is put back into place on the board or faceplate, and the flat surface is trimmed off after the arms are

glued together. This part of the work is shown in Fig. 2. Each arm should be completely finished before it is returned to its place. It is much easier to work the oval, or elliptic, section on each arm separately, than it is to try to shape them up after the arms are fastened together permanently. Arms 3 and 5 are then finished and put back where they belong. Those numbered 2, 4, and 6 are next in order, and are glued in place as soon as they are finished.

While the glue is drying on the arms, a suitable faceplate is turned up in the lathe, and the rim built up. If the arms are not too thick, one course of segments will do for the bead that is to be turned on the inside of the rim, but if the arm is thick, like the one illustrated, two courses will be necessary. The rim is built up and turned, as shown in Fig. 3, the joint between courses 1 and 2 being the center of the rim. One-half of the bead is finished in this operation, a template being used to get it the proper shape.

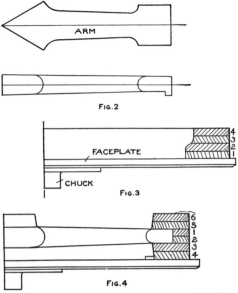

Layout for the Arms, and the Manner of Building Up the Rim Segments

When the rim has reached this stage, it is taken from the faceplate and rechucked on thin segments, which are fastened with brads to the faceplate and turned to fit the finished side of the arm. The other half of the bead is then finished to the template.

The next operation is to fit the arms to the rim. This is done by cutting recesses through the segment courses 1 and 2, to receive the arm ends. If the job has been carefully laid out and turned, the joint between the segment courses 2 and 3 will be the bottom of these recesses.

The cope hub is a loose one and is turned separately and pinned to the arms, but the nowel hub should be fastened to the arms before the latter are fastened in place in the recesses cut for them in the rim. A screw with glued surfaces, through each arm, secures the hub and gives added strength where it is most needed. The work proceeds as shown in Fig. 4, by applying the courses 5 and 6, and then finishing the inside and outside, and turning the hub to size.—Contributed by J. A. Shelly, Brooklyn, N. Y.

To Prevent Round Stock from Slipping on a Planer Bed

It is frequently necessary to cut a key seat in a long shaft and the work must be done on a planer. There is always a possibility of the shaft sliding along with the tool, even though it is well clamped in one of the slots in the planer bed. A holding device may be had by fastening a lathe dog on the shaft where the dog will rest against the rear end of the table. Of course, if the shaft is short enough, or the key seats so located that a stop can be placed on the front end, it will hold much better.

Sand Bucket for Loosening Dirt

Where a sand bucket is used in digging wells the pounding sometimes packs the dirt or sand instead of loosening it. The dirt may be easily loosened and small stones dislodged more readily if the lower edge of the sand bucket is cut in sawtooth fashion. —Contributed by J. V. Day, Stratton, Nebraska.

Sheet-Metal Lifting Hook

The illustration shows a hook for lifting and carrying sheet metal in a vertical position. The construction of this hook makes the grip draw tighter as the load increases. The hook can be made in any size to suit the kind of work. The face of the clamping lever can be corrugated or smooth, as desired.—Contributed by Joseph K. Long, Renovo, Pa.

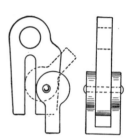

Extension Handle for a Paintbrush

Desiring to use an extension on my paintbrush handle, I quickly made one with the use of an old bicycle-lamp bracket clamp. A discarded broom handle was slotted to receive the shank of the clamp, and a small bolt held it in place. The thumb nut on the bolt of the clamp made it easy to clamp the brush handle in the opening.—Contributed by Elvin L. Hartlett, Wausau, Wis.

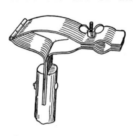

Staging Clamp

The illustration shows a clamp which will save much time and many nails when erecting staging. This clamp is made of 5/8-in. round iron rod. It is applied to the studding, and the board it holds is clamped firmly by driving a wedge between the board and the rod.— Contributed by Abner B. Shaw, N. Dartmouth, Mass.

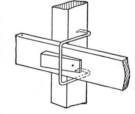

Temporary Pipe Line Attached to a Tank

A certain piece of work made it necessary to use water temporarily from a tank. The outlet pipe was insulated to keep it from freezing, and it was not considered advisable to connect to this pipe. Also, the new line had to be con-

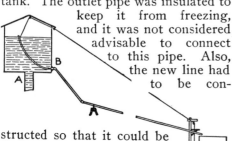

structed so that it could be drained to keep it from freezing.

The water was run out of the tank until a man could wade in it with rubber boots, and a hole was cut in the tank near the lower edge and pipe connections made from this point. A long hose was attached to the pipe on the inside of the tank so that its open end could be raised above the water level. A rope was attached to the end of the hose and run over pulleys to a weight near the place where the water was to be used. A shelf was provided for the weight, and when water was wanted, the weight was placed on the shelf. This lowered the hose into the water and started it to run. When the hose was raised out of the water the line drained itself quickly.—Contributed by James E. McCormack, Haliburton, Ontario.

Lighted Box for Tracing Drawings on Heavy Paper

In the drafting room of a railroad office it was necessary to make copies of a large number of tracings on sheets of thick and hard paper. The paper was too thick to trace through in the usual way, and as it would have taken a great deal of time to copy each drawing, the arrangement shown in the sketch was made, to light the drawing from the under side.

An ordinary drawing board was used for the top, and a hole, 22 in. square, was cut in the center. A piece of plate glass, 24 in. square, was procured and the wood of the board cut away to let it in flush with the top. A drawer was then made and fitted to hold four 40-watt tungsten globes, placed horizontally under the glass. The tracing to be copied was placed on the glass and the paper over it. When the current was turned on, the lines to be traced could be easily seen through the heavy paper.

The globes were held in sockets of the ordinary wall type, which were mounted on blocks of wood, the latter being fastened with ¼-in. bolts on two boards, 4 in. wide, which were placed lengthwise through the center of the drawer, as shown. These boards were made with a ¼-in. longitudinal slot extending to within 1 in. of the ends. The bolts of the socket mountings were passed through this slot. With this arrangement the lights can be slipped to any desired position in the drawer and held tightly with the bolts.

The sockets were connected up, and the terminal ends run out through a hole in the bottom of the drawer and attached to a standard plug. The drawer was 8 in. deep, 22 in. wide and 30 in. long, inside measurements. The entire interior was painted with a gloss white.

The device is useful not only for tracing through heavy paper, but also

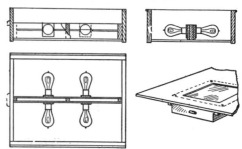

The Lamps in the Drawer beneath the Glass will Light a Drawing on Heavy Paper Sufficiently

for making tracings of indistinct blueprints, where the white lines would not show through the tracing cloth.—Contributed by J. C. Jacobs, Freeport, Illinois.

Chalking a Line

A line must be coated with dust from a piece of charcoal or chalk before it can be snapped, which alone requires some time when there are many lines to be made. The sketch shows a simple method of making a chalker for a line, which is of great assistance to a scenic artist, but equally applicable to other work.

Procure an empty tin box, remove the cover, and punch a hole in its center with a nail; also make a hole in the center of the bottom in the same man-

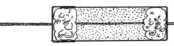

The Coloring Powder is Evenly Distributed on the Line by Drawing It through the Box

ner. Run the line through these holes. Place a small moistened sponge in the bottom of the box and fill the box on top of the sponge with lampblack, or any dry, powdered paint, then place another piece of sponge on top and put on the cover. In chalking the line, it is only necessary to run the box the entire length of the line. The sponges will prevent too much color from adhering to the line. As the color has no binder, it is easily brushed off when dry.—Contributed by Mrs. Harry Marcelle, Honolulu, Hawaiian Islands.

Drip Catcher on an Oilcan Spout

The drip of an oilcan spout running down on the outside keeps the can covered with grease and in an unclean condition. To catch this drip, I made a cup from a large cartridge shell, cut off on the lines A and B and attached to the spout with solder, as shown at C. A little clean waste or cotton packed in the cup will catch any oil that runs down on the outside of the spout.—Contributed by Chas. G. England, Washington, Pa.

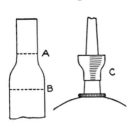

Air-Hose Uncoupling Lever

When uncoupling passenger coaches it is very difficult to disconnect the air hose without a leverage. With the

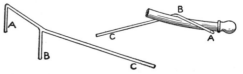

Lever to Use in Disconnecting the Air Hose When Uncoupling Railroad Passenger Coaches

device shown, the proper leverage may be had by placing the prong A under the hose and the prong B above, and bearing down on the handle C. This raises the coupling and loosens the connection. The device is made of 5/8-in. round iron.—Contributed by Benjamin H. Baird, New York City.

Lace-Hole Marker for Belts

A very practical tool for laying off holes to be punched for wire lacing in belts is shown in the illustration. The

tool is made of hard wood, 1 1/2 in. thick, 4 in. wide and 6 in. long. A row of w i r e nails or brads, spaced 3/8 in. a p a r t, are driven part way into the end and lined up evenly, whereupon the heads are filed off and the ends pointed. Finish the block to make a handle, as shown. I find this simple tool very rapid and accurate in scribing holes for punching.—Contributed by John M. Pipp, Muncie, Ind.

To Lengthen a Twist Drill

Sometimes when drilling a hole in a difficult piece of work, it is found that the drill is just a little too short. The drill can be easily extended to cut through the metal by wrapping the shank with a layer of fine emery cloth or several layers of paper before inserting it into the taper hole.—Contributed by John A. Cook, Birmingham, Alabama.

A Drill Jig

A simple drill jig that will locate holes centrally in a shaft, or other round stock, accurately and quickly is shown in the sketch. It may be pro-

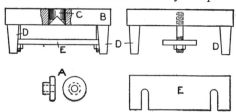

A Jig to Use on a Drill Press for Drilling Holes in Round Stock Centrally

vided with any number of hardened and ground slip bushings, A, to take various sizes of drills and reamers.

The body B is a gray-iron casting with a 90-deg. angle groove machined the full length of it. A permanent bushing, C, is hardened, ground and located exactly in the center of the groove. The result of the work depends on the accuracy of the location of this bushing. The legs D are made of cold-rolled steel and pressed into holes drilled in the corners of the plate.

The clamp E should be slotted, as shown, for rapid work. A small pin may be located close to the lower edge of the bushing C, to prevent the slip bushings A from turning while in use. A slot is made in the bushing A to accommodate the pin.—Contributed by A. Dane, Pottstown, Pa.

How to Make a Hydrogen Generator

The hydrogen-gas generators used in establishments where a great deal of lead burning is being done, such as storage-battery plants, usually consist of two wooden boxes, one being mounted about 3 ft. above the other. The lower box is made air-tight, but it is connected to an opening in the bottom of the upper box by means of a piece of rubber tubing which is provided with a stopcock or pinch valve, and the upper box is usually partly open. These boxes are both lined with some material, such as lead or rubber paint, that is not acted upon by the sulphuric acid used in the production of the hydrogen gas. The operation of the device is as follows:

A small quantity of commercial zinc is placed in the lower box through an air-tight opening provided for this purpose, and the upper box is partly filled with sulphuric acid diluted with about 10 volumes of water. When the valve in the tube connecting the two boxes is opened, the acid runs down into the lower box and a reaction takes place, the result of which is zinc sulphate and hydrogen gas. If the outlet from the lower box is closed, a pressure will be established, due to the hydrogen gas, which will force the excess acid back into the upper box—the tube into the lower box should extend inside and the end almost touch the bottom—and reduce or stop the chemical action of the acid on the zinc. As the gas is drawn from the lower box the acid is allowed to run down and again start the chemical reaction.

The arrangement shown in the sketch operates in the same manner, and its construction is a great deal less trouble- some. Instead of two boxes, use two 5-gal. water bottles. One bottle should be supported in an inverted position at least 3 ft. above the other. Each bottle should be provided with a large rubber stopper with two openings in

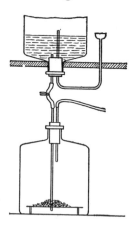

them, through which small glass tubes may be inserted. The proper length and arrangement of these tubes is shown in the sketch. The inside end of the air inlet in the upper bottle should extend up to within a very short distance of the bottom of the bottle; while the acid inlet into the lower bottle should almost touch the bottom. The remaining two tubes should extend just inside the corks. A pinch cock should be provided in the tube conducting the acid from the upper bottle to the lower. Some kind of a small, light support should be made from thin lead and placed on the bottom of the lower bottle, to hold the zinc above any acid that cannot be forced back up into the upper bottle.

Be very careful to get all the air out of the lower bottle before any attempt is made to light the gas, as an explosion is sure to follow if any air remains.

The gas thus generated may be used in many ways, but especially in producing a pure, hot flame. For this purpose a burner is required, which may be purchased at most chemical houses, and a foot bellows to supply air pressure. The air pressure can be produced by using a large can and connecting it to the water faucet; when the water is turned on, the air is forced out.

Trapping Killies

While out catching crabs one day, we ran short of meat and could get no other bait than killies, but had no net. Having an empty milk bottle in our lunch box, it was tied to a line so that it would hang in a horizontal position. A piece of meat was weighted and placed near the bottom end. The bottle was then hung over the side of the boat. The killies would enter the neck and nibble the meat and thus attract others, and as a result we caught plenty to bait the crabs.—Contributed by Robert Meier, Lynbrook, L. I.

Binding Bales of Hay on a Wagon

In hauling baled hay on rough roads, the bales can be bound together to keep them from slipping off with wood pins, about 4 in. long, sharpened on both ends and stuck into a bale about halfway before placing another bale on top of it.—Contributed by Ray C. Evans, Meyers Cave, Virginia.

Bed Desk for an Invalid

An adjustable desk or table for an invalid or convalescent can be made as shown in the sketch. The arrangement

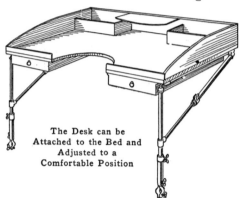

The Desk can be Attached to the Bed and Adjusted to a Comfortable Position

of the top may be in this or any other manner to suit the maker. The length of the desk should be the same as the width of the bed. Two vertical standards made of two pieces of tubing, one telescoping in the other, are used as the supports. Clamps are attached to the upper ends of the larger, or outside, tubes for use in holding the desk at the height set. A brace, also made of two telescoping tubes, is used at each end to adjust the rear part of the desk to a comfortable height for the user. Thumb nuts are used to clamp the desk to the bed.—Contributed by Louis Stankewitz, New York City.

Homemade Expansion Bolts

When expansion bolts are not available, substitutes can be made of pieces of gas pipe of the required size, each cut slanting with a hacksaw to divide it into two pieces, as shown. A bolt is passed through the center and a large washer holds the bolt head. 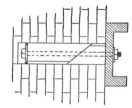 When drawn up, the sloping parts clamp on the sides of the hole.—Contributed by James E. Noble, Toronto, Canada.

Belt Holder for a Shaft

The unused belt, when there is no loose pulley to shift it on, is usually hung on the running shaft or attached

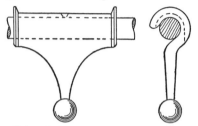

The Holder Swings on the Shaft and is Ready to Carry the Belt When Not in Use

to a wire fastened to the ceiling or joist. A much better way is to make a belt hanger, as shown in the sketch, to hold the belt. It consists of a piece of wrought iron, forged out as shown, to fit over the shaft and an extending end to prevent its turning with the shaft. An oil hole is provided to keep the bearing well lubricated. When a belt is hung on this holder there is no danger of its catching on the shaft and being wound up and broken.—Contributed by S. Gulbransen, Chicago.

Sanitary Drinking Fountain for a Shop

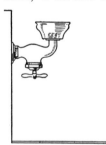

Wishing to install some sanitary drinking fountains as cheaply as possible, I struck on a very good idea which proved both satisfactory in every respect and strictly sanitary. There were three large wash sinks in the shop, and each was fitted with three plain bibbs and one hose bibb. I merely turned the hose bibb around, allowing the hose end to face upward. I then secured three vitreous-china drinking cups which fitted snugly over the hose end and then, by screwing a locknut on the top, the cups were held secure. Each fountain head had four small holes to allow the water to drain and was so constructed as to make it impossible for the lips to come in contact with the bibb, thus making the device just as sanitary as any drinking fountain on the market.—Contributed by D. Marcus, Madisonville, Ohio.

Combination Lathe or Planer Tool

The lathe or planer tool illustrated is one that holds cutters made of self-hardening steel, ¼ by ⅜ in. These cutters will stand more rough usage and take heavier cuts than a like sectional volume, ½ by 1½ in. in size, used on combination tool holders. A wedge instead of a setscrew is used for holding the cutters. The wedge has more bearing on a cutter than a screw and it will not break. If there is any wear, the wedge will take it up.

A Combination Tool Holder Using a Wedge Instead of a Screw for Clamping the Cutter

For cutting-off tools, place two pieces, ⅛ by ¾ in., side by side in the holder, allowing the one ground for the cutter to project farthest from the holder.—Contributed by Fred B. Stoner, Masontown, Pa.

Removing Tarnish from Silver by Electricity

There is no solvent for silver sulphide, or tarnish on silverware, that is not a better solvent for the silver itself. Therefore the tarnish cannot be removed in a solution. However, this coating can be removed electrically. Make a dilute acid solution, 1 part chemically pure sulphuric acid to 10 parts of water, and use a carbon electrode. The tarnish will disappear in a few minutes without injury to the silver.

In the absence of a battery, suspend the silverware in the solution and bring a piece of aluminum in contact with it. This will restore the luster.

INDEX TO VOLUME XI

SHOP NOTES FOR 1915